DATE DUE

CONSTRUCTION ESTIMATES
FROM TAKE-OFF TO BID

Dedicated to Jessica's future

CONSTRUCTION ESTIMATES
FROM TAKE-OFF TO BID

NORMAN FOSTER

F. W. DODGE CORPORATION, NEW YORK • A McGraw-Hill Company

Foreword

There are books on almost every aspect of building construction, including many that deal with pricing the estimate. Until the publication of this one, however, there has not been one devoted to the daily work of the construction estimator—one that shows how he extracts the quantities from the drawings, compiles and prices the estimate, and prepares the bid. This book, then, could be called "The Estimator at Work."

Here, although the general approach to estimating has not been overlooked, the emphasis is on showing it in action. Examples are included to show how quantities are taken off for all of the trades customarily handled by the general contractor, each with its particular working drawing. In order that the reader may keep the appropriate drawing before him while he follows each take-off, item by item, these have been bound into a separate booklet for which a pocket in the back cover has been provided.

The examples show a methodical system of taking-off. Many short cuts and time-saving devices are included, showing how computations may be simplified and initial calculations made to do extra duty by being retained for reuse at several stages of the take-off.

The chapters on alterations, overhead, and sub-bids—usually given scant attention in estimating books—have been treated rather fully, in recognition of their importance to all who work on estimates.

Also included is the entire take-off and estimate for a school building of almost $1,000,000, including all the pricing right down to the final bid figure.

To round out the presentation, there is a chapter giving full details of many unit prices, showing how the prices of labor and material are compiled.

This book, then, is the estimator at work, from the opening of the drawings to the closing of the bid.

The aim throughout has been to show you how to save time, work, and money while achieving greater accuracy than is yielded by less systematic estimating methods. You may be in a general contractor's office; in the masonry, carpentry, excavation, or steel business; or you may be preparing budget estimates for architects, engineers, or building owners. Whatever your concerns or your interests, if they are connected with construction estimating, this book was written for you.

ACKNOWLEDGMENTS

The author wishes to thank The Architects Collaborative (Cambridge, Mass.); Kilham, Hopkins, Greeley & Brodie, Architects (Boston, Mass.); and Korslund, LeNormand & Quann, Architects (Norwood, Mass.) for permission to use certain details and drawings. Thanks are also extended to Mr. Vincent Iannone who made the finish drawings from the author's rough sketches.

Contents

Abbreviations

alum.	aluminum
arch.	architect
av.	average
B.	bottom
bast.	basement
bd.	board
bdg.	boarding
BF	board feet
bit.	bituminous
bldg.	building
bm.	beam
B. P.	base plate
b. s. m.	both sides measured
c.	courses (on masonry drawing)
carbo.	carborundum
C. B.	catch basin (on utilities drawing)
C.B.	chalkboard (on carpentry drawing)
c-c	center to center
ceram.	ceramic
cert.	certified
CF	cubic feet
C. I.	cast iron
clg.	ceiling
col.	column
com.	common
comb.	combination
comm.	commercial
conc.	concrete
cont.	continuous
C. P.	concrete pipe

cupb.	cupboard
C. of W.	clerk of works
CY	cubic yards
D. H.	double hung
dia.	diameter
dist. box	distribution box
dr.	door
drg.	drawing
D. U.	dwelling units
ea.	each
e. f.	each face
e. w.	each way
exc.	excavation
exp.	expansion
ext.	exterior
fcg.	facing
Fig.	figure
flr.	floor
fr.	frame
frmg.	framing
F. T.	facing tile
ftg.	footing
galv.	galvanized
gen.	general
G. F. T.	glazed facing tile
gl.	glazed
G1F	glazed one face
G2F	glazed two faces
G1S	good one side
gr.	grade
grano.	granolithic
G. W. L.	ground water level
gyp.	gypsum
H.	header (on masonry drawing)
H. B.	heavy bending
H. D. C. I.	heavy-duty cast iron
H. M.	hollow metal
hor.	horizontally
H. W. L.	heavyweight Lally
I. D.	internal diameter
ins.	insurance
int.	interior
inv.	invert
jnt.	joint
jntd.	jointed
kit.	kitchen
L. B.	light bending
lb	pounds

LF	lineal feet
lg.	long
lino.	linoleum
L. S.	lump sum
M	thousand
magn.	magnesium
max.	maximum
M.H.	manhole
min.	minimum
opg.	opening
pcs.	pieces
perim.	perimeter
pl.	plate
plmg.	plumbing
ply.	plywood
porc.	porcelain
pr.	pair
psi	pounds per square inch
psf	pounds per square foot
ptn.	partition
R.	risers (as in "14R")
rad.	radius
R. C. P.	reinforced concrete pipe
reinf.	reinforcing
retg.	retaining
rm.	room
R. T.	rubber tile
S.	stretcher (on masonry drawing)
san.	sanitary
S. E.	square edged
sect.	section
SF	square feet
span.	spandrel
sqr.	square
st.	station
str.	straight
susp.	suspended
SY	square yards
T.	top
T.B.	tackboard
temp.	temporary
T. & G.	tongued and grooved
typ.	typical
V. C.	vitrified clay
vert. (or V.)	vertically
W. D.	working drawing
W. I.	wrought iron
wind.	window

CHAPTER 1   **General Methods and Procedures**

Every construction estimate is based on a quantity survey, sometimes called the take-off, being the extraction from the drawings and specifications of all of the labor and material required for the structures. No bid can be more accurate than the quantity survey on which the estimate is based. A quantity survey, properly made, is much more than simply a list of so many cubic yards of concrete, so many bricks, so much of this, and so much of that. A good take-off shows everything necessary to enable a proper estimate to be made for the job—not for *any* job, but for the particular job that is being bid. An office engineer-estimator must be able to work accurately, quickly, and methodically in taking off. There are many "tricks of the trade" that will save time, reduce errors, and improve accuracy; there are no short cuts, however, that can be taken at the expense of accuracy. "Near enough" is not sufficient. Fractional figures may be rounded off for some items, but such adjustment must be judicious and controlled. For example, consider a concrete item that is 120 ft 9 in. × 1 ft 3½ in. × 11 ft 10 in. This item cannot be altered to 121 ft × 1 ft 4 in. × 12 ft just because those figures would be easier to work with—an error would result of almost 3½ CY. However, having properly computed the item in cubic feet, the conversion to cubic yards may be adjusted to the nearest half cubic yard. This principle of control in rounding off quantities will be evident in the examples shown throughout this book.

Before beginning the take-off, the specifications must be studied; in fact, a "specifications take-off" is of tremendous value and is a great time-saver.

THE SPECIFICATIONS

Reading the specifications need not be a laborious job. You will find, as you become more used to them, that although there are certain items to look for in particular, they also contain many standard paragraphs that you are familiar with and need only scan. It is not necessary to read the subcontractors' sections of the specifications, except to ascertain what items are included, or perhaps to see what reference is made to "work by others" (particularly insofar as "others" refers to the general contractor).

A specifications take-off shows the name of the job, the architect, the date bids close, and the amount of the bid bond or other bid security. The general conditions are read and all salient factors noted—such as completion time, retainage, scope of the work, items not in the contract, items by others, allowances, and alternates. The specifications take-off should be concise, using abbreviations wherever the meaning will not be lost to you.

In the detailed chapters of the specifications, however, all sections that are general contractor's work must be read carefully and the various items and materials that are required must be noted. Subcontractors' sections should be scanned, and any special inclusions or exclusions noted. It is especially important to check the mechanical trades for items such as temporary heat, storm and sanitary sewers, water service, duct lines, and concrete pads for mechanical items. It may be necessary to check other sections of the specifications against the mechanical-trade sections in order to determine which of these items are to be provided by the general contractor.

Subtrade sections that contain "supply only" items should also be read carefully, to ascertain the extent of the general contractor's responsibility for setting.

A typical specifications take-off follows (boldface type indicates sub items):

South Elementary School	Arch.—Nodder & Pulski
Baysville, Mass.	Bids—June 9, 1959, 2 p.m.
Completion—340 cal. days	Cert. check—$18,000

General conditions

By gen. contractor—permits, progress photos, temporary heat (fuel only), C. of W. shack, 2 phones.

Not in contract—fire ins. on bldg., utilities beyond site boundary, furniture, drapes.

Generally—no overtime work, 10 per cent retained 90 days. 1 year maintenance.

Alternates

1. Add for roof changes (see Drg. 12A)
2. Deduct terrazzo & add resilient flooring—Rms. 1A, 3, 9, & 27.

Allowances

Finish hardware	$5,600	(supply only)
Stage curtains	$900	(installed)
Kitchen equipment	$14,200	(installed)

Section 1.   Excavation & site work

Clear site of trees, etc. & grub up roots.

Strip & stockpile loam.	Pumping.
Bldg. excavation.	Sheathing.

Backfill—clean bank gravel 3 ft around all walls.

12 in. bank gravel under ground slabs, platforms, & walks.

Site grading—6 in. low for lawns; 15 in. low for roads; 16 in. low for walks.

Excavate utilities—storm sanitary, water, telephone, fire, oil tank, oil line, electric.

Storm drain—V.-C. pipe; catch basins, head walls.

Sanitary sewer—exc.; catch basins, & manholes *only* (plumber does piping).

Concrete envelope (2,500 psi) for electric service.

Water service (street to bldg.).

Pavings—12½ in. graded gravel + 2½ in. bitumen + bit. curbs

Walks—12 in. bank gravel + 4 in. concrete (2,000 psi) + 6-in. × 6-in. × 10/10 mesh. Broom finish.

½-in. × 4-in. expansion jointing on 30-ft centers.

Flagpole base.

Rebuild stone wall at west boundary.

Lawns & planting.

2. *Concrete*

2,500-psi concrete—footings, foundation walls, ground slabs.

3,000-psi—all other.

Reinforcing steel.

Mesh—6 in. × 6 in. × 6/6 for ground slabs.

Rub exposed walls, ceilings, etc.

Trowel floors + 2 coats liquid hardener for exposed concrete floors.

Grano. floor topping 1:1:2 as drgs. + color admix.

Stair fill (1:1:1) + abrasive grits ¼ lb per SF.

Entrance platforms and steps—float + abrasive ¼ lb per SF.

Lightweight concrete roof fill—1:7 (min. 2 in.)

Set col. base plates, bolts, etc.

Concrete tests (3 cylinders per day of pour).

Waterproofing admix for boiler rm. floor & walls.

3. **Structural steel** (shop paint + field paint 1 coat)

   Bar joists.

4. *Masonry*

Ext. face brick—waterstruck; flemish header in 6th course? Backparge.

Common brick—backup at beam bearings.

Concrete block—backup for gym. walls.

Cinder block—backup & ptns.

Gypsum block ptns.

Limestone + dowels & anchors.

Block reinforcing mesh—all backup block & ptns., continuous at every 2nd course.

Facing tile (5 × 12) clear glazed + plain trim shade caps as drgs. Bull-

nosed jambs and quoins. Coved base in toilets only.
Brick anchors & straps.
Mortar—1:2:6 (ext. walls + waterproofing).
16-oz. copper dam at expansion joints.

5. **Miscellaneous metal** (check specs. for items)
   Hollow metal doors & frames.
   Kalamein doors.
6. **Metal toilet ptns. & screens**
7. **Accoustical tile**
8. **Gypsum roof + formboard + subpurlins**
9. **Fire extinguishers**
10. **Furring, lathing, & plastering**
11. *Carpentry*
    Roof nailers & eaves blocking (pressure treated).
    Framing canopy + 2-in T. & G. deck.
    2-in. batt insulation at eaves.
    Cemesto panels ($1\frac{1}{4}$-in. & $1\frac{1}{16}$-in. at window walls).
    1×3 furring on 16-in. centers—ext. walls for plaster.
    1×2 furring on 12-in. centers—clg. for acoustic tile.
    Grounds for chalkboards, tackboards, & wood paneling.
    2×3 studding at wardrobes and closets.
    Framing & 1-in. T. & G. deck—catwalks.
    Blocking for cabinets & casework.
    Rough bucks and window blocking (treated).
    Frmg. stage floor + 1-in. S.E. subfloor (diagonally).
    Finish wood floor.
    Millwork.
    Wood door & frames.
    Wood windows.
    Overhead doors.
12. **Glass & glazing**
13. **Painting**
14. **Terrazzo & ceramic tile**
15. **Resilient floors**
16. **Plumbing** (includes sanitary sewers except excavation & manholes)
17. **Heating & vent.** (includes labor & set units for temp. heat)
18. **Electrical** (includes *all* temporary wiring: gen. contractor pays for power)

Double lines should be drawn under what will be sub items in colored
pencil (indicated by boldface type in the list above). Blue pencil is best; use
of a red pencil should be restricted to deductions and queries. The reason for
underlining the sub items in colored pencil on the specifications take-off is
to make them stand out ready for when you write up the sub sheet of the
estimate.

If there is any doubt about the intent of the specifications, a small question mark should be made against the item in question (see, for example, the face-brick bond item in the sample specifications take-off) and the specifications can be rechecked when that item is being taken off. Except for such items, the specifications can now be put aside and only the specifications take-off used. The preparation of a specifications take-off will take only two or three hours for most jobs; only very complex or very large (multimillion-dollar) jobs should require more than four hours for this task.

The purposes of a specifications take-off are: to give you an over-all knowledge of the items before you start taking them off individually, to determine the allocation of items between the general contractor and the subcontractors, to subdivide sections that include more than one trade, and to save you time in taking off by providing a convenient summary of the items required.

BEFORE TAKING OFF

Before starting to take off quantities, examine the drawings—*all* of them. Take a quick look through the entire set of drawings for an idea of the layout, type of building, number of floors, and general design, and also the order of the drawings. This quick look takes only a few minutes, yet many little things will stick in your mind and save you time later.

There are three basic rules for taking off quantities:

1. Measure everything as it shows.

2. Take off everything that you can see.

3. If it is different, keep it separate.

1. The first rule—"measure everything as it shows"—simply means take it off exactly as it shows on the drawings; do not "approximate," do not "average," do not "round it off," and do *not* change something because you think you know better than the architect. A measurement of 21 ft 9 in. is not 22 ft; if calculations involving odd inches are beyond your mathematical ability, then estimating is not the work for you! You want to save time? There are ways—many ways—to save hours of your take-off time; they are evident throughout this book. But as for changing something because you think you know what is intended, remember that your take-off is to be used for an estimate on a building "as per plans and specifications"—not for what you imagine is required. If there is a discrepancy between details or between drawings and specifications, you may have to ask the architect for clarification; but never take off what is not called for. Do not attempt to superimpose your own construction knowledge on the architect's drawings, for you are bidding only on what is shown. If changes are made subsequent to the award of a contract, they are a matter for adjustment between the contractor and the owner.

2. The second rule—"take off everything that you can see"—means take it *all* off; do not deliberately leave out anything. You will undoubtedly make some mistakes; we all do. You cannot hope to break down a building into hundreds of small parts and not miss something or make some kind of error. But in order to reduce the probability of error—and so minimize the risk inherent in any bid—you must take off everything that you can see.

If you follow these two rules—taking off everything that you see and taking it off exactly as it shows—you should have a good take-off so far as quantities go.

3. The third rule—"if it is different, keep it separate"—means that you must separate items that will require special consideration, and that you must not mix items that will require different unit prices. Ordinary foundation walls should be carried separately from walls "up in the air" (which will involve a crane for pouring and may also entail more costly formwork). Curved concrete walls mean expensive formwork; keep them separate. Special face-brick patterns, brick arches, and herringbone brick paving are all examples of items that are abnormally expensive and should be kept separate. Machine trench excavation costs more than machine bulk excavation; they should not be lumped together. Work that will require more than normal consideration in pricing the estimate, is often best handled by taking off extra-cost items. The quantities must fully describe and measure all of the work involved. For example, formwork for foundation walls may be taken off as a main item—"Exterior foundation walls—14,340 SF"—plus separate extra-cost items: "Formwork 4-in. brick shelf—1,620 SF; Wall pilasters average 1–6 × 8–0 × 7–3—25 each; 1-in. chamfer strip to walls—386 LF." The take-off should describe the various items; if there is something very unusual about an item, then it should be notated: "See Drg. . . . ." or "Bottom 2 ft below G.W.L.," or whatever is applicable. Pricing an estimate is always a difficult and problematical matter, but a good take-off will reduce the difficulties.

If the take-off is correct and complete, the estimate can be priced with confidence. A poor take-off, a rough, half-guessed take-off, a take-off that does not reflect the special requirements of the job concerned, will mean an unsatisfactory estimate. Errors in the field can be costly, but they *can* be found and corrected. Errors in the take-off, however, have to be swallowed; there is no adjustment possible once the bid has been submitted. The estimating department always works under pressure. There is no time for checking back and forth; it is not possible to do things twice in order to be sure. A certain amount of checking of extensions must be done, but the accuracy of the take-off itself cannot be checked. Contractors involved in competitive bidding cannot double their estimating staffs so as to have enough help to take off each job twice. The office engineer-estimator taking off the job must know what he is doing, must work quickly and methodically, and must have self-confidence.

ORDER OF TAKING OFF

There are several orderly ways for a take-off to progress. One cannot be dogmatic and say that a particular trade must be taken off first for every job; many jobs must be handled quite differently from the normal way. Such jobs excepted, however, the take-off should proceed in a definite pattern—not only trade by trade, but also item by item within each trade. Excavation should *not* be taken off first. The excavation items depend on and follow the below-ground structure, so the substructure items should be taken off before the excavation. That way you will know just what is involved when you start taking off the excavation items, and you will have many needed quantities and measurements already computed. The suggested order of take-off is:

1. Concrete	Substructure
	Superstructure
	Finishes
2. Masonry	Exterior
	Interior
3. Carpentry	Rough
	Finish
4. Finishing trades	Any that the general contractor must do
5. Excavation	Building
	Site
6. Site work	
7. Alternates	

Having completed the concrete (or even just the substructure concrete) items, it would be perfectly in order for you to turn then to the excavation and take off either just the building excavation or the entire excavation and site work before proceeding with the masonry. I prefer the order indicated above because I like to work through the building methodically, trade by trade, before starting on the excavation and site work. This preference is not just a personal prejudice. Very often during the process of taking off an opportunity will occur to visit the site, and a preliminary look at the site will often help one's approach to the excavation items. There may even be specific considerations that necessitate a site visit before taking off the excavation—considerations such as the depth and quality of topsoil, the water condition, street and curb conditions, trees, and access. For a job that is heavy on excavation or site work, making two visits to the site—one before taking off the excavation items and one when ready to price the estimate—is good practice.

The order of taking off should not vary except for very special jobs. The purpose of establishing and keeping a particular order is to so order your mind that one item will follow another in a methodical pattern not only from trade to trade but through the entire take-off. Consider a specific trade—say, concrete. The take-off should progress through the building: pier footings, foundation piers, wall footings, foundation walls, entrances, steps, platforms, ground slabs, and other substructure items; columns, beams, suspended slabs (first floor, second, and so on), roof fill, and other superstructure concrete; floor finishes, rubbing, curbs, bases, and sundries. And so it should go through each trade. Having developed an order of taking off, stay with it—use it always. Every item will have its place, the take-off will go smoothly and swiftly, and the probability of missing an item will be reduced to a minimum; also, a particular item will be easily found when you refer back to the take-off sheets to check something.

TIME-SAVING PRACTICES

Many "tricks of the trade" that save time will be shown in the take-off examples that follow, but certain basic rules may be stressed now.

1. Never use a long word if a short word will do.

2. Abbreviate words whenever possible. "Exc.," "Conc.," "Forms.," "San. Sewer," and "tel." are simple examples. The examples of take-off sheets throughout this book will use many such abbreviations. (A list of abbreviations is given at the beginning of the book.)

3. Keep all dimensions, figures, and areas that might be useful later. A prime example of such a figure is the total exterior-wall perimeter. This figure, first obtained when taking off the concrete walls, could be needed for damp-proofing, rubbing concrete, concrete footings, exterior masonry, plates, stone bands, copings, and eaves items.

4. Learn the "27 times" multiplication table. It is a simple table, quickly learned, and can be used constantly in converting concrete and excavation items from cubic feet to cubic yards.

$$
\begin{array}{rcrcr}
1 & \times & 27 & = & 27 \\
2 & \times & 27 & = & 54 \\
3 & \times & 27 & = & 81 \\
4 & \times & 27 & = & 108 \\
5 & \times & 27 & = & 135 \\
6 & \times & 27 & = & 162 \\
7 & \times & 27 & = & 189 \\
8 & \times & 27 & = & 216 \\
9 & \times & 27 & = & 243 \\
\end{array}
$$

Always be ready to take advantage of combinations of figures that lend themselves to speedy reckoning. The "27 times" table is often especially useful. For example:

$$94{-}0 \times 1{-}0 \times 13{-}6 = 47 \text{ CY}$$

13–6 being half of 27–0, the computation can be reduced to 94 divided by 2. Or, in figuring the excavation of wall trenches:

$$216\text{–}0 \times 4\text{–}6 \times 4\text{–}0 = 144 \text{ CY}$$

216 is a multiple of 27 (8), so to convert to cubic yards the calculation becomes 8 times $4\frac{1}{2}$ times 4, or 8 times 18.

Another example, for 2×8 joists:

$$30 \times 14 \text{ LF} = 560 \text{ BF}$$

Since 2×8 requires $1\frac{1}{3}$ BF per LF, the calculation is actually $30 \times 14 \times 1\frac{1}{3}$; it is simplest, however, to multiply 30 by $1\frac{1}{3}$ first, giving 40, and then multiply 40 by 14 (560).

MATHEMATICAL SHORTCUTS

There are many aids to speedy calculating, as will be seen in the take-off sections of this book. Reference to the sample take-off sheets will show that all dimensions for building items throughout this book are written in feet and inches, *not* in decimals. Even if you intend to use a slide rule or calculating machine, it is best to book the figures in the units that are used on the drawings, and architectural and structural drawings are usually dimensioned in feet and inches. If one is using a machine the conversion to decimals can be made when putting the figures into the machine; and for those who wish to compute the quantities without using a machine or do not have a machine at hand, feet and inches are as easy to work with as decimals. The disadvantage of changing the figured dimension into decimals is that the more conversions the more steps, and the more steps the greater the probability of error. Every step saved when taking off must reduce the probability of error. For each of us, there is a certain probability of error—whether an average of one error per 10 calculations or one per 1,000; thus if we reduce the number of operations, we also reduce the number of errors.

Estimators usually use either a slide rule or a comptometer in converting their quantities and pricing the estimate. There are some small contractors, however, who do not own a comptometer, and there are also many occasions when we have to make computations without access to a calculating machine (such as on the site or on one of those weekends of working on a bid at home). There are even a few mathematically minded purists who prefer to do all their computations without using a calculating machine. Whether you are calculating manually by necessity or choice, however, the quickest and simplest method is by duodecimals or ratio, or (more often than not) a combination of these two methods, which are explained in the Appendix.

The basic rule for multiplication is to multiply the whole numbers and the largest factors first, before multiplying small fractional parts; so the error involved in rounding off fractions or decimals is reduced to a minimum.

Given three dimensions to produce a cubic quantity, two of them small figures and one large, if the two small figures were multiplied first and a fraction or a couple of decimal points dropped, then the error would be multiplied by the amount of the larger figure.

Consider the following calculation for concrete foundation walls:

Concrete foundation walls

$$\textit{By feet and inches: } 327\text{--}0 \quad \times \quad 1\text{--}2 \quad \times \quad 5\text{--}8$$

Method 1	1–2	×	5–8	=	6–8
	327–0	×	6–8	=	2,180 CF

Method 2	327–0	×	5–8	=	1,853–0
	1,853–0	×	1–2	=	2,162 CF

[handwritten: 1852.9999]
[handwritten: 2161.8332]

$$\textit{By decimals: } 327 \text{ ft} \quad \times \quad 1.17 \text{ ft} \quad \times \quad 5.67 \text{ ft}$$

[handwritten: 1'–2"]   *[handwritten: 5'–8"]*

Method 1	1.17	×	5.67	=	6.64
	327.0	×	6.64	=	2,171 CF

Method 2	327	×	5.67	=	1,854
	1,854	×	1.17	=	2,169 CF

The exact answer is 2,161.84 CF.

There are many legitimate shortcuts, most of them simply a matter of seeing combinations of figures that lend themselves to speedy computations. A little thought is also helpful! In every take-off, there are dozens of opportunities to combine items to simplify the extensions. Reducing the number of steps not only saves time, but also reduces the probability of error.

The take-off for concrete beams might read:

[handwritten: 1.14.666]

Concrete beams

L		W		D		Bottoms	Sides
122–0	×	1– 4	×	2–2	} 594 CF	163 SF	1,102 SF
132–6	×	0–10	×	2–2		111	
114–8	×	0–10	×	1–1½	} 138	96	272
27–0	×	1– 0	×	1–1½		27	
					732 CF	397 SF	1,374 SF
				=	27 CY		

[handwritten left margin: 2)54'–6"]
[handwritten: 1.25]
[handwritten: 110.41666]
[handwritten: .8333]

The method used in the above example eliminated eight calculations, reducing the number of steps from sixteen to eight. The extensions on the left are for the concrete, those on the right are for the formwork for beam bottoms and beam sides respectively. First the formwork items for beam bottoms (163 SF and so on) are extended. Each of these items is also the first step in computing the concrete ($L \times W$). Using these items, therefore, go on to compute the concrete items. The first two items have a common beam depth of 2–2, so the 163-SF area may be added to the 111 SF, giving 274 SF times 2–2, or 594 CF. Repeat this procedure for the other two items: 96 SF plus 27 SF gives 123 SF; 123 SF times 1 ft 1½ in. gives 138 CF. Finally, the beam-side forms are computed by first combining those having a common depth; thus the first two beams are handled in one item—254–6 times 2–2, doubled (for two sides). It should be noted that fractional parts of a foot are adjusted to the nearest whole number only in the final figures. Also, if computing only two out of three dimensions—as for beam bottoms—a pencil should be laid over the column of figures not being used, to prevent "jumping" to the wrong dimension.

Length × Depth

It should further be noted that beams of the same width and depth were combined into one item before being entered on the take-off sheet. This is yet another time-saving device; the value of a preliminary "collection sheet" will be shown in the take-off sections that follow.

The general idea is to "use your head," making every calculation work for you, so as to save time and increase accuracy. Quantities to be used for estimating do not have to be set out in the same way as quantities for purchasing schedules. This book is primarily intended to show how to take off items for estimating, for which it is perfectly proper to combine quantities that will carry a common unit price. A great deal of time is wasted by taking off bidding quantities in dozens of separate items that will be priced at the same units. When preparing job schedules, it may be necessary to take off, say, glazed brick or structural glazed tile by rooms; but for estimating, such a room-by-room breakdown would be a waste of time. Only items that will require special consideration when the estimate is being priced should be taken off separately.

COLLECTION SHEETS

The purpose of these sheets is to collect together items that are similar, so as to simplify the take-off sheets, save time, and reduce the probability of error. Collection sheets are *not* scrap paper to be thrown away after the items have been transferred to the take-off sheets; they are part of the take-off, and should be retained in the take-off folder. Consider, for example, concrete foundation walls for a medium-sized building—say, 20,000 SF of floor area. There may be variations in thickness and height of exterior walls; wall footings probably would vary; there might be a brick shelf that varies. The exterior concrete walls, footings, forms, and brick shelf could be taken off in hundreds of separate pieces, with each item being laboriously computed. But the collection sheet will do much of that work for you. It will bring together all the concrete foundation walls 12 in. thick, all the 15-in. walls, and

COLLECTION SHEET FOR FOUNDATION WALLS

Foundation walls

	14 in. *thickness*				16 in.	
height 3–9	4–2	5–8	7–2		4–2	5–4
length 121–4	21– 8	84–8	18–7		19–0	31–6
13–2	17– 9	19–2	43–5			
19–7	32–11	13–6	62–0			
35–4	15– 6	11–4				
189–5	87–10	128–8				

so on; moreover, it will bring together the 12-in. walls 4 ft high, the 12-in. walls 5 ft 3 in. high, and so on. It will enable the wall footing items to follow the wall take-off; it will collect the various pilasters; it will reduce the brick shelf to a few items of specific heights. Ordinary 8½-in. × 11-in. white ruled paper, turned sideways, is excellent for "collecting." For very large jobs, any large ruled or squared paper may be used.

After the various quantities that make up an item have been collected, the total is transferred to the take-off sheet. For the concrete foundation walls described in the previous paragraph, the collection sheet would read as shown above.

If there were openings in the walls, they would be entered on the collection sheet and transferred as deductions to the take-off sheet. From the figures shown above, the take-off sheet would read:

Ext. fdtn. walls

								FORMS
14 in.	189– 5 × 3–9	= 710 SF	⎫					2 × 2,496
	87–10 × 4–2	= 366	⎬ 2,249 SF	= 2,624 CF				= 4,992 SF
	128– 8 × 5–8	= 729	⎪					
	62– 0 × 7–2	= 444	⎭					
16 in.	19–0 × 4–2	= 79	⎫ 247	= 329				
	31–6 × 5–4	= 168	⎭					
Perim.	518–5		2,496 SF	2,953 CF				
				= 109½ CY				

Note that sixteen figures are collected into six items; also that on the take-off sheet the wall surface areas are extended and totaled before being multiplied by the wall thickness. The total perimeter of the walls is computed (518–5), and so becomes available for several items that will come up later. The wall surface area is doubled to obtain the contact area for formwork.

The extensions made in the above example are worth noting:

1. 189–5 × 3–9. Without rewriting the figures,

189–5 is multiplied by 3		= 568–3	
Since 0–9 is a quarter of 3–0, add ¼ × 568–3		= 142–1	
		710–4	= 710 SF

2. In the other items, inches were also converted to fractions of a foot; for example, 87–10 × 4–2:

$$87\text{–}10 \ \times \ 4 \ = \ 351\text{–}4$$
$$+ \ 87\text{–}10 \ \times \ 1/6 \ = \ 14\text{–}8$$
$$366\text{–}0 \ = \ 366 \ SF$$

SUMMARY OF GENERAL RULES FOR TAKING OFF

Always start in the same place on each drawing and progress around the building in a particular direction. (The examples in this book generally start the take-off at the bottom left-hand corner of a drawing and proceed clockwise.)

Do not be afraid to mark up the drawings as you clear a piece of wall or an item. Check off *everything* that you have completed, using a small check mark: details, sections, completed drawings (that is, drawings from which you have taken off everything), items on the specifications take-off, items on the collection sheets that have been transferred to the take-off, and items on the take-off sheets transferred to the estimate. Check them off *immediately after the clearance has been made.*

Always take advantage of duplications of design. Is the building symmetrical about its center line? Are there two or more structural floors with the same design? Do certain beams repeat through two or more floors? Do the room layouts repeat either floor-to-floor or in different sections of a floor? What features do the rooms have in common?

A design is repeated somewhere in most buildings; it might be nothing more than similar bathrooms in the north and south wings, or it might be the whole floor layout of a hospital that is exactly the same on each of three floors. If there are only slight variations from floor to floor, then the items that vary should be taken off before repeating the common items. Make an item work for you as many times as it is repeated. If you see that the interior partitions in the north and south wings are alike and that they are duplicated on the next two floors, then you can handle two wings on each of the three floors—that is, six wings—all alike. Mark one of the wings on the first applicable plan "6 times" or "1 × 6" in bold colored pencil, draw cutoff marks through the plan to delineate the repeated section, and check off all the five duplicate areas on the three drawings. Then take off the partitions in the *one* wing (on a collection sheet), add up the completed items, and multiply each total by six; the six wings are thus all taken off. Probably the best way

COLLECTION SHEET FOR PARTITIONS

Cinder-block partitions

	4-in. ptns.		*8-in. ptns.*	
	9–2	*10–6*	*9–2*	*10–6*
	31– 0	18– 2	111–0	82–4
	42– 6	16–10	27–0	92–8
	93– 4	24– 0	58–0	32–0
	166–10	59– 0	196–0	207–0
6 wings	× 6	× 6	× 6	× 6
√	1,001– 0	354– 0	1,176–0	1,242–0

to mark off the five wings that will not be used is to cross out those areas on the drawings with a large X, as in Fig. 1.1.

The "1 × 6" notation at the right is checked off as the items are done; the first check mark is made when one wing has been completed, and the other when the items have been multiplied by 6.

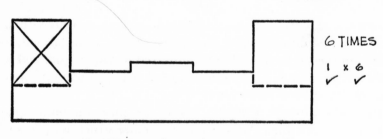

6 TIMES

1 × 6

Fig. 1.1   Duplication of floor plan

Great care must be taken in using this "times-ing" method, but properly applied and carried out it is of tremendous help in both saving time and reducing the probability of error. The notation "6 times" or "1 × 6" must be large enough to stand out, and the check marks must be made as soon as the clearance is completed. The collection sheet must be neat, and must clearly show the multiplication by 6, as in the example shown.

Should further repeating items occur, list them under the applicable items, bracket them for totaling, and then add on the "similars" total (that is, the total of this set of items times the number of duplicates). If, for example, this set of items applies to four areas, you have one area already listed and so have only to add three times the total of this set of items (with a notation "Add 3"). You cannot multiply beyond your first group, except by carrying the subtotals out into another column:

```
                          166–10
              6 wings      × 6
                         _____
                         1,001–0
                           22–6  ⎫
                           14–4  ⎪
                           18–3  ⎬  147–9
                           92–8  ⎪
           Add 3          443–3  ⎭
                         _____
                         1,592–0
```

or

```
        166–10  ×   6   =   1,001–0
         22–6
         14–4
         18–3
         92–8
        _____
        147–9  ×   4   =     591–0
                           _____
                           1,592–0
```

Look for the predominant item of design or detail and make it work for you. For example, the structural floors may be 7-in. concrete slabs for the most part, with small areas of 4-in., 5-in., and 6-in. slabs. Take off the total slab areas—floor by floor—and add them up; you will need the gross floor area anyway for several other items. Then take off all the minor areas of 4-in., 5-in., and 6-in. slabs, and deduct their total from the gross slab area so as to obtain the area of 7-in. slabs. This method is quicker and better than taking off each separate area of 7-in. slab.

Practice adding two items simultaneously, as, for example, in adding windows taken from the elevations. Let us say that there are six types of window in the building, designated A, B, C, D, E, and F. Instead of counting each type of window separately, try two at a time; carry the totals for both types A and B simultaneously. Starting at the top left-hand corner of the elevation sheet, you come first to an A (that is, "1 and 0"), then a B (that is, "1 and 1"), two A's ("3 and 1"), a B ("3 and 2"), and so on. As you count, check off each window with your colored pencil. After a little practice it will become quite simple, and you can step it up to doing three types at a time. It is just a little trick of concentration and practice. (Four items at a time is rather difficult—and is not recommended.)

Do you know the "27 times" table yet?

Always write your items in a set order. Throughout this book, all items are written in the order of *length* times *width* times *height* (or *depth*); any combination of two items also follows that order.

Generally, an item should indicate all three dimensions somewhere; if not in the quantity, then in the description—or between the two. For example:

Concrete in ext. walls   =   27 CY

1-in. T. & G. roof boarding   =   *1,200 SF*

2-in. × 4-in. plates   =   *1,840 LF*

To summarize the basic rules:

Learn the "27 times" table.

Use a red pencil for deductions and queries.

Underline in blue pencil the final total of every item on the take-off sheets —that is, the items that will go onto the estimate sheet.

Make a specifications take-off.

Always check off an item or a drawing as you clear it.

Measure everything as it shows.

Take off everything that is shown.

If it is different—*keep it separate.*

Make the collection sheet work for you.

CHAPTER 2   **Excavation and Site Work**

Excavation is a difficult trade to take off. By contrast, structures are of definite and fixed dimensions; the take-off for them follows a clearly defined procedure and method. Taking off excavation, however, entails several unknown factors which require knowledge and judgment. Consider, for example, that a hole is to be dug; the calculation is simple. But how big is the hole to be? Will the banks stand up? What slope should be figured? What may be reasonably inferred from the borings? Where is the water level? How is the drainage? Is there loam to be stripped? If so, how deep is it? For what is the excavated material to be used? How much of it can be used for fill? Is it going to be trucked away? If so, where to? Is the surplus excavated material enough for the fill areas? Does the material to be excavated meet the requirements for backfill, for general fill, or for sub-beds for pavings? These are only a few of the questions that must be answered in taking off the excavation.

Excavating never conforms to exact quantities; in fact, there is always an element of "intelligent approximation" involved. There can be no certainty about the actual width for a trench, and even if there were, no machine or shovel operator would be able to dig it dead to line. Nor can one be certain about the extent to which excavated material will bulk up when in the loose. Ten CY in the ground might be 12 CY on the truck, or perhaps 11 CY, or— who knows? Knowledge of the district, study of the borings, previous experience, and examination of the site will all help in estimating the increase in bulk—but that is what it is: an estimation, an approximation.

The excavation take-off should not be attempted until all of the substructure concrete has been taken off. Whether the excavation is taken off immediately following the belowground concrete, after the entire concrete work, or even after all trades for the entire building proper, is a matter of choice. But you cannot determine the problems of the building excavation until you have taken off the foundations, the ground slabs, and all the rest of the belowgrade concrete.

17

VISITING THE SITE

Always try to see the site *before* starting the excavation take-off. An idea of what the site is like will often help you to decide how to handle some of the excavation problems. Often it is possible to visit a site when picking up the bid drawings or while en route to another job or appointment, but sometimes a special trip will be necessary. It might also be necessary to revisit the site when the estimate is ready to price. The problems involved and the overall value of the excavation and site work should determine whether or not two visits to the site are justified.

For many reasons, it is imperative that the site be visited. The plot plan *should* show all items present on the site, but plot plans are sometimes so sketchy that one must examine the site for anything—old foundations, curbs, buildings, trees, shrubs—that would have to be removed. It is quite common to discover that a site is completely wooded, although no trees have been shown on the plot plan.

Determining the depth and quality of the loam may present a problem. For bidding jobs that include considerable excavation or a fair amount of loam stripping, a hand shovel should be taken along when visiting the site. The entire bid may turn on one question: how much loam is there and is it good enough to meet the requirements for lawns? The quantity of loam affects other aspects of the job too. On a site-cut job (for which the grading is essentially cut) more loam means less cutting. If fill must be added to raise a low site, however, then the more loam to be stripped the more fill to be supplied.

Rock is another vital consideration. If rock excavation is specified as an extra-cost item over the amount of the contract, the unit price for rock may be very important. A given unit price (that is, a unit price embodied in the specifications by the architect) that is very low may have to be compensated for in the bid if there is much rock on the site. Or a large amount of rock excavation with a good unit-price extra, may cause a contractor to tighten his bid. The size of boulders not classified as extra-cost rock may also be important. For example, a certain architect invariably includes boulders up to 4 CY with the unclassified "earth" excavation. The amount of rock, of course, depends on the nature of the site, but on a recent bid for which the specifications included this provision, rock outcroppings were found all over the site. A 4-CY boulder is quite an item—8 tons of rock at no extra cost!

Of course, the general nature of the ground will have to be considered. A good set of borings will help you; two or three test pits may only fool you! If other construction is going on near the site, you may be able to see there how the banks stand up, what the water condition is like, and what the ground material is like. All these observations can help, but cannot be conclusive.

Access to the site must also be evaluated. Are you going to be hemmed in? Will you have to construct a temporary access road? Will you be tight for storage room? How far is the nearest electric power line? How far to the water main? Where is the telephone line?

Utilities may present several problems. Where do your lines go to from the building? Where do the permanent power, water, and gas supply lines, fire alarm, and telephone lines come from? Will you have street digging, or road and sidewalks to cut and make good? Will there be any utility companies to pay? Any city fees for street work? Any traffic protection or police control to be paid by the contractor when working in the public road?

Surplus earth may have to be removed from the site. Where is it to go? Can it be sold? Is there a dump handy? Is there a charge for dumping? How many miles is it to the dump?

Fill may have to be transported to the site. Is there a pit nearby? If so, what is the material like? How will it compact?

These are only the most common problems that must be considered. Particular jobs may have their own site problems—anything from radio control for hauling earth around airports to problems of logistics for a job in a remote area.

SITE CLEARING

If possible, all items to be removed should be measured; otherwise they should be described for a lump-sum price. Walls, curbs, fences, and the like can be taken off in lineal feet; isolated trees can be counted. Wooded areas are measured in acres, with some indication given as to the extent and nature of the trees, such as "heavily wooded" or "small trees" or "mostly scrub."

The site area will probably be taken off at this time. The limits of contract lines on the plot plans should be clearly marked with colored pencil. If the

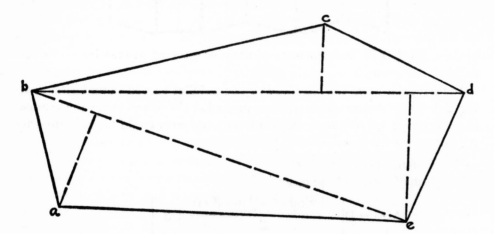

Fig. 2.1 Determination of site area—triangulation

site is irregular in shape, it may have to be broken up into triangles to compute the area—a procedure called "triangulation." An irregular site with
curved boundaries might require offsets for calculating the area.

To compute the area of a site that has been split into triangles, note the
areas that have a common base. In Fig. 2.1, triangles b-c-d and b-e-d have a
common base (b-d). Those two triangles may be computed as one item: the
length of b-d times the average perpendicular height. Scale off the perpendicular height of each of the two triangles, add them together, and divide by
two for the average height, which multiplied by b-d will give the total area
of the two triangles.

Short irregular boundaries may be treated as straight-line boundaries in
marking off the limit lines, as in Fig. 2.2. The curved lines are the actual site
boundaries; the dotted lines are the boundaries superimposed for computing
the area.

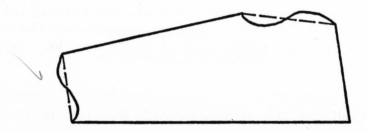

Fig. 2.2   Determination of site area—irregular boundaries

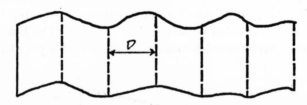

Fig. 2.3   Determination of site area—curved boundaries

For irregular areas having more or less parallel curved boundaries, as in
Fig. 2.3, the area of the site may be expressed as the length times the average
of the seven offsets. Or, for greater accuracy, the area could be computed by
the midordinate method:

D = Distance between offsets
S = Sum of intermediate offsets

$$\text{Area} = D\left[\frac{(\text{1st offset} + \text{last offset})}{2} + S\right]$$

Still another method is "Simpson's Rule of One-Third," which is more complicated and is not usually used for estimating.

STRIPPING LOAM

As in all excavation work, there is an element of guesswork in this item; not blind guesswork, but without certainty. The depth of the loam shown on the borings can be averaged, the areas in which loam is shown can be marked off, the site can be examined, and certain conclusions may thus be drawn. But a great deal depends on the quality of the loam and the nature of the site. What is classified as loam on the borings may prove to be very poor loamy sand when you start stripping. If the site is wooded with fair-sized stumps to be grubbed up, much loam may be lost in loading roots and stumps to haul off the site.

The quantity of loam required for the lawns and planting may affect the take-off for loam stripping. What happens to the surplus loam: does it become the property of the owner or the contractor?

Loam stripping is taken off in cubic yards, with the thickness stated in the description: "Strip and stockpile loam (8 in.)—........CY."

BUILDING EXCAVATION: EXAMPLE NO. 1

The building excavation must be taken off in several separate items, such as: "Machine bulk excavation, building; Machine trench excavation, building; Hand excavation, footings; Excavate pier footings." The bulk excavation is measured to the underside of the basement slab or to the underside of the gravel bed for the slab, allowing for the depth of loam stripping already

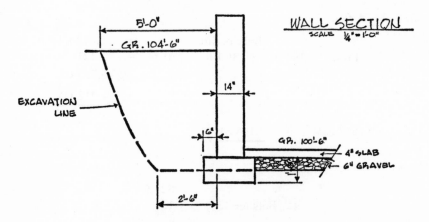

Fig. 2.4   Section through foundation wall

taken off. The top grade must be averaged from the grades shown on the plot plan. The allowance for working space depends on the depth of the excavation and the nature of the material. The excavation can seldom be less than

3 ft outside the building lines, but the distance cannot be determined exactly. It is often useful to set up the excavation lines on a wall section. This setting up takes only a few minutes, and then, knowing the type of material (from the borings), you can see what appears to be a reasonable slope for the banks. If the excavation cut is to be sheeted, of course there is no problem of banks or slope.

An excavation line superimposed on a foundation-wall section is shown in Fig. 2.4. The average width of the bulk excavation is 3 ft 9 in. outside the building line; hand work for the wall footing is taken off separately.

Working Drawing 2.1 shows the foundation walls of a building, with the wall section the same as that in Fig. 2.4. The perimeter and the floor area are given because they would have been taken off and determined as part of the foundation concrete.

THE TAKE-OFF (W. D. 2.1)

Machine bulk exc. bldg.

$$
\begin{array}{rrrrrr}
 & 4,534 \text{ SF} & \times & 4\text{--}10 & = & 21,912 \text{ CF} \\
\text{Perim.} \quad 309\text{--}0 & \times \quad 3\text{--}9 & \times & 4\text{--}10 & = & \underline{5,602} \\
 & & & & & 27,514 \text{ CF} \\
 & & & & = & \underline{\underline{1,019 \text{ CY}}}
\end{array}
$$

Hand exc. wall ftgs.

$$
\begin{array}{rrrrr}
289\text{--}4 & \times \quad 3\text{--}0 & \times \quad 0\text{--}6 & = & \underline{\underline{434 \text{ CF}}} \\
 & & & = & \underline{\underline{16 \text{ CY}}}
\end{array}
$$

Backfill: walls & ftgs.

$$
\begin{array}{rrrrrr}
 & & \text{Bulk perim.} & = & 5,602 \text{ CF} \\
\text{Ftgs.} \quad 289\text{--}4 & \times \quad 0\text{--}10 & \times \quad 0\text{--}6 & = & \underline{121} \\
 & & & & 5,723 \text{ CF} \\
 & & & = & \underline{\underline{212 \text{ CY}}}
\end{array}
$$

Hand trim for ground slab   = $\underline{\underline{4,196 \text{ SF}}}$

Surplus material to remove

$$
\begin{array}{rrr}
 & & 823 \text{ CY} \\
+ \quad \text{Bulkage } 15\% & & \underline{123} \\
 & & \underline{\underline{946 \text{ CY}}}
\end{array}
$$

NOTES ON THE TAKE-OFF (W. D. 2.1)

The perimeter is separated from the building area in order to have the quantity for backfilling available without having to recalculate it. The method by which the perimeter and floor area are obtained is explained in

Chap. 3. The gross building area is the floor area plus the perimeter wall area —4,196 SF—plus (289–4 times 1–2); that is, 4,196 plus 338, or 4,534 SF. The depth of 4–10 is from the present grade to the underside of the gravel bed.

The length of the perimeter item is figured as follows:

Wall perimeter				=	289–4
+ to outside lines	4	×	1–2	=	4–8
+ to excavation line	4	×	3–9	=	15–0
					309–0

The hand-excavation length is the same as the wall perimeter, since the footing excavation is equidistant from both sides of the wall. The footing is 2–2 wide, so an excavation 3 ft wide would be sufficient to allow for erecting the edge forms.

The take-off for the backfill is the perimeter quantity (5,602 CF) plus the backfill around the footing. The footing backfill is the 10-in. working space included in the 3-ft-wide footing excavation. Very often, having taken off the concrete, we can use those quantities to figure the backfill. In this instance, reference to the concrete quantities would show the wall footings (289–4 × 2–2 × 1–0) to be 627 CF. The hand excavation item is to half of the 12-in.-deep footing, so the concrete used in that space will be 313 CF. Deducting that figure from a total excavation of 434 CF, gives 121 CF to be backfilled.

The item for hand trim is the floor area that must be graded before pouring the slab. The actual leveling may be to the ground or simply of the gravel fill, but whichever it is, an item has to be carried for it.

The surplus for removal is the total excavated material less the quantity needed for backfill. An allowance must be made for the increase in bulk when the material is in the loose. For rock on trucks, the increase may be as much as 30 per cent. Normally the balancing of excavation and backfill is not made until all excavation work has been taken off. It is shown here as if there was no further excavation, but on most jobs there would be site cut and fill still to take off, plus various site-work excavations, before striking the balance.

BUILDING EXCAVATION: EXAMPLE NO. 2

The foundation plan and section are shown in W. D. 3.1 for a building whose slab-on-ground is above the natural grade. Since the excavation take-off will follow the quantities for the foundation items, the concrete take-off (p. 52) should be read in conjunction with this example.

The excavation will be for wall trenches (no bulk excavation) and footings.

The footing is 2 ft wide, and so the trench should be 4 ft wide at the bottom. At a slope of about 1 in 2, the trench will be 8 ft wide at the top, for a 6-ft average width. The wall bottom varies. The trench excavation item is taken off to within 3 in. of the bottom of the footing, and that last 3 in. taken off as hand work.

THE TAKE-OFF (W. D. 3.1)

*Strip & stockpile loam**
$$107\text{--}0 \quad \times \quad 77\text{--}0 \quad = \quad 8,239 \text{ SF} \quad \times \quad 0\text{--}6 \quad = \quad 4,120 \text{ CF}$$
$$= \quad \underline{153 \text{ CY}}$$

Machine trench exc. bldg.

$314\text{--}10 \times 6\text{--}0 \times 5\text{--}0 = 9,445$ CF	Wall area	$= 2,232$ SF
$= \underline{350 \text{ CY}}$	Wall perim.	$= 314\text{--}10$
	Average height	$= 7\text{--} 1\frac{1}{2}$
	$101\text{--} 3$	$- \quad 2\text{--}10\frac{1}{2}$
	$-\ 98\text{--} 4\frac{1}{2}$	$4\text{--}3$ below grade
	$2\text{--}10\frac{1}{2}$ Add	$0\text{--}9$ footing
	Exc. height	$= \underline{\underline{5\text{--}0}}$

Exc. pier ftg.†
$$12/ \quad 8\text{--}0 \quad \times \quad 7\text{--}0 \quad \times \quad 5\text{--}0 \quad = \quad 3,360 \text{ CF} \quad = \quad \underline{125 \text{ CY}}$$

Hand exc. wall ftgs.
$$314\text{--}10 \quad \times \quad 3\text{--}0 \quad \times \quad 0\text{--}3 \quad = \quad \underline{9 \text{ CY}}$$

Backfill walls

	Total exc. material		$= \quad 484$ CY
Wall	$314\text{--}10 \times 1\text{--}0 \times 4\text{--}3 =$	$49\frac{1}{2}$ CY	
Wall ftg.		$23\frac{1}{2}$	83
Pier ftg.		10	
			$= \quad \underline{401 \text{ CY}}$

Fill to ground slab
$$4,777 \text{ SF} \quad \times \quad 1\text{--}6\frac{1}{2} \quad = \quad 7,365 \text{ CF} \quad = \quad \underline{\underline{273 \text{ CY}}} \text{ (see below)}$$

Site material	$=$	$\underline{83 \text{ CY}}$
Material to buy	$=$	190 CY
$+ \ 15\%$		29
		$\underline{219 \text{ CY}}$

* Taken off approx. 8 ft outside max. bldg. lines.

† The oblique line (/) is a multiplication sign (an "×" may be used if preferred). The only advantage in using the "/" sign is to differentiate the quantity from the dimensions, so that one can quickly see, for example, that there are 12 footings — each 8–0 × 7–0 × 5–0.

NOTES ON THE TAKE-OFF (W. D. 3.1)

The loam strip is taken off to a rectangle approximately 8 ft beyond the building lines. The extent of this item would be indicated on the drawings or in the specifications. The excavation for wall trenches is based on a width of 8 ft at the top and 4 ft at the bottom, an average width of 6 ft. For the depth of the trench, note that on the concrete foundation wall take-off (p. 52) there is 314–10 of wall with a total surface area of 2,232 SF. Dividing 2,232 SF by the 314–10 perimeter gives an average depth of 7–1½. The distance from the top of the wall to the grade after the loam stripping is 2–10½, leaving 4–3 of wall below ground. Adding 9 in. for the footing gives a total depth of 5 ft for the trench; this leaves 3 in. of hand excavation.

The pier footings item follows the grades of the walls nearest to them (as can be seen in W. D. 3.1); therefore they too must be 5 ft below grade. The average size of the 12 pier footings is 4 × 3 ft (or 12 SF of "on the ground" area). The 2-ft wall footing required a 6-ft trench, so a 4-ft footing for the same slope would require an 8-ft trench, and the 4 × 3-ft footing an 8 × 7-ft hole. Thus 12 holes are required, each 8 × 7 × 5 ft. The take-off for backfill starts with the total excavation (350 plus 9 plus 125) in cubic yards, from which the concrete is deducted. The concrete wall is 4 ft 3 in. in the ground, so there is 49½ CY in that item. The wall footings are entirely below ground. The backfill item for piers and pier footings consists of all the footings (8 CY) plus 2 CY of the 3 allowed for the piers.

The fill to ground slab item is the floor area times the distance from the underside of the gravel bed down to the natural grade after loam strip. This gives 273 CY, but since some surplus earth is available at the site, that quantity is broken down as follows: 83 CY of site material, and 190 CY to buy. To the 190 CY to buy is added 15 per cent for truck measure (which is the way the material is bought); thus, 190 plus 29 CY is 219 CY to buy.

ROCK EXCAVATION

Rock excavation must be measured as accurately as is possible from the available information. The excavation lines for rock do not require quite so much working clearance as earth excavation. In general, the rock excavation line at the bottom would be the same as for earth, but the banks would not be sloped. If the wall section in Fig. 2.4 was to be in rock, for instance, the excavation lines would extend 2½ ft outside the wall lines. Rock cannot be excavated to an exact grade, and any attempt to do so would almost inevitably result in failure to "get the bottom" in many places and incur almost a double expense for redrilling. In order to be reasonably sure of getting down to grade everywhere, the rock should be drilled to an extra depth of 6 in. or more, depending on the nature of the rock and the depth being drilled.

For the building shown in W. D. 2.1 and the wall section in Fig. 2.4, the rock excavation would be taken off to 6 in. below the gravel (that is, to the bottom of the wall footing) and around the perimeter the rock would be drilled 6 in. deeper (say, 4 ft wide) to ensure getting the footing.

THE TAKE-OFF (W. D. 2.1)

Exc. rock (bulk) — bldg.

	Bldg.				=	4,534 SF	
+ Perim.	304–0	×	2–6		=	760	
						5,294 SF	× 5–4 = 28,235 CF
+ Ftg.	289–4	×	4–0	× 0–6			= 579
							28,814 CF
							= 1,067 CY

Load & truck rock from site

		1,067 CY
+	Bulkage 40%	427
		1,494 CY

Level off rock for footing

$$289\text{–}4 \quad \times \quad 2\text{–}6 \quad = \quad \underline{724 \text{ SF}}$$

Gravel bed for ground slabs

		4,196 SF	× 12 in.	=	156 CY
			+ Compaction 15%		24
					180 CY

Backfill — walls & ftgs.

	Perim.	760 SF	×	5–4	=	4,053 CF
+	Ftg. (all)					579
						4,632 CF
					=	172 CY

NOTES ON THE TAKE-OFF (W. D. 2.1)

The excavation area is the building area previously determined (p. 23): the floor area (4,196 SF) plus the walls (289–4 × 1–2)—4,534 SF, plus the working-space perimeter. That outer perimeter is:

	Wall perimeter			=	289–4
+	to outside wall lines	4	× 1–2	}	14–8
+	to excavation lines	4	× 2–6		
					304–0

The depth is from grade 104–6 to 99–2 (5–4), which allows for excavation 6 in. below the bottom of the gravel bed.

The trucking allows an increase of 40 per cent in the rock volume for bulking up. The bulk-up allowance will vary considerably; much depends on how the rock is broken up. The larger the pieces, the lesser the yardage per truckload. One or two large, irregularly shaped pieces of rock can make a truckload—a load consisting half of voids, but nevertheless a load.

Some leveling for the footings will usually be needed. If the walls are to rest on rock without footings, it may be necessary to take off items both for leveling and for doweling the walls to the rock.

The gravel bed is taken off at 12 in. deep because the rock excavation item was taken off an extra 6 in. deep. Actually, the amount of gravel required will vary according to how the rock blows when dynamited. The projection of the footing under the slab is *not* deducted from the gravel quantity.

The backfill is taken off only for the outside of the walls. The 12 in. taken off for the gravel bed will allow sufficient surplus material to fill the small area around the inside of the excavation at the footings.

Like most excavation items, rock excavation involves many unknown factors, and the quantities are at best a close approximation. Hard granite with the seam diagonal to the drilling line may break, leaving a toe, so that after a few unlucky blasts it becomes necessary to drill deeper to remove the toe. It is usually considerably cheaper to drill a little deeper the first time.

Even if rock excavation is specified at extra cost over contract, it might be necessary to take off rock quantities. In figuring a unit price for rock, you should check the specifications for payment lines. Pay lines that are too tight must be allowed for in your own unit price for extra-cost rock; if the unit price has been set up by the architect, pay lines are just as important to your thinking. You may be paid for rock excavation as measured to a pay line 2–0 outside the building lines, but in actuality have to excavate 3–0 outside the building lines to allow for footings and formwork.

Rock excavation in trenches must be taken off separately from open rock excavation. Rock excavation where blasting is prohibited must also be taken off separately. Similarly, separate any rock excavation that must be blown in small pieces, such as when blasting close to another building.

SHEETING FOR EXCAVATIONS

Sheeting for excavations is measured in square feet, allowing sufficient length both for driving the sheeting into the ground below the excavation grade and for the top of the sheeting above ground. Driven sheeting will "go" according to the material and obstructions encountered, and so the sheeting will be up and down; thus the length figured should never be less than the next even-foot length (that is, 6 ft, 8 ft, 10 ft, and so on) greater than the net depth of the excavation.

Special sheeting, such as steel columns, interlocking steel sheeting, or something similar, should be taken off in detail and fully described, as in the following: "H-cols. for sheeting (50 pcs. at 18 ft)—31.7 tons; Interlocking sheet piling (2,200 SF)—33.4 tons; I-beam spreaders for trench sheeting—4.1 tons."

Ordinary plank sheeting of the type used in a sewer trench of moderate depth and width, is measured as the net square-foot face area of the trench, doubled for the two sides, and the item notated "b.s.m." (both sides measured).

SITE GRADING

Cut and fill for site grading is an item for which the quantities will vary considerably; even if taken off twice by the same person, the totals might not be exactly the same. On a scale of 1 in. to 40 ft, each 1-in. × 1-in. square represents 1,600 SF, so that in estimating the cut or fill for that area, there is a variation of 5 CY of material for every 1-in. difference in depth. It is impossible to take off cut and fill to within 1 in.—in fact, those items are usually measured in multiples of 3 in. or 6 in. It should also be noted that the finished area when graded will probably vary slightly from the drawings. If road profiles are shown on the drawings, the cut and fill for roads should be taken off separately and measured more accurately than general grading.

General grading is usually taken off from the site plan by blocking off the drawing into suitable squares and taking each square separately. But before considering the actual amount of cut and fill, there are other factors

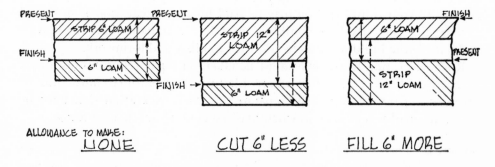

Fig. 2.5 Grading cut and fill, working from present and finish grades

that must be determined. The loam stripping would already have been taken off, and now the depth of the loam to be stripped and the specified depth of the loam for finish grading must be compared (Fig. 2.5). If the loam stripped was the same depth as the loam required for finish grading, there would be no problem, because the difference between the present grades and the finish grades would be the same as the difference between the present grade after stripping and the finish subgrade. If there was no loam to strip, however, and 6 in. of loam was to be allowed for finish grading, then cuts would be increased by 6 in. and the fill decreased by the same amount. If, on the other hand, there was 12 in. of loam to strip but only 6 in. required for finish grading, then cuts would be decreased by 6 in. and fill increased by that amount.

One other factor should be considered before taking off cut and fill. Any peat, silt, or other spongy or unstable material specified for removal must be taken off and notated "remove from site" if it has to be hauled away. The extent of that item will have to be allowed for in taking off the cut and fill.

In taking off cut and fill by gridding the site, it is better to use a transparent plastic sheet than to mark off the drawing itself. Heavy plastic sheets can be bought marked off in 1-in. squares, which, laid on the drawing, will save time and prevent the drawing from becoming so marked up that it cannot be read. It is also helpful to mark off the plastic sheet with letters for one direction and numbers for the other, so that each block is identified.

Working Drawing 2.2 shows an area to be graded ("Loam stripped 6 in.; allow 6 in. for loam for finish grading"). The broken lines are present grades, and the solid lines finish grades. The drawing is marked off in 1-in. squares, each square (or block) representing 40 ft × 40 ft, or 1,600 SF. The letters along the top and the numbers down the side identify the squares: A1, B1, C1, and so on. Starting at A1 and working across the drawing, we would consider each square separately. We might take off the present grade at each corner of a block to obtain an average present grade, and then do the same for the finish grades, with the difference between the two averages being the cut or fill needed for that square. This is a laborious and slow method, however, and, despite all the work involved, the result is still an approximation. It is much simpler to take the present and finish grades at the *center* of each block, allowing for any abrupt changes, and so determine each cut or fill depth in a single mental calculation.

Let us compare these two methods, taking at random three blocks—say A1, B3, and B5 (see tabulation on next page).

The three blocks taken off at the four corners (4.55 ft plus 4.35 ft plus 2.73 ft) show a total cut of 689 CY, while the three blocks taken the simpler way (4.5 ft plus 4.5 ft plus 2.5 ft) give a total cut of 682 CY; the difference of 7 CY is negligible for grading quantities. It must be remembered that grading cut and fill items are always approximate quantities. The present grades shown are themselves approximations, being simply contours drawn in to connect spot grades taken at intervals. The finish grading will be done to grade stakes, and will not necessarily conform to the exact contours shown on the drawing; between the stakes, the grades will be shaped to pleasing

		4-Corners Method		Center Method	
		Present	*Finish*		
Block A1	1.	90.1	85.1	Present	88.5
1 2	2.	88.3	85.0	Finish	84.0
	3.	88.9	83.5	Cut	4.5 ft
	4.	87.5	83.0		
3 4		354.8	336.6		
		336.6			
		4)18.2			
	Cut	4.55 ft			
Block B3	1.	86.0	80.5	Present	83.8
	2.	83.7	79.8	Finish	79.3
	3.	84.3	78.8	Cut	4.5 ft
	4.	81.0	78.6		
		335.0	317.7		
		317.7			
		4)17.3			
	Cut	4.35 ft			
Block B5	1.	82.9	78.1	Present	79.7
	2.	79.0	77.6	Finish	77.2
	3.	80.4	76.9	Cut	2.5 ft
	4.	77.8	76.6		
		320.1	309.2		
		309.2			
		4)10.9			
	Cut	2.73 ft			

contours. Thus the simplest and fastest satisfactory way in which to take off cut and fill is by using the grades at the center of each block. The collection sheet for W. D. 2.2 is shown on page 31.

Notice that D6 is an example of a block that must be adjusted to allow for abrupt changes in contours. Although there is 4 ft of fill at the center, this decreases to 2 ft at the outside, and so this block is taken off for 3 ft of fill.

For a small site such as that shown in W. D. 2.2, the advantage of using a collection sheet is slight, but the method would be the same no matter how large the site; thus for large grading jobs there would simply be more items in each of the groups, and cut and fill for the entire site could still be taken off in only twenty or thirty calculations.

COLLECTION SHEET FOR CUT AND FILL

	Grading (1,600-SF blocks)	
	Cut	*Fill*
0–6	D2	D1
1–0	C4, C5	
1–6	C1, B6	C6
2–0		D5
2–6	C2, B5, A6	
3–0	C3	D6
3–6	B1, B2, B4	
4–0		
4–6	A1, B3	
5–0	A2	
5–6	A5	
6–0	A4	
6–6	A3	Loam strip 6 in.
		Lawns, 6 in. loam

No change — D3, D4

THE TAKE-OFF (W. D. 2.2)

Site grading — cut

1/	1600 SF	×	0–6	=	800 CF
2/	1600	×	1–0	}	8,000
2/	1600	×	1–6		
3/	1600	×	2–6	=	12,000
1/	1600	×	3–0	=	4,800
3/	1600	×	3–6	=	16,800
2/	1600	×	4–6	=	14,400
1/	1600	×	5–0	}	36,800
1/	1600	×	5–6		
1/	1600	×	6–0		
1/	1600	×	6–6		
					93,600 CF
				=	3,466 CY

Site grading — fill

1/	1,600 SF	×	0–6	}	11,200 CF
1/	1,600	×	1–6		
1/	1,600	×	2–0		
1/	1,600	×	3–0		
				=	415 CY

Material to remove from site

$$3,051 \text{ CY}$$

$$+ \quad \text{Bulking up} \quad 15\% \quad \underline{449}$$

$$\underline{3,500 \text{ CY}}$$

Area to subgrade

$$240 \text{ ft} \quad \times \quad 160 \text{ ft} \quad = \quad \underline{38,400 \text{ SF}}$$

Lawns — spread loam (from site stockpile)

$$38,400 \text{ SF} \quad \times \quad 6 \text{ in.} \quad = \quad \overline{\underline{19,200 \text{ CF}}}$$

$$= \quad \overline{711 \text{ CY}}$$

$$+ \quad 10\% \quad \underline{71}$$

$$\overline{782 \text{ CY}}$$

Spread lime (10 lb per 1,000 SF)	=	400 lb
Comm. fertilizer (20 lb per 1,000 SF)	=	800 lb
Grass seeding (5 lb per 1,000 SF)	=	38,400 SF
Maintain lawns until 2nd cutting	=	L.S.

NOTES ON THE TAKE-OFF (W. D. 2.2)

In taking off a job, the entire excavation section would be completed before balancing the excavation and fill items to determine the quantity of material to be removed or bought. In the calculation of the grading cut and fill, certain items are combined to save multiplications; for example, the second and third items of the grading cut (two at 1–0 and two at 1–6) are combined (as one at 5–0), so that 1,600 SF times 5–0 gives 8,000 CF.

The details of the lawn items would be taken from the specifications take-off. The quantities of lime and fertilizer are rounded off to the next 50 lb above the net quantity.

MISCELLANEOUS LANDSCAPE ITEMS

Lawn sodding is taken off in square feet separately from the seeding quantities. Any special lawn items are measured and taken off item by item; for example, swales are measured as an extra-cost item: "Form grass swales—........SF."

Planting is usually treated as a sub item; if taken off, however, the various types of shrubs are listed separately by sizes.

Tree wells are taken off by number and fully described; for example: "Field stone tree wells 6-ft dia. × 1–6 deep—8 ea."

ROADS AND PAVINGS

The cut and fill for pavings may be taken off as part of the general grading cut and fill, making allowance for the paving subgrades where they differ from the subgrade for the lawns; thus doing the entire grading in one operation. Alternatively, roads, parking areas, drives, and the like can be marked off on the drawing, and the excavation for them taken off separately from the general grading. Either method may be used, depending on the site layout and personal preference. If road profiles are shown on the drawings, they should be used for the road cut and fill.

Still another method is to first take off the entire site with the general grading—that is, *all* the exterior areas (such as lawns, roads, and walks)—measured as at the lawns subgrade; then take off the paved areas for extra depth. Thus, if the subgrade for the lawns is 6 in. low and the road subgrade is 14 in. below the finish grade, having previously taken off the entire site as at 6 in. below the finish grade, we can use the road profiles for the additional 8 in. of cut or fill. Cuts for roads should be taken off wide enough to include the curb, or the width of the gravel or stone bed if it extends beyond the actual road width. Fill for roads must be taken off wide enough to allow for the slope of the banks. If a road is to be built on an embankment that varies in height, it will be necessary to take a number of cross sections in order to determine an average cross section for the embankment fill.

When preparing a collection sheet for the roadwork, you should also include thereon the areas for *all* pavings, driveways, courtyards, curbs, walks, and similar work connected with the pavings. Guard rails, parking lines, wheel stops, fencing, and the like should also be included. Then, using the collection sheet and the cross sections and details on the drawings, complete the take-off sheet.

Working Drawings 2.3 and 2.4 show a partial site plan: a road, a parking area, bitumen walks, concrete walks, and curbs. We note that the road is 30 ft wide and has a granite curb at one side and a bitumen curb at the other. The subgrade for the road (14½ in. below finish grade) and the distances between points where cut and fill depths change, are details that we would mark on the profile when starting our take-off for the paving; they are *not* part of the profile drawing.

This is an example of a plan that does not show the finish contours; the only information on them is shown on the profiles. Therefore we must use the profiles for our take-off.

Assume that the grading (except for the road) has been taken off previously. In this take-off, we will include cut and fill for the road, the extra excavation for the curb, all of the gravel, surface material for all pavings, the bitumen curb, and the granite curb.

The curbing around curves is measured best by using a steel scale tape on edge, following the curve. The scale measurement may be converted to the actual dimension by laying it off on the proper engineer's or architect's scale. Since the two radius pieces at the street are not detailed, they should be taken off as scaled (as 5-ft curve pieces). All dimensions not given are scaled off. The collection sheet is shown:

COLLECTION SHEET FOR WALKS AND ROADS

Roads

						Bit. walks					

Roads

344–0 × 30–0 = 10,320 SF

80–0 × 25–0 = 2,000

12,320 SF

Bit. walks

25 × 10 ft = 250 SF

75 × 6 = 450

700 SF

Conc. walks   *Forms*

259–0 × 6–0 = 1,554 SF   518 ft

72–0 × 8–0 = 576   144

30–0 × 23–0 = 690   68

2,820 SF   730 ft

Bit. curb

52 ft

220

272 ft

Gran. curb   *Pkg. area — grades*

195 ft

85   *Present*   *Sub*

63   (rad.)   34.0   33.8

20   35.2   35.8

2/25 = 50   37.5   2.0 cut

80   36.5

493 ft   4)143.2

Gran. curb 5-ft rad. corners = 2 pcs.   35.8

THE TAKE-OFF (W. D. 2.3 AND 2.4)

ROADS AND PAVINGS

Exc. for roads

	33–0	×	31–6	×	1–0	=	1,040 SF	=	1,040 CF
+	10–0	×	31–6	×	1–4	=	315	=	420
$\frac{1}{2}$/	53–0	×	31–6	×	1–3	=	1,670	=	1,046
$\frac{1}{2}$/	70–0	×	31–6	×	2–3	=	2,205	=	2,480
Pkg.	82–0	×	25–6	×	2–0	=	2,091	=	4,182
							7,321 SF	=	9,168 CF
								=	340 CY

Fill for roads

$\frac{1}{2}$/	18–0	×	31–6	×	0–3	=	567 SF	=	71 CF
$\frac{1}{2}$/	170–0	×	31–6	×	1–4	=	5,355 SF	=	3,571
							5,922 SF	=	3,642 CF
								=	135 CY

Shape & roll subbase for road

$$
\begin{array}{r}
7,321 \text{ SF} \\
- \quad 315 \\
\hline
7,006 \\
+ \quad 5,922 \\
\hline
12,928 \text{ SF} \\
\end{array}
$$

Grading for walks — taken off previously

Shape & trim subbase for walks

$$
\begin{array}{r}
2,820 \text{ SF} \\
700 \\
\hline
3,520 \text{ SF} \\
\end{array}
$$

Graded gravel base for pavings

Road	12,928 SF	×	12 in.		=	12,928 CF	
Walks — conc.	2,820	×	6		=	1,410	
Walks — bit.	700	×	8		=	467	
+ Curbs	500–0	×	1–6	× 1–0	=	750	

$$
\begin{array}{r}
15,555 \text{ CF} \\
= \quad 576 \text{ CY} \\
+ \quad 87 \quad (15\%) \\
\hline
663 \text{ CY} \\
\end{array}
$$

$2\frac{1}{2}$-in. bitumen paving — roads   =   1,370 SY

2-in. bitumen paving — walks   =   78 SY

6-in. × 6-in. bit. curb   =   272 LF

Edge forms for conc. walks   =   730 LF

4-in. conc. walks (2,500 psi)

2,820 SF   =   940 CF   =   35 CY

Broom finish conc. walks   =   2,820 SF

Reinf. mesh for walks   =   ? (none shown)

Cure conc. walks   =   2,820 SF

Hand exc. for curbs

750 CF   =   28 CY

Granite curbs 6 in. × 18 in.   =   430 LF

Granite curbs rad. pcs.   =   63 LF

Granite curbs 5-ft rad. corner   =   2 pcs.

NOTES ON THE TAKE-OFF (W. D. 2.3 AND 2.4)

Road cut and fill is taken off from the profiles. The first item (33 ft × 31–6 × 1–0) is the 33-ft length on the profile measured below the hump; the hump is the "add" item taken off next (10 ft × 31–6 × 1–4). (The 31–6 width is the 30-ft road plus 6 in. at the side that has a bitumen curb and 1 ft to the outside of the gravel at the side that has a granite curb—all as shown on the road cross section.) Generally, the items are triangular in longitudinal section; therefore the depth is measured at the maximum point, and the item is "one-half times."

The areas of the items are converted to cubic feet and totaled, so that they can be used for the gravel take-off and for the shape-and-roll item.

The parking-area excavation is taken off by averaging the present grade at the four corners and deducting that figure from the finish subgrade, as shown on the collection sheet.

Shape and roll is an item that should always be taken off for the road sub-base. The walks would have a similar item, but for hand trim rather than roller work.

In taking off the gravel around the curb, the estimator does not deduct for the curb; the 12-in. gravel roadbed is taken off across the entire width of 31 ft 6 in., and an additional 18 in. × 12 in. of gravel is taken for under the curb. For waste and compaction, 15 per cent is added to the gravel item. Also an item for hand excavation must be taken off for the trench at the curb, its quantity being the volume of the extra gravel (750 CF).

Notice that when the bitumen paving items are transferred from the collection sheet to the take-off sheet, the conversion from square feet to square yards can be done mentally and the result entered directly on the take-off sheet. A note is made of the fact that there is no reinforcing shown for the concrete walks. The specifications should be checked later for the queried items.

UTILITIES

Before taking off the utilities, you must decide whether they are going to be installed before or after the site grading; that is, whether the utilities excavation is to be figured from present or finish grades. The depth of the trenches and the nature of the ground must be examined to decide where sheeting will be needed. In many states there are laws governing requirements for sheeting. Usually, trenches over 6–0 deep will be measured for sheeting even if no local law requires it. The width of the trench is governed by its depth, the nature of the ground, and the size of the pipe. City regulations must also be checked for such requirements as fees for connections to mains and permits for street work, traffic control, barriers, and lights.

COLLECTION SHEET FOR UTILITIES

Storm sewers

M.H.		C.B. (+2.5 ft)		6-in. C.P.	10-in. C.P.	12-in. R.C.P.	18-in. R.C.P.
1.	2.85	1.	2.5	44 ft	74 ft	56 ft	80 ft (6.4 ft)
2.	4.00	2.	3.6	20			
3.	5.50	3.	3.0	32			*San.*
	3)12.35	4.	3.6	52			
	4.12 ft		4)12.7	40		*8-in.*	*M.H.*
			3.2 ft	188 ft		96 ft (6.15 ft)	5.8 ft

2 in. water = 99 ft   Present grade 6 in. below finish (top of M.H.)

Working Drawing 2.5 shows a storm drain system, an incoming water line, and a sanitary sewer. The rough grading has been done; the present and finish subgrades are 6 in. below the top of the manholes and catch basins. The length of the pipe runs are shown, as is customary on many engineering site drawings. The site grades are not required, and so have been omitted.

Taking off the excavation of utilities trenches can be a long and tedious process if each run of piping is taken off separately at its exact depth. The storm-drain excavation (W. D. 2.5) will be taken off by two methods, so that we may see how the total quantity obtained by the recommended method compares with the slower and more detailed itemizing of every separate run. The collection sheet is shown above.

The parenthetical notation "(+2.5 ft)" is a reminder that the depths of the catch basins are 2 ft 6 in. greater than the depths listed, which are depth-to-invert figures (as required for trench excavations).

The manholes and catch basins are totaled and averaged. The parenthetical notation (6.4 ft) for the 18-in. reinforced-concrete pipe represents the average depth of the trench; that is, 5.5 ft at manhole No. 3 and 8.3 ft at the street manhole, or an average of 6.9 ft, less the 6 in. that the present subgrade is below the finish grade. The 6.15-ft notation for the 8-in. vitrified clay pipe is the average depth of the trench.

The trench excavation will be taken off by averaging the depths of catch basins and manholes for all the storm drains except the 18-in.:

M.H.	4.12 ft
C.B.	3.20
	2)7.32
	3.66
Less	0.50
	3.16 ft

= 3–2 (storm 6-in. to 12-in.)

UTILITIES

Trench exc. & backfill

Storm	6-in. to 12-in.		318–0	×	3–3	×	3–2	=	3,273 CF	
Storm	18-in.		80–0	×	5–0	×	6–5	=	2,566	5,839 CF
Sanitary			96–0	×	4–6	×	6–2	=	2,664	
Water			99–0	×	3–0	×	3–6	=	1,040	
C.B.		4/	11–0	×	11–0	×	5–9	=	2,783	
M.H.		4/	11–0	×	11–0	×	4–6	=	2,178	

$$14,504 \text{ CF}$$
$$= \quad 537 \text{ CY}$$

Sheeting util. trenches

$$\left.\begin{array}{l} 2/ \quad 80\text{–}0 \ \times \ 6\text{–}6 \\ 2/ \quad 96\text{–}0 \ \times \ 6\text{–}6 \end{array}\right\} \quad \underline{2{,}288 \text{ SF}} \ (\text{b.s.m.})$$

Conc.-pipe storm sewer — 6-in.   =   188 LF

Conc.-pipe storm sewer — 10-in.   =   74 LF

Reinf.-conc.-pipe storm sewer — 12-in.   =   56 LF

Reinf.-conc.-pipe storm sewer — 18-in.   =   80 LF

8-in. V.-C. pipe sewer   =   96 LF

Connect 18-in. storm sewer to main   =   1 ea.

Connect 8-in. san. sewer to main   =   1 ea.

Street barricades & lights   =   L. S.

Repair street paving

$$34\text{–}0 \ \times \ 9\text{–}0 \ = \ \underline{34 \text{ SY}}$$

Permits & fees   =   L. S.

C. B. 4–0 dia.   ×   *5–9 av. depth (8-in. conc. block)*   =   4 ea.

M.H. 4–6 dia.   ×   *4–6 av. depth (8-in. com. brick)*   =   4 ea.

H.-D. C.-I. M.H. cover & fr. 24 in.   =   4 ea.

H.-D. C.-I. C.B. grated cover & fr. 24 in.   =   4 ea.

2-in. W.-I. water service   =   99 LF

Connect water service to city branch main   =   L. S.

NOTES ON THE TAKE-OFF (W. D. 2.5)

Compare with the quick, tidy method used above, the take-off of excavation for the storm sewers with each run of sewers taken off at its proper average depth:

6-in.	44–0	× 3–0	× 2.43 ft	= 107 SF	⎫				
	20–0	× 3–0	× 2.20	= 44	⎪	413 SF	× 3–0	=	1,239 CF
	32–0	× 3–0	× 3.30	= 106	⎬				
	52–0	× 3–0	× 3.00	= 156	⎪				
	40–0	× 4–0	× 4.05	= 162	⎭			=	648
10-in.	74–0	× 3–0	× 2.93					=	650
12-in.	56–0	× 3–6	× 4.25					=	833
18-in.	80–0	× 5–0	× 6.40					=	2,560
									5,930 CF

The difference between the detailed take-off and the "average depth" take-off is only 91 CF, or 3½ CY, which is very small for excavation. That system of averaging the depth must, however, be carefully controlled. Many instances will require a modified method; for example, if there were a considerable number of 4-in. or 6-in. branch lines leading into 8-in. or 12-in. lines, it might be advisable to take off the branch lines as one collected item and the 8-in. and 12-in. lines between manholes as another. The change in depth at drop manholes may require separation of excavation items beyond those points.

The method we used for the trench excavation is quick and simple, and will be accurate in most instances. The 18-in. pipe requires a wider trench than the smaller pipes and so is kept separate. The 12-in. pipe requires a trench of about 3 ft 6 in.; the 10-in. pipe may have a slightly narrower trench; the 6-in. pipe will need a 3-ft trench, which is about as narrow as should be figured for any drainage lines. Thus the average trench is 3 ft 3 in. wide. The first excavation items (combining the 6-in., 10-in., and 12-in. pipe) becomes 318 ft × 3–3 × 3–2. (Figuring the depth of the trench is explained on p. 37).

The other trench depths are determined in a similar fashion. The pipe runs are measured between manholes (or between catch basins and manholes); therefore the excavation for manholes and catch basins must be added. That excavation will actually be less than we take off, because in one direction our square hole will overlap two or three feet of the pipe-trench excavation. The few yards of excavation duplicated is not deducted, however, because it will make up for the extra excavation required if a bank should cave in.

The trenches over 6 ft deep are measured for sheeting. Since one is 6 ft 2 in. deep and the other 6 ft 5 in., 6 ft 6 in. of sheeting is a logical depth to use in both trenches. The height of the walers will probably depend on what material is available at the site. The notation "b.s.m." (both sides measured) will be a consideration when the item is priced.

The pipe items are taken off at net length, in even feet. For pipe sold in 2-ft lengths, this is satisfactory. In a case such as concrete pipe that comes only in 6-ft lengths, the items would be taken off in multiples of 6 ft (for example, 188 LF of 6-in. concrete pipe, would be taken off as 192 LF).

Street connections, barricades, and the like should be checked with the local authorities.

It is not necessary to take off the manholes and catch basins in detail (separating concrete, forms, and brick). Having made two or three estimates using the descriptive method shown in our take-off, an estimator will have worked up a price for a certain depth and a per-lineal-foot price for variations on that basic price, and he will thus be able to give a lump-sum price for any manhole of that particular design and diameter. An example of this is given in Chap. 13.

UTILITIES: SEPTIC TANKS AND DISTRIBUTION BOXES

Working Drawing 2.6 shows a concrete septic tank with cast-iron fittings, brick manholes, and a 5-in. siphon. The piping is shown diagrammatically. The small sketch under W. D. 2.6 shows the natural (and finish) grades in the vicinity of the sanitary system. Working Drawing 2.7 shows the sanitary system extending from the septic tank: the outfall line, distribution box, headers, and field piping.

Starting with the septic tank and the 6-in. length of cast-iron pipe that connects the sewer line to the building (not included and not shown), we will take off all the items for W. D. 2.6 and 2.7.

THE TAKE-OFF (W. D. 2.6 AND 2.7)

UTILITIES — SEWER SYSTEM

Exc. — septic tank

35–0	×	22–6	×	12– 7	=	9,916 CF
8–6	×	22–6	×	9–10	=	1,878
						11,794 CF
					=	437 CY

Hand exc. — siphon   =   1 CY

Exc. & backfill sewer trenches

	68–0	×	4–6	×	6–6	=	1,989 CF
	42–0	×	4–6	×	4–0	=	756
+ Box	5–0	×	4–0	×	5–6	=	110
							2,855 CF
						=	106 CY

Exc. disposal field

$$93\text{--}0 \quad \times \quad 57\text{--}0 \quad \times \quad 6\text{--}8 \quad = \quad 5{,}301 \text{ SF}$$
$$= \quad 35{,}340 \text{ CF}$$
$$= \quad \underline{1{,}310 \text{ CY}}$$

Hand trim for septic tank floor

$$35\text{--}0 \quad \times \quad 14\text{--}0 \quad = \quad \underline{490 \text{ SF}}$$

Backfill — septic tank

		Exc.			=	437 CY
Tank	33–8 ×	12–6 ×	9–1 =	3,824 CF	=	142

$$\underline{295 \text{ CY}}$$

Trench sheeting

$$(\text{part — outfall line}) \quad 2/ \quad 35\text{--}0 \quad \times \quad 8\text{--}0 \quad = \quad \underline{560 \text{ SF}} \ (\text{b.s.m.})$$

Pumping = $\underline{L.\ S.}$

Septic tank — conc. (waterproof admix)

			FORMS
Floor			
34– 8 × 13–6 × 1– 0	= 468 CF		110 SF
Walls			
81–10 × 1–0 × 7– 3	= 594	2/ 594 SF =	1,188
27– 6 × 1–0 × 4– 6	= 124	2/ 124 =	248
Roof			
33– 8 × 12–6 × 0–10	= 351	29–8 × 10– 6 =	312
	1,537 CF	93–0 × 0–10 =	78
	= 57 CY		1,936 SF
Add Around siphon		2 × 4 keyways	
2– 0 × 2–0 × 2– 9 = 11 CF =	$\frac{1}{2}$	2 × 110–0 =	220 LF
	$57\frac{1}{2}$ CY	52-in. dia. hole	
		through roof =	2 pcs.

Common brick — M.H.'s over tank

$$(\text{8 in.}) \quad 2/ \quad 3\tfrac{1}{7} \quad \times \quad 3\text{--}8 \quad \times \quad 3\text{--}6 \quad = \quad 81 \text{ SF}$$
$$\text{At } 13\tfrac{1}{2} \text{ per SF} \quad = \quad 1{,}094 \text{ pcs.}$$
$$+ \text{ Waste } 4\% \quad 46$$
$$\underline{1{,}140 \text{ pcs.}}$$

24-in. C.-I. cover & fr. = $\underline{2 \text{ ea.}}$

Galv. step irons (none shown) = $\underline{20 \text{ pcs.}}$

Conc. distr. box

FORMS

Flr. & roof
    2/   4–9 × 3–9 × 0–6 = 18 CF | 17–0 × 3–9 = 64 SF
Walls   15–0 × 0–6 × 2–9 = 22 | 13–0 × 2–9 ⎫
                        40 CF | 3–9 × 2–9 ⎭ 46
                   = 1½ CY | 110 SF $\left(\begin{smallmatrix}\text{L.}\\\$0.50\end{smallmatrix}\right)$

6-in. C.-I. sewer pipe = 6 LF

5-in. C.-I. sewer pipe
          6–0 + 3/ 2–0 + 2/ 2–0 = 16 LF

5-in. C.-I. tees = 5 pcs.

6-in. C.-I. tee = 1 pc.

6-in. × 4-in. C.-I. tee = 1 pc.

Adapter (6-in. C.I. to 6-in. V.C.) = 2 pcs.

Adapter (5-in. C.I. to 6-in. V.C.) = 1 pc.

5-in. anti-siphon = 1 pc.

4-in. C.-I. pipe = 6 LF

6-in. V.-C. sewer pipe
          68–0 + 54–0 = 122 LF

4-in. V.-C. sewer pipe
    2 (16–0 + 6–0 + 2–0 + 2–0) = 2/ 26 ft = 52 ft
                                  + 2
                                 54 LF

4-in. V.-C. elbows = 4 pcs.

6-in. × 4-in. V.-C. tees
          5 + 8 = 13 pcs.

6-in. V.-C. elbows = *2 pcs.*

4-in. V.-C. pipe disposal field (open joints)   =   900 LF

Graded gravel bed ($\frac{1}{2}$ in. to $1\frac{1}{2}$ in.)

$$5,301 \text{ SF} \quad \times \quad 1\text{--}8 \quad = \quad 8,835 \text{ CF} \quad = \quad 327 \text{ CY}$$
$$+ \quad 15\% \quad \underline{\quad 49}$$
$$\underline{376 \text{ CY}}$$

Graded gravel bed ($\frac{3}{4}$ in. to $1\frac{1}{2}$ in.)

$$5,301 \text{ SF} \quad \times \quad 2\text{--}0 \quad = \quad 10,602 \text{ CF} \quad = \quad 393 \text{ CY}$$
$$+ \quad 15\% \quad \underline{\quad 59}$$
$$\underline{452 \text{ CY}}$$

9 in. loam (supply and spread)

$$5,301 \text{ SF} \quad \times \quad 0\text{--}9 \quad = \quad 3,976 \text{ CF} \quad = \quad 148 \text{ CY}$$
$$+ \quad 20\% \quad \underline{\quad 30}$$
$$\underline{178 \text{ CY}}$$

Backfill over disposal area (site material)

Exc.		= 1,310 CY
Less	327 CY	
	393	868
	148	
		442 CY

Surplus material for removal from site

$$142 \text{ CY}$$
$$\underline{868}$$
$$\underline{1,010}$$
$$+ \text{ Bulkup} \quad \underline{\quad 150}$$
$$\underline{1,160 \text{ CY}}$$

Clean up & regrade area disturbed   =   L. S.

NOTES ON THE TAKE-OFF (W. D. 2.6 AND 2.7)

All the excavation items are taken off first, the structures next, then the pipe fittings for the structures, the sewer piping, and finally the disposal field.

The septic tank (Fig. 2.6) is 33–8 × 12–6, the bottom being 12–7 below the present grade. The deep part of the tank is 25–2 long. If we allow about 5–0 for clearance around the tank, the excavation for the deep section is 35–0 × 22–6. For the siphon area, no working clearance is required in the length, because the 5–0 clearance was taken off in the first item; 1 CY of hand excavation is taken off for around the siphon.

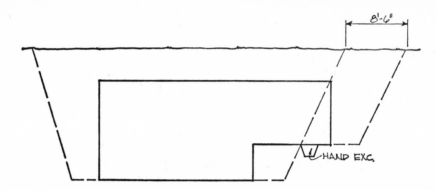

Fig. 2.6   Excavation lines for septic tank

The excavation for the sewer lines includes, as its first item, the outfall line—68–0 from the tank to the distribution box at an average depth of 6–6 (it is 9.35 ft deep at the tank and 3.5 ft at the box). In the second item, 42–0 is the length of the trenching for the lines from the distribution box. The two lines out of the side of the box (one of which is only 6–0 long) both go in one trench; so for excavation there are two lengths **at** 16–0, plus five 2–0 stubs, or a total of 42–0. Since considerable trenching has been taken off all around the box, the extra excavation for the box is taken off at about its net size. The box is 18 in. deeper than the pipe invert and consequently its excavation is 18 in. deeper (that is, 5 ft 6 in. instead of 4 ft). Notice that the header line in the disposal field is *not* measured for trench excavation. The disposal-field excavation will be 1 ft 6 in. outside the pipe lines to provide sufficient room for the header line, which is part of the field piping.

For a concrete slab such as the septic-tank floor, some hand labor is always needed for clearing out loose dirt, leveling, and the like; therefore a hand-trim item is taken off.

The backfill at the septic tank is taken off by simply deducting the volume of the structure from the total excavation item. If we consider the structure as a simple box 33–8 × 12–6 × 9–1, the small excess volume taken where the siphon chamber is 6–5 deep will offset the minor items not deducted (the two manholes, the concrete around the siphon, and the 6-in. projection of the tank bottom slab).

The trench sheeting item includes about half of the 68-ft line. That line is 9.35 ft deep at one end and 3.5 ft deep at the other, so that at about 35 ft from the septic tank the excavation will become less than 6 ft deep; sheeting is not taken off beyond that point. The 8-ft depth of the sheeting is an average for the walers, which will vary from 10 to 6 ft in height. Notice the "b.s.m." notation, indicating "both sides measured."

Pumping is taken off, because although the water level is below the deepest excavation grade, surface water can always be a problem in bad weather.

The concrete and formwork for the septic tank are taken off as single items. The two items are sufficient for such a small structure, because overlapping job costs make it difficult to separate or price the items in greater detail. The openings through the roof are not deducted. The item for roof forms consists of the inside surface area (the width—10 ft 6 in.—times the sum of the lengths of the 3 chambers) plus the area of the 10-in. edge forms (the outside perimeter times 10 in.).

The concrete around the siphon was missed; picked up later, it is shown as an "add" to the total for the septic tank.

The manhole is taken off—at its mean diameter of 3 ft 8 in.—"twice times," for two manholes. The 8-in. brick is taken off at $13\frac{1}{2}$ bricks per SF—a factor that is about right for common-brick work in minor items. (The entire question of brick quantities is discussed in Chap. 6.)

Step irons have been taken off, although they are not shown. Reference to the specifications may clarify an item such as this.

The distribution box is a straightforward take-off; except that although the top slab is not shown as such, it would have to precast. With this in mind, a note is made "$\left(\dfrac{L}{\$0.50}\right)$" as a reminder that this small item is worth $0.50 per SF for formwork labor, and that $0.50 will be entered in the labor unit-price column of the estimate when the take-off item is entered.

The cast-iron pipe is measured in 2-ft multiples for the short pieces that are connected to the tees inside the septic tank. Lengths of cast-iron pipe that have a collar are measured in 6-ft multiples. The 6-in. cast-iron tee is for inside the distribution box; the adapters are to join the cast-iron pipe to the vitrified clay pipe.

The 4-in. vitrified clay pipe specials are for the bends in the four lines from the distribution box. The 6-in. × 4-in. tees connect the distribution lines to the header line (5 tees), and the header line to the field lines (8 tees). A 6-in. elbow is needed for each end of the header line.

The gravel for the disposal field has 15 per cent added for compaction and waste; the loam has a 20 per cent allowance. The surplus material for disposal item is the sum of the septic tank displacement and the disposal field displacement.

MISCELLANEOUS UTILITIES ITEMS

Precast concrete septic tanks are taken off as a lump sum; a unit price should be obtained from suppliers. The excavation, setting, and piping must be taken off separately.

Cesspools may be described fully for lump-sum pricing of labor and material, or they may be taken off item by item.

Drain inlets are described and the average depth stated for lump-sum pricing, as for manholes and catch basins.

Headwalls for storm-drain outfalls are taken off in detail: excavation, concrete, forms, and stone bed.

Dry wells are taken off in the same way as cesspools.

Sewer or drain piping: If in doubt, check on the material specified. Some corrugated culvert pipe comes only in long lengths; some large-diameter sewer pipe is amazingly heavy and must be unloaded and placed by crane, or even by two cranes. Heavy sewer piping (24 in. and larger) should be considered as material requiring special handling, and the take-off must provide for such handling: engineering, excavation, unloading and distributing the pipe, method of laying, shoring the trench, and the cost of pipe cut to length.

Footing drains are taken off in the same way as other drainage items; except that if the footing drains are around the perimeter of a building, the pipe usually cannot simply be dropped into the working area excavated for the foundation walls. Since the grade of the pipe will vary, some hand excavation will be required, and must be included in the take-off. If the footing drain is to be surrounded by porous gravel, forms may have to be taken off for the outside face of the surround. This is a small but expensive operation, involving the gradual withdrawal of the form as the outside backfill is placed in order not to disturb the gravel around the drain.

Dewatering: Water can become a major problem, and may have to be handled as a special item. If there is a definite water condition to be met, all aspects of the situation must be carefully examined. A well-point company may have to be consulted. Generally, it is not the policy of well-point companies to give firm prices for dewatering. They will advise on the amount of equipment required and give rental rates for the various pieces of equipment, but usually the general contractor will be responsible for finally evaluating the item.

Every job of this sort must be considered as a special case presenting its own problems; there is no common approach. But one important question should always be asked: when were the borings taken and what has the weather been like since then? A long dry spell could have lowered the water level considerably. If it will be necessary to divert water, temporary drainage ditches should be measured and taken off as "Exc. temp. drainage ditch—........CY"; if the diversion is to be effected by damming the ditch and pumping, then items should be taken off for that work and properly described.

SUNDRY SITE WORK ITEMS

Fieldstone paving is measured in square feet and fully described. The sand or concrete bed for paving is taken off separately from the stone paving.

Edge forms for pavings are taken off in lineal feet, and the size described.

Steel edging for lawns and the like is taken off in lineal feet and described. The price obtained from the manufacturer will usually include the stakes.

Concrete curbing if precast may be a standard manufactured item, for which a price can be obtained. If that is so, take it off per lineal foot with separate items for excavation and the like. Cast-in-place concrete curbing must be taken off in several separate items, such as excavation, concrete, forms, and rubbing.

Fence postholes and concrete for setting the posts are taken off as one item: "Concrete surround for fence posts, incl. exc.—29 ea." Ordinary fence postholes without concrete are not taken off—both the hole and the setting are included in the post item.

Wood fences are taken off in several items, as for example: "3-in. × 4-in. creosoted fence posts 8 ft long—........pcs.; 2 × 4 creosoted fence rails —........BF; and 1-in. × 3-in. cedar fencing 5 ft long, pointed—........pcs." Boarding for close boarded fencing is taken off in board feet; chestnut fencing in lineal feet of stated height.

Chain-link fencing is measured in square feet or lineal feet of the specified type, gauge, and height, with the extra items, such as posts, stays, and gates, taken off separately.

Retaining walls of concrete are included in Chap. 3. Stone retaining walls are taken off in cubic feet and the type of stone described.

Seats are usually treated as a separate item, fully described for a lump-sum unit price, if they are a standard manufactured item. Specially designed seats are taken off item by item.

Flagpole bases may be taken off in several separately priced items, such as excavation, concrete, forms, and set sleeve. Having priced a few jobs including flagpole bases, the estimator may reduce this item to a single unit price; for example, "3-ft dia. × 4 ft deep flagpole base—L. S."

Baseball fields require, in addition to the grading and seeding (which are taken off in the usual manner), several special items. Items such as excavate, base course (gravel or as specified), and clay and sand (1 to 1) top course (all for skinned area) are taken off in cubic yards; fine grade (skinned area) is taken off in square feet; form pitcher's mound is a lump-sum item. Exact details would be as specified.

Cinder running tracks require the following items, taken off in cubic yards: excavation (or fill), stone base course (as specified), cinder bed, and surface course (usually brown clay and cinders mixed 1 to 2). In addition, an item for roll and shape sub-base and another for fine grade and roll are taken off in square feet. The entire take-off for athletic fields will follow the requirements of the specifications.

CHAPTER 3   **Concrete**

In taking off quantities for a building, it is customary to start with the foundation concrete; therefore the exterior-wall perimeter should be one of the first computations made.

WALL PERIMETER

The rules for computing building exterior-wall perimeters are very simple. In any rectangular building (either a true rectangle or a rectangular design with corners that step in and out) the wall perimeter is twice the sum of the length and the width, expressed as

$$2\,(L + W)$$

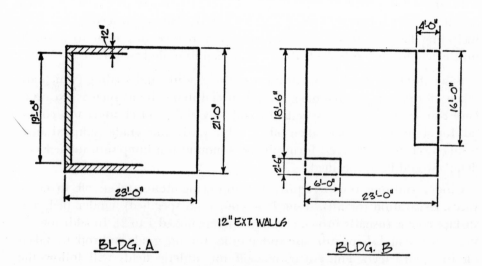

12" EXT. WALLS

BLDG. A   BLDG. B

Fig. 3.1   Building perimeters

48

In making this computation, the four corners must be deducted to allow for the overlap; therefore one outside and one inside dimension should be used in the computation. For Building A in Fig. 3.1, for example:

$$\text{Wall perimeter} = 2(23\text{--}0 + 19\text{--}0) = 84 \text{ LF}$$

It should be noted that 19–0 is 21–0 less 2 times 12 in., the wall thickness.

In the drawing of Building B, it is obvious that the wall lines of the two indented steps are the same length as the dotted lines that superimpose the outline of Building A on it. Thus Building B, having outside dimensions of 23–0 × 21–0, must have a wall perimeter equal to that of Building A (84 LF). If walls should step in as a recess in the *middle* of one side of a building, however, *twice* the depth of the recess must be added to the total of 2 times the sum of L and W.

In the working example (W. D. 3.1), the wall perimeter is computed as follows:

		79– 5
		11– 2
Outside	=	90– 7
Inside	=	58– 4
		148–11
	+	148–11
+ Recess	=	8– 6
+ Recess	=	8– 6
Wall perimeter		314–10

No matter how often a wall perimeter line steps in or out, there are only four corners to deduct in computing it. This rule may be expressed as: The wall perimeter is the sum of the outside dimensions less four times the wall thickness.

Having obtained the wall perimeter, that figure can be adjusted to obtain other items. For W. D. 3.1, the outside-wall-*surface* perimeter will be 314–10 plus 4 times 1–0, or 318–10. The brick-shelf perimeter will differ from the wall perimeter, because the 5-in. shelf is a deduction from the *outer* face of the 12-in. wall; therefore the brick shelf is 7 in. longer than the wall at each of the four outside corners. Thus for W. D. 3.1, the total brick shelf is 314–10 plus 4 times 0–7, or 317–2.

These perimeter rules can be applied to any building; for example, Fig. 3.2. (The dimensions not shown have been omitted because they are not required for the perimeter computation.)

The wall perimeter for a circular building would be computed using the diameter to the center of the exterior wall.

It should only be necessary to compute the perimeter of a building *once*—you should then make that figure work for you.

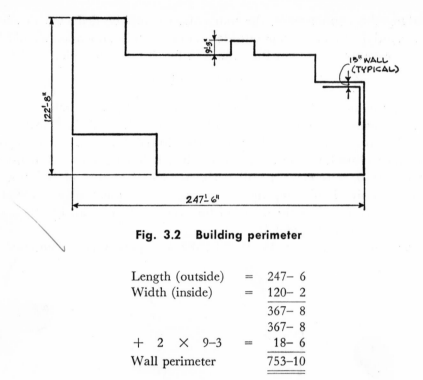

Fig. 3.2   Building perimeter

$$
\begin{array}{llr}
\text{Length (outside)} & = & 247-\ 6 \\
\text{Width (inside)} & = & 120-\ 2 \\
\hline
& & 367-\ 8 \\
& & 367-\ 8 \\
+\ \ 2\ \ \times\ \ 9\text{--}3 & = & 18-\ 6 \\
\hline
\text{Wall perimeter} & & 753\text{--}10 \\
\hline
\end{array}
$$

CONCRETE FOUNDATIONS

Working Drawing 3.1 shows a sketch of the concrete foundations for a building with 12-in. foundation walls, a brick shelf, a section of 16-in. wall, and wall and interior footings. Each interior footing has a 12-in. × 12-in. pier. Proceeding in a predetermined, orderly manner, the foundation concrete is taken off in the following order: pier footings; piers; wall footings; walls; ground slabs (except that the walls are used to obtain the wall footings).

Concrete (3,000 psi unless noted)

Conc. pier ftgs.

									FORMS
A	7/	3–0	×	3–0	×	1–2	=	74 CF	98 SF
B	3/	4–6	×	3–0	×	1–4	=	54	60
C	2/	5–0	×	4–0	×	2–0	=	80	72
								208 CF	230 SF
							=	8 CY	

Having completed this first item, which was simple enough to be entered directly on the take-off sheet, it is time to use a collection sheet, which is shown below.

COLLECTION SHEET FOR FOUNDATION WALLS

Foundation walls

	12-in.			16-in.	5-in. brick shelf		Piers		
6–3	*7–3*	*8–3*	*7–3*		*1–4½*		*12 in.* × *12 in.*		
49–11	29– 6	25–0	19–6		90–7	(A)	2/ 6– 9	=	13– 6
28– 4	33– 4	40–5	══		59–6	(A)	1/ 7– 9		7– 9
11– 2	13– 8	65–5			150–1	(A)	4/ 5– 9		23– 0
17– 8	8– 6	══			8–6	(B)	1/ 7– 7		7– 7
107– 1	8– 6				8–6	(B)	2/ 5– 7		11– 2
══	17– 0				317–2	(C)	1/ 5–11		5–11
	12– 4				══	(C)	1/ 4–11		4–11
	122–10						(12)		73–10
	══								══

Wall ftgs.

24 × 12   28 × 12

295–4   19–6

The collection sheet may be followed through item by item (taking off the walls first, the items started at the lower left-hand corner of the figure and proceeded clockwise):

The top of the wall is at a grade of 101–3 and the bottom of the 12-in. footing at 94–0; therefore the wall height is 6–3 for a distance of 49–11, until it steps down to elevation 93–0 for a 7–3 wall 29–6 long. The 79–5 side gives both these first two items. The next wall must be taken off at its inside dimension—58–4—which, less 25–0 at a height of 8–3 (grade 92–0), leaves 33–4 at 7–3. This method is further applied in taking off the remaining portions of the perimeter.

The 5-in. brick shelf is a straightforward perimeter addition: the outside dimension one way (90–7) and inside dimension the other way (60–4 less 0–10), plus the 8–6 side of the recess, all doubled.

The piers can be followed using top and bottom grades, starting with the A piers. For simplicity these are not listed clockwise; they start with the top line (A footing—pier bottom at grade of 94–2, top of pier at 100–11, a height of 6–9, 2 in quantity).

The footings follow the walls: the 16-in. wall has a 28-in. × 12-in. footing, 19–6 long; the length of the 24-in. × 12-in. footing is the sum of all the 12-in. walls (107–1 plus 122–10 plus 65–5).

The total length of the exterior walls (which is also the footing length) is 314–10, which checks with our previous calculation of the perimeter.

After transferring these items from the collection sheet, the take-off sheet
will read as follows:

THE TAKE-OFF (W. D. 3.1)

Wall ftgs.

295– 4 × 2–0 × 1–0 =	591	CF
19– 6 × 2–4 × 1–0 =	46	
314–10	637	CF
	= 23½ CY	

2 × 315

630 SF *Form*

2 × 4 footing
keyway = 315 LF

Foundation piers

(12)   1–0 × 1–0 × 73–10 = **3 CY**

296 SF

(12 piers,
12 in. × 12 in.)

Conc. ext. fndtn. walls

FORMS

12-in.

107– 1 × 6–3 =	669 SF
122–10 × 7–3 =	892
65– 5 × 8–3 =	530

2,091 SF = 2,091 CF

2 × 2,232 SF =
4,464 SF

16-in.

19– 6 × 7–3 =	141
314–10	2,232 SF

= 188
2,279

Less Brick shelf
317–2 × 0–5 × 1–4½   = 182
                              = 2,097 CF
                              = 78 CY

5-in. brick shelf = 436 SF

1-in. chamfer strip to walls
= 320 LF

12-in. gravel for ground slab

	88–7 × 58–4	=	5,167 SF	
Less	18–8 × 11–2 =	208		
	21–6 × 8–6 =	182	390	
			4,777 SF	
	× 12 in. =		4,777 CF	
		=	177 CY	
+ Waste & compaction 15%		=	26	
			203 CY	

6-in. × 6-in. × 10/10 wire mesh

$$
\begin{array}{r}
4{,}777 \text{ SF} \\
+ \quad \text{Waste } 10\% \quad \underline{473} \\
\underline{5{,}250 \text{ SF}}
\end{array}
$$

Concrete (2,500 psi) ground slab

4 in. × 4,777 SF	=	1,592 CF	*Screeds for 4-in. slab* =
	=	59 CY		480 LF

Cure slab = 4,777 SF

Trowel finish floor = 4,777 SF

½-in. × 4-in. premolded expansion jointing = 320 LF

Carbo. rub exterior walls

$$319\text{--}0 \quad × \quad 1\text{--}3 \quad = \quad \underline{400 \text{ SF}}$$

NOTES ON THE TAKE-OFF (W. D. 3.1)

Being all 12 × 12, the foundation piers were added to make one item, but the number of piers (12) is noted; on the estimate the item will read "Concrete foundation piers (12)—3 CY." Note that the final figure was rounded out. Concrete items should be rounded off to the nearest cubic yard if the item is over 50 CY. On the estimate sheet, the formwork for this item is also notated with the number of piers. It is unnecessary to waste time writing the details for the formwork computations, as the concrete items show all that information.

The concrete side of the wall footings item is self-explanatory. As there is only one depth of footing, the formwork is simply 2 times 315 SF, or 630 SF. This item is an "automatic" mental calculation, so the total is inserted without unnecessary detail. The keyway is shown on the drawing; it is the same length as the wall footings.

Foundation walls of uniform thickness are kept together and the surface areas extended and totaled, so that the total volume can then be obtained by a single operation. As these walls are to be 1 ft thick, no multiplication is necessary to convert square feet to cubic feet; with any other wall thickness, however, it is very advantageous to total the areas before multiplying by the thickness. The brick shelf is deducted from the concrete total, but added (as an extra-cost item) to the formwork side; this takes care of the double forming required at the brick shelf. Various extra-cost items for walls (such as pilasters, slab keys, and the like), are handled later (pp. 70 and 71).

The gravel for slab item is the ground-slab area; note that the isolated piers or pier footings are *not* deducted. The required quantity of gravel cannot be computed exactly; truck measure is not itself an exact quantity, and the compaction varies according to the grading of material, its moisture content, and the percentage of compaction required. All factors considered, however, 15 per cent is a reasonable allowance for spillage, waste, and compaction, although sometimes it might be necessary to carry 20 per cent.

The wire mesh item is also the ground-slab area, with an additional 10 per cent for laps and waste. For large areas, the waste and laps may be reduced to 8 per cent; for small, cut-up areas, 12 per cent may be needed. Note that in adding the waste, the figure used is adjusted slightly so as to round off the total quantity (10 per cent of 4,777 SF is 478 SF, which is decreased by 5 SF to 473 SF, to round off the total to 5,250 SF).

The floor slab item is straightforward. The formwork for screeds is one of those items that are needed but do not show on the drawings. Screeds should be figured at about 1 LF of screed to every 10 SF of floor, which assumes the use of a 12-ft to 14-ft straight edge, with the screeds set on between 10-ft and 12-ft centers.

If specified, the type of curing should be described. If burlap covering is called for, take it off and add 10 per cent waste: "Burlap for curing slab, sealed joints, 3 days wetted—5,250 SF."

The trowel finish item is straightforward. Normally the concrete finishing items are not taken off until all the structural items have been taken. The finish items are then taken off from the floor finish schedule onto the collection sheet. For floors, measure the areas that differ from the predominant finish and deduct their total from the gross floor area to obtain the area of the predominant finish.

The expansion jointing item was not mentioned on the plans, but on the section there is a dark line between the floor and the wall; you would go to your specifications take-off for the item. The quantity is the building perimeter with a slight waste allowance added.

Although only 12 in. of wall is to be exposed, the finish grade could hardly be expected to be on a perfect line; thus the rubbing item should extend a little lower than the required line. At least 3 in. extra should always be allowed.

This completes the take-off of items that are either shown in W. D. 3.1 or can reasonably be assumed to be included in that drawing. The specifications take-off should determine items such as expansion jointing, rubbing, curing, and trowel finish.

AREAWAY AND STAIRS

Figure 3.3 shows a basement entrance. The main wall of the building is not to be included in this example.

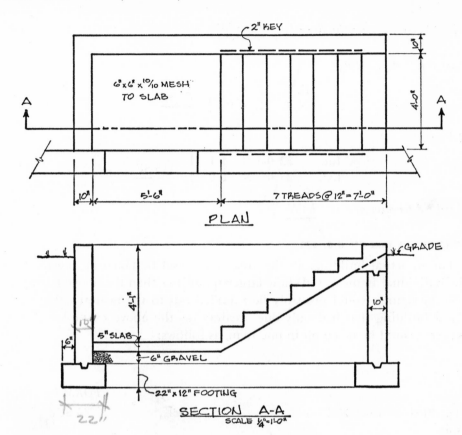

Fig. 3.3   Basement stairs

length × width ×
height

THE TAKE-OFF (FIG. 3.3)

Conc. wall fittings. (footing?)

21–4	×	1–10	×	1–0	= 39 CF
		22"			= 1½ CY

FORMS
43 SF
2 × 4 *ftg. key* = 22 LF

Conc. foundation walls

17–4	×	0–10	×	5– 0	= 87 SF
4–2	×	0–10	×	3–10	= 16
					103 SF = 86 CF
					= 3¼ CY

206 SF
Wall key = 4 LF

Conc. — bast. stair and slab

Slab

5–6 × 4–0 = 22 SF × 5 in. (thickness / slab) = 9 CF

Stair

8–6 × 4–0 × 1–0 = 34

43 CF

= 1½ CY

8–6 × 4–0 ⎤
4–1 × 4–0 ⎦ 51 SF

6-in. $\times$ *6-in.* $\times$ *10/10 mesh* = <u>25 SF</u>

Float or rub, steps and slab

$$\left.\begin{array}{ccc} 12\text{--}6 & \times & 4\text{--}0 \\ 4\text{--}1 & \times & 4\text{--}0 \end{array}\right\} \quad \underline{67 \text{ SF}}$$

Rub walls

$$\begin{array}{lccc} \text{Int.} & 22\text{--}0 & \times & 4\text{--}1 \\ \text{Ext.} & 23\text{--}0 & \times & 1\text{--}0 \end{array}\right\} \quad \underline{113 \text{ SF}}$$

Gravel bed for areaway = $\frac{1}{2}$ CY

NOTES ON THE TAKE-OFF (FIG. 3.3)

For an actual building, all the areaways would be taken off together, so the individual items would show larger quantities than the above example; also the figures would probably be rounded out to the nearest cubic yard. For a building that had only one areaway (as the above example) all the concrete could be taken off in one item, as follows:

Conc.—areaways, stairs

		FORMS
Ftg. 21–4 × 1–10 × 1– 0	= 39 CF	43 SF
Walls		
$\left.\begin{array}{l} 17\text{--}4 \times 0\text{--}10 \times 5\text{--} 0 = 87 \\ 4\text{--}2 \times 0\text{--}10 \times 3\text{--}10 = 16 \end{array}\right\}$ 103	= 86	206
Slab 22 SF × 0–5	= 9	
Stair 8–6 × 4–0 × 1– 0	= 34	
	<u>168 CF</u>	<u>51</u>
	= <u>6 CY</u>	<u>300 SF</u>
		2 × 4 *keyways* = <u>26 LF</u>

The stair is taken off by measuring the soffit (8 ft 6 in.) and multiplying it by the width (4 ft) and the thickness (1 ft). Although the actual thickness of the stairway may be 9 or 10 in., it is advisable to use 12 in. for all ordinary steps, to allow for the high percentage of waste in pouring. The stair formwork item is the "contact area": the area of the soffit plus that of the risers. For an open stair, the area of the sides would be added in the formwork. If the walls are to be poured and stripped, and the area behind the stairs backfilled and graded off to the stair slope without using forms, the cost will be about the same as would be carried for the forms; therefore one may simply carry soffit forms rather than backfill and "Hand trim of slope."

The rubbing item includes the three sides of the entrance slab section (5–6 plus 4–0 plus 5–6) plus half the wall at the stairs (2 sides at 3–6 each) for a total of 22–0 in length—4–1 high. Note that the rubbing of the main building wall is included in this item. The finishing of the slab, risers, and treads is carried as a single total. It would be impossible to separate the cement finisher's time into three individual items of cost.

EQUIPMENT PADS

TAKE-OFF OF EQUIPMENT PADS IN FIG. 3.4

Conc. eqpt. pads

$$8/\ 8–8 \times 3–0 \times 1–0 = 208\ \text{CF}$$
$$8/\ 4–2 \times 3–3 \times 1–0 = 108$$
$$\overline{316\ \text{CF}}$$
$$= \overline{\underline{12\ \text{CY}}}$$

Trowel finish eqpt. pads $= \underline{316\ \text{SF}}$

Rub sides eqpt. pads $= \underline{120\ \text{SF}}$

FORMS

$$\left.\begin{array}{l} 8 \times 30\ \text{ft} = \underline{240\ \text{LF}} \\ \\ \end{array}\right\}$$
(12-in. edge form)

3-in. chamfer strips $= \underline{240\ \text{LF}}$

$\frac{1}{2}$-in. $\times$ 6-in. exp. jointing $= \underline{240\ \text{LF}}$

NOTES ON THE TAKE-OFF (FIG. 3.4)

The formwork is taken off in lineal feet rather than square feet; the estimate sheet will read: "12-in. edge forms for equipment pads—240 LF." This method is used for items involving edge forms up to 12 in. high; pads, curbs, and bases over 12 in. high should be taken off in square feet. There is no concrete deduction for the chamfer strip.

The rubbing and the trowel finish could be lumped together, providing a suitable unit price is used. If rubbing is worth $0.17 per SF (for 120 SF) and trowel finish $0.12 per SF (for 316 SF), then the combined item ("Finishing concrete pads") would be priced at $0.14 per SF—the average price of the two items after rounding off.

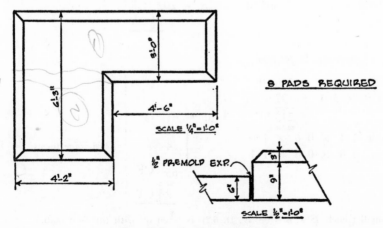

8 PADS REQUIRED

SCALE ¼"=1'-0"

½" PREMOLD EXP.

SCALE ½"=1'-0"

Fig. 3.4 Equipment pads

TAKE-OFF OF CONCRETE FLOOR PIPE TRENCHES IN W. D. 3.2*

Conc. ground slab (5 in.)

		FORMS

54–6 × 48–8 = 2,652 SF

23–0 × 12–2 =   280

                    2,932 SF   2,932 SF

Less trench C-C   29–6 × 4–4 = 128 ⎫

Less trench C-C   39–6 × 4–2 = 165 ⎬   320

Less trench B-B   17–0 × 1–0 = 27 ⎭

                                  2,612 SF

5-in. slabs   = 1,088 CF

+ B-B   28–3 × 2–0 × 0–6   =   28

            58–6 × 0–6 × 0–7   =   17

                                  1,133 CF

                          =   42 CY

FORMS

5-in. edge form   = 98 LF

Trench B-B

59–0 × 1–1 =   64 SF

57–0 × 1–0 =   57

                121 SF

5-in. slab screeds = 300 LF

Set angle-iron frame = 58 LF

Pipe trench C-C

Conc. wall ftg.

98–2 × 1–4 × 0–8 = 88 CF

              = 3½ CY

                                132 SF

Ftg. key   = 99 LF

Conc. pipe trench walls

8 in. 54– 8 × 2–7 = 141 SF

       38–10 × 3–7 = 139

        4– 8 × 4–8 = 22

              302 SF × 8 in. = 202 CF

                    =   7½ CY

                                604 SF

Conc. — pipe trench & pit floor

39–10 × 3–8 = 146 SF

29– 0 × 3–4 = 97

             243 SF × 3 in. = 61 CF

+ Drop 3–4 × 0–6 × 1–0 ⎫

       3–8 × 0–6 × 1–1 ⎬   4

                            65 CF

                    =   2½ CY

12-in. edge forms = 8 LF

* The small trench (Sec. B-B on W. D. 3.2) is taken off with the floor slab.

Conc. slab over pipe trench

$$65\text{--}0 \times 4\text{--}4 = 282 \text{ SF} \times 5 \text{ in.} = 118 \text{ CF}$$
$$= \underline{4\tfrac{1}{2} \text{ CY}}$$

260 SF (note stripping)

6-in. $\times$ *6-in.* $\times$ *10/10 mesh for slab* = $\underline{270 \text{ SF}}$

NOTES ON THE TAKE-OFF (W. D. 3.2)

All parts poured with the slab are taken off with it as part of the slab concrete item. On the formwork side, however, the various items are taken off separately. The top slab of a pipe trench such as Sec. C-C is often a continuous part of the floor; in that case, the entire floor slab would be taken off as one item with the formwork for the slab over the trench described and measured.

In the 4-ft-wide pipe trench, the wall of the pit has been taken off at 4 ft 8 in. deep from the underside of the floor, although in the drawing the pit could be 4 ft 8 in. from the top of the slab. The difference would be very slight.

The "drop" items added to the Sec. C-C type pit floor are for the changes in floor grade (Fig. 3.5), for which the 12-in. edge forms are also taken off.

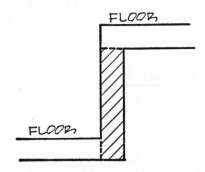

Fig. 3.5 Floor drop in pit

The notation "(note stripping)" against the pipe-trench top slab item is a reminder to the estimator that stripping forms from this low trench will be expensive.

Precast concrete trench covers are taken off by pieces and described. Consider Sec. C-C (W. D. 3.2), with precast covers in 4-ft lengths, 3 in. thick. For the 35–6 length, 9 pieces would be required; for the 29–4 side, 8 pieces. The item would be: "3-in precast conc. trench covers, approx. 16 SF each—17 pcs." Here, all labor and materials (formwork, concrete, and setting) would be part of the one item for unit pricing.

Reinforcing steel has not been shown as part of the concrete take-off in any of the examples in this chapter; it is covered in Chap. 4. Where shown in the figures, wire mesh has been included as part of the concrete quantities, because mesh is usually a material purchase item that is set by the general contractor's own crew.

TAKE-OFF OF CONCRETE RETAINING WALL IN W. D. 3.3

Conc. retg. wall

			FORMS

Ftg.   51– 6 × 1–0 × 1–0 =   52 CF   105 SF
              51– 6 × 6–0 × 1–5 =   438   120–0 × 1–5   =   170
Steps   2/ 1– 3 × 6–0 × 1–2 =   18   14
14½-in. wall 10– 8 × 7–9 =   83 SF
              7– 4 × 6–6 =   48
              5– 5 × 7–8 =   42
              14– 0 × 6–5 =   90   2 × 344 SF   =   688
              3– 7 × 5–9 =   21   + 1–5 × 18–0 =   25
              3–11 × 6–11 =   27   1,002 SF
              5– 7 × 5–11 =   33
                    1–2½ × 344 SF   = 416 CF
                                        924 CF
                                     = 34 CY   *Ftg. key*   = 50 LF

Rubbing walls

          104–0 × 3–6 = 364 SF

NOTES ON THE TAKE-OFF (W. D. 3.3)

Retaining walls with wide footings should be taken off as one item (footing plus wall). The formwork for a wide footing is more expensive than that for the ordinary 20-in. × 10-in. or 24-in. × 12-in. footings, and in fact the formwork for the footing in the above example would cost as much per square foot as the wall forms themselves; thus those items need not be separated. Notice that the ends are included in the formwork for the footing, and that the steps are also included on both the concrete and formwork sides of that item.

The exposed area for rubbing is the average of the two faces above ground.

CONCRETE COLUMNS

The column schedule (W. D. 3.4) is typical of the schedules found on structural drawings. The totals for each group (the circled figures above the schedule) and the notations (E, I, 8E, 2I, and the like) would not be given on the schedule; they are our own notations made in colored pencil. The totals

COLLECTION SHEET FOR COLUMNS

Cols.	10 × 12	12 × 12	12 × 14	14 × 14	16 × 16
Ext.	18/ 8–11	18/ 10–10	8/ 8–11	8/ 10–10	None
		18/ 9–11		8/ 9–11	
		26/ 8–11			
	161 ft	606 ft	72 ft	166 ft	
Int.	43/ 9–5	19/ 9–5	2/ 9–5	16/ 9–5	8/ 10–5
	13/ 10–5		17/ 10–5	2/ 10–5	8/ 11–4
	13/ 11–4		17/ 11–4	2/ 11–4	
	688 ft	179 ft	388 ft	194 ft	174 ft

+ 4 col. base plates 24 in. × 24 in.

---

for each group would be obtained from the plans and inserted on the schedule to simplify the take-off. The E and I notations denote the exterior and interior columns. Note that unless both exterior and interior columns appear in the same group, the I notation need not be used; the exterior groups having been so marked, the rest must be interior. It is necessary to separate the two not only because their heights vary, but for the following reasons also: (1) the exterior columns are probably deductions from the exterior masonry; (2) dovetail slots may be required in the exterior columns; (3) the finishing of the columns probably differs. The column heights should be marked on the schedule if not already shown. When taking off the columns, check off the schedule as each item is counted and entered on the collection sheet.

The collection sheet is shown. Because of space, the totals of the various columns items have been omitted; using wider spacing, the extensions could be shown as follows:

$$12 \times 12$$

$$
\begin{array}{l}
18/ \quad 10\text{–}10 = 195\text{– }0 \\
18/ \quad 9\text{–}11 = 178\text{– }6 \\
26/ \quad 8\text{–}11 = 231\text{–}10 \\
\hline
\phantom{26/ \quad 8\text{–}11 = }605\text{– }4
\end{array}
$$

The columns take-off is now simple.

THE TAKE-OFF (W. D. 3.4)

Conc. cols.

								FORMS
Ext.	0–10	×	1–0	×	161 ft	=	134 CF	590 SF
	1– 0	×	1–0	×	606	=	606	2,424
	1– 0	×	1–2	×	72	=	84	312
	1– 2	×	1–2	×	166	=	226	775
Int.	0–10	×	1–0	×	688	=	573	2,523
	1– 0	×	1–0	×	179	=	179	716
	1– 0	×	1–2	×	388	=	453	1,682
	1– 2	×	1–2	×	194	=	264	905
	1– 4	×	1–4	×	174	=	309	928
							2,828 CF	10,855 SF
						=	105 CY	

NOTES ON THE TAKE-OFF (W. D. 3.4)

The exterior-column height is the floor-to-floor height less the depth of the spandrel beam; for example, on the third floor the column height is 10–9 less a 1–10 beam, or 8–11. The interior columns are the floor-to-floor height less the 1–4 beam depth.

If there are numerous beams of varying depth, it may be necessary to take them off onto the collection sheet before figuring the columns. From a study of the beam take-off, it should be possible to determine an average beam depth to use as the deduction required to obtain the column height. If a particular beam depth is predominant at the column lines, that depth may be used when the column heights are determined.

If the columns are larger in cross section than the beams, they should be measured to the underside of the slab above, and the beams measured between columns.

CONCRETE BEAMS AND SUSPENDED SLABS

Beam sizes are usually shown in beam schedules on the structural drawings, with the beams numbered—B1, B2, and so on. The easiest way to take off beams is to mark the sizes on the plans, checking off the beam schedule item by item, and then, dispensing with the schedule, compile the collection sheet from the plans. For a large building that has entire structural sheets of schedules, it is best to extract the schedule sheets and place the pertinent sheet (folded, if that is more convenient) alongside the plan. This method will simplify the tedious job of marking the beam sizes on the plan, and is much easier than constantly turning back from one drawing to the other.

In the example (W. D. 3.5), the beam sizes have been marked on the plan; note that this is the first-floor plan and that it has been notated: "Second floor similar; roof similar except as noted." The spandrel beams will be taken off at full depth, the slab measured inside the spandrels, and the interior beams taken off to the underside of the slab. The formwork item for beam sides will have to be adjusted if the slab depth changes at a beam. Sometimes such adjustment of the beam sides is very minor and not worth the time spent figuring it, but only experience will enable you to know when to ignore this item and when to measure it. If a particular slab depth predominates, the adjustment of the beam-sides formwork may be ignored. If the design shows a consistent change (such as a 7-in. thickness in the rooms and 5 in. through the corridors), the additional formwork (2 in., for the corridor beams) should be taken off. The collection sheet for W. D. 3.5 is on p. 64.

THE TAKE-OFF (W. D. 3.5)

Conc. beams

			FORMS	
			Bottoms	*Sides*
Spand.	$900\text{--}0 \times 0\text{--}8 \times 1\text{--}10$	$= 1{,}100$ CF	600 SF	2,850 SF
Int.	$54\text{--}4 \times 0\text{--}10 \times 0\text{--}8$	$= 30$	45	72
	$27\text{--}2 \times 0\text{--}10 \times 0\text{--}9\frac{1}{2}$	$= 19$	23	43
	$122\text{--}4 \times 0\text{--}10 \times 1\text{--}3\frac{1}{2}$	$= 132$	102 ⎫	
	$122\text{--}4 \times 1\text{--}0 \times 1\text{--}6$	$= 183$	122 ⎬	1,081
	$122\text{--}4 \times 1\text{--}0 \times 1\text{--}7\frac{1}{2}$	$= 201$	123 ⎭	
	$27\text{--}0 \times 1\text{--}0 \times 0\text{--}5\frac{1}{2}$	$= 12$	27	24
	$227\text{--}0 \times 1\text{--}3 \times 0\text{--}11\frac{1}{2}$	$= 272$	284	435
		$1{,}949$ CF	1,326 SF	4,505
				— 231
		$= 72$ CY		4,274 SF

Conc. susp. slabs

			Slabs	$= 14{,}778$ SF
6 in.	5,280 SF	$= 2{,}640$ CF	Less bm. bot. 726	
$4\frac{1}{2}$ in.	5,793	$= 2{,}173$		14,052 SF
10 in. + 3 in.	3,705	$= 4{,}014$		
	14,778 SF	8,827	*Slab screeds*	
				$= 1{,}500$ LF
Less Pans $1{,}665\text{--}0 \times 1\text{--}8 \times 0\text{--}10$		$= 2{,}313$		
		6,514 CF	*20-in.* $\times$ *10-in. long*	
		$= 241$ CY	*pans* $= 1{,}665$ LF	

Trowel finish floors $= 10{,}252$ SF

Float roofs $= 5{,}126$ SF

COLLECTION SHEET FOR W.D. 3.5

Span. Bms.			Int. Bms.					Beam sides (adjustment)				
								Add		Deduct		
8×22	10×8	$10 \times 9\frac{1}{2}$	12×18	$12 \times 19\frac{1}{2}$	$10 \times 15\frac{1}{2}$	$15 \times 11\frac{1}{2}$	$12 \times 5\frac{1}{2}$	$1\frac{1}{2}$ in.	$4\frac{1}{2}$ in.	$8\frac{1}{2}$ in.	$1\frac{1}{2}$ in.	7 in.
88- 9	27-2	27-2	61-2	61-2	122-4	37-10	27-0	61-2	36	25-5	24-3	47-6
61- 2	27-2		61-2	61-2		× 6		61-2	× 3	37-10	24-3	26-0
149-11	54-4		122-4	122-4		227-0		122-4	108	63-3	48-6	9-8
149-11										× 3		83-2
299-10										189-9		× 3
× 3												249-6
899-6												

```
          +                    —
         16                   135
         40                     6
         56                   146
                              287
                              -56
                              231 SF (deduct)
```

To take-off sheet — 231 SF (deduct)

Total slabs

1st	77–9 × 61–2 =	4,756 SF
	26–0 × 9–8 =	251
		5,007
Less Stair	9 ft × 9 ft =	81
		4,926
2nd	=	4,926
3rd (roof)	=	4,926
		14,778 SF

10 in. + 3 in.

47–6 × 26–0   = 1,235 SF
                × 3
                  3,705 SF

6 in.

61– 2 × 28–2	=	1,723 SF
37–10 × 24–3	=	917
1st		2,640
2nd		2,640
		5,280 SF

$4\frac{1}{2}$ *in.*

total	= 14,778 SF	
6 in.	= 5,280	8,985
10 in. + 3 in.	= 3,705	5,793 SF

Pans

12 × 46–3 = 555 ft
          × 3
            1,665 ft

The collection sheet for W. D. 3.5 (beams and slabs) is shown on p. 64. In figuring the slabs the total slab area is taken off first; then, taking off the 6-in. slabs and the 10-in. + 3-in. slabs, their combined area is subtracted from the total area to obtain the 4½-in. slab area. This method is invariably both quickest and best; first take off the total area of all the suspended slabs, then measure the simpler, less numerous areas, and finally subtract the sum of these from the total area to obtain the area of the predominant type of slab.

NOTES ON THE TAKE-OFF (W. D. 3.5)

The total length of the spandrel beams being 899–6, the item is entered at 900–0 on the take-off sheet (p. 63); it is reasonable to round out this item, as 6 in. in 900 ft is of little consequence.

The beam bottoms are figured first, and then used to obtain the concrete quantities (beam-bottom area times depth). The spandrel-beam sides are 1–10 on the outside and 1–4 on the inside; 900–0 × 3–2 gives 2,850 SF. The interior-beam formwork is the length times twice the depth (for two sides). The three beam items that are 122–4 long are combined for convenience in computing the beam sides; adding the beam depths together (1–3½ plus 1–6 plus 1–7½, totaling 4–5) the area of the forms for the beam sides will be 122–4 times twice 4–5, or 1,081 SF.

The deduction from the beam sides (231 SF) was computed in detail on the collection sheet.

The slab forms are the total slab area less that of the interior beam bottoms. If the slab is taken off to the outside face of the spandrels, then the total of all beam bottoms is deducted to obtain the slab forms, the spandrels are measured to the underside of the slab (8 in. × 16 in. in the example), and 6 in. is added to the face side of the spandrel-beam formwork (22 in. plus 16 in., or 3 ft 2 in.).

The concrete for the 10-in. + 3-in. slab (10-in. pan with 3-in. concrete over) is first figured as a solid 13-in. slab, and then the volume of the pans is deducted. Very often a floor plan does not show all of the pan layout, but simply a typical layout of one small area. If that is so, there are two methods that may be used to compute the items for the concrete and the pans: (1) the pans can be laid out by marking them off, either throughout the entire floor plan or in complete areas that are repeated, or (2) a typical area can be computed so as to arrive at factors that can then be projected for the entire pan area. To illustrate method 2, consider the quantities for the pan slabs in W. D. 3.5 as being for a typical area of a large floor, a floor having, say, 20,000 SF of that type of slab (see example on top of p. 67).

This second method, although much simpler than laying out all the pans, is not as accurate as the first method, and it is not recommended except for

Typical area	3,705 SF	×	1– 1		=	4,014 CF
Less Pans	1,665–0	×	1–8	× 0–10	=	2,313
						1,701 CF

concrete = 0.46 CF per SF of floor
pans   = 0.75 SF per SF of floor

or

pans   = 0.45 LF per SF of floor

For the entire pan slab area of 20,000 SF

Concrete	20,000 SF	×	0.46	=	9,200 CF
20-in. pans	20,000 SF	×	0.45	=	9,000 LF

rough-checking of quantities. Slab layouts usually repeat design patterns, so the entire pan quantity can often be computed by laying out the pans in one of each of the different areas and making the repetitions work for you.

Regarding the total slab area, the collection sheet should separate floors from roofs. Also note that the slab finish area is the slab area plus the spandrel-beam-bottom area (because the slabs were measured to the inside of the spandrels).

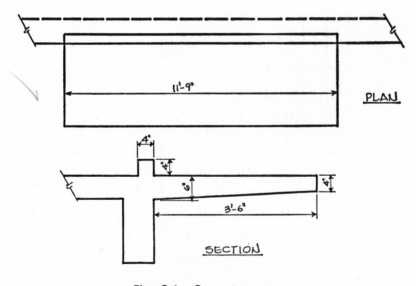

Fig. 3.6   Concrete canopy

CONCRETE CANOPY (FIG. 3.6)

The spandrel beam would have been taken off with the building slab and beam items. The canopy, although to be poured with the slabs, is kept separate because the formwork is expensive. The take-off would read:

Conc. canopy

$$
\left.\begin{aligned}
& 11\text{--}9 \ \times \ 3\text{--}6 \ \times \ 0\text{--}5 \ = \ 17\ \text{CF} \\
+\ & 11\text{--}9 \ \times \ 0\text{--}4 \ \times \ 0\text{--}4 \ = \ \underline{1} \\
& \phantom{11\text{--}9 \ \times \ 0\text{--}4 \ \times \ 0\text{--}4 \ = \ } 18\ \text{CF} \\
& \phantom{11\text{--}9 \ \times \ 0\text{--}4 \ \times \ 0\text{--}4 \ } = \ \overline{\underline{\ 1\ \text{CY}}}
\end{aligned}\right.
$$

	FORMS
Soffit	41 SF
Edges	9
Curb	8
	58 SF (cantilevered)

Rubbing canopy = 58 SF

NOTES ON THE TAKE-OFF (FIG. 3.6)

The small curb over the spandrel is part of the canopy and is taken off with the canopy. The thickness is averaged for the concrete item, but the forms are taken off at the maximum thickness (6 in.) around the three sides. The rubbing item is the same area as the formwork—the exposed soffit and sides.

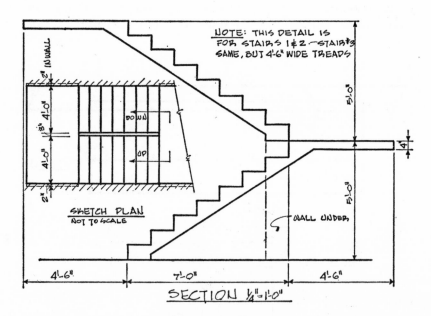

NOTE: THIS DETAIL IS FOR STAIRS 1 & 2. STAIR #3 SAME, BUT 4'-6" WIDE TREADS

SKETCH PLAN
NOT TO SCALE

WALL UNDER

SECTION ¼"=1'-0"

Fig. 3.7 Concrete stairs

CONCRETE INTERIOR STAIRS (FIG. 3.7)

Notice that this is stair No. 1. Stair No. 2 is similar; stair No. 3 is also similar, except that it is 6 in. wider. The wall under the second flight may be assumed to have been taken off previously. The section is drawn to a scale of ¼ in. to 1 ft; the underside of the stairs is exposed and must be rubbed. The take-off would read:

Conc. int. stairs

$$FORMS$$

No. 1 & 2	2/2/8–8 × 4–0 × 1–0 = 139 CF	4 × 35 SF	
		4 × 9	256 SF
		4 × 20	
	2/2/8–7 × 4–6 × 0–4 = 52	4 × 37 = 148	
No. 3	2/8–8 × 4–6 × 1–0 = 78	2 × 39	
		2 × 9	142
		2 × 23	
	2/9–7 × 4–6 × 0–4 = 29	2 × 42 = 84	
	298 CF	630 SF	
	= 11 CY		

Rub risers = 126 SF

Trowel treads and landings

2/16–0 × 8–3 }
16–0 × 9–3 } 412 SF

Rub stairs, soffits, etc. = 504 SF

NOTES ON THE TAKE-OFF (FIG. 3.7)

The stair soffit is scaled off the drawing at 8 ft 8 in., and—as for basement stairs—the thickness is taken off at 12 in. to allow for spillage and waste. The stair forms are the soffit, (8–8 × 4–0) 35 SF, the open side, (8–8 × 1–0) 9 SF, and the risers, (4–0 × 5–0) 20 SF—all multiplied by 4 (for 4 flights, 2 flights each for stairs No. 1 and 2). The landings are taken off full size for concrete but "wall to wall" for forms.

The rubbing item is the formwork total area less that of the risers (630 SF less 126 SF, or 504 SF).

MISCELLANEOUS FORMWORK ITEMS

Grade beams are taken off in the same way as foundation walls, except that the formwork may be a little different. It will be necessary to study the drawings to decide whether or not grade-beam bottoms will be needed. If in doubt at the time of taking off, keep the beam-bottom forms item separate from the sides. The item "Grade-beam bottoms" may then be entered on the estimate sheet with a query or similar notation that will draw special attention to it.

In taking off grade-beam sides, no special procedure is involved if the beams are to be poured separately from the slab. For grade beams poured with the ground slab, however, the area of the inside forms, which will be lost, should be listed separately from the outside form, which will be recovered. Forms that will be covered up and therefore cannot be recovered should always be shown separately.

For framed ground slabs, beam bottoms will not usually be required. The lost beam sides should be taken off separately, the same as for grade-beam forms.

Formwork for high slabs should be a separate item from that for the normal slab areas. "Normal slab areas" may be considered as being slabs that can be formed using a single jack system. Whether wooden tee jacks or tubular metal shores are used, 13 ft to 14 ft is the maximum height obtainable with a single jack. Slabs requiring a shore of over 14 ft must be taken off separately (for formwork at least) and the height noted.

Foundation-wall formwork should be separated into two items—walls up to 10 ft high, and those over 10 ft high—so that the labor costs can be properly considered. Walls requiring difficult or intricate formwork—such as curved walls or Y-walls—should always be taken off separately and the formwork described.

Wall openings should be deducted from the concrete and the extra formwork items taken off. There is no deduction from the normal formwork item; instead, a separate extra-cost item is taken off. That item can be the measured perimeter of all the openings, taken off as "Boxing for wall openings—........ LF"; or the openings may be counted in groups, and the item taken off as "Box out for wall openings up to 10 SF—........opgs.," then similarly for openings from 10 SF to 25 SF, and so on.

Brick shelf is usually taken off in square feet (see p. 52). A one- or two-course brick shelf, however, should be taken off in lineal feet and the size described. A brick shelf of up to two courses will not require special formwork make-up.

Haunches on walls are described by size and taken off in lineal feet—for example, "5-in. × 8-in. haunch to wall—120 LF"—and if necessary a sketch may be drawn in the left-hand margin of the estimate sheet. Haunches of odd design can be a very expensive formwork item. All items such as haunches, pilasters, and brick shelf that are extra-cost items for formwork, are included in the main item on the concrete side; that is, they are added into or deducted from the wall concrete item, and are ultimately contained within the one final item "Concrete foundation walls"—but they appear as separate extra-cost formwork items in the estimate.

Pilasters are added into the wall concrete item. The pilaster forms may be taken off as an extra-cost item in square feet and the number of pilasters noted: "Extra for wall pilasters (14)—250 SF."

Slab stops for concrete pourings are taken off in lineal feet. If the slabs have to be poured checkerboard fashion, the quantity of stops can be measured. If the pouring need not be done in any particular pattern, the item can only be figured by gauging the extent of each day's pour and allowing stops accordingly. If reinforcing is to be continuous through the stops, that fact should be noted and described in the slab stops item.

Slab stops at openings (such as holes through the slab where the formwork is not stopped) are measured as the perimeter of the openings in lineal feet. Usually, openings for stairs and elevator shafts are not decked in, but minor openings would be decked in and stopped off.

Chamfer strips for columns, beams, and the like are taken off in lineal feet.

Screeds for pitched slabs are measured in lineal feet and described as "Slab screeds to pitch." Such an item is common for roof fill pitched to roof drains, and also for floors pitched to drains; it should be kept separate from the ordinary slab screeds item.

Metal forms "left in place" for slabs are corrugated metal forms supplied by the manufacturer in widths suitable for spans up to about 8 ft. The item should be taken off in square feet allowing 8 to 10 per cent for waste. Some types of corrugated metal slab forms will require temporary shoring, which must also be taken off; such shoring, however, may only amount to a row of jacks with a 3-in. × 4-in. or 4-in. × 6-in. header. Having decided what is required, take off an item—"Temporary shoring for metal slab forms"—in lineal feet, with all rows measured.

Gallery step seating formwork must be carefully taken off. Take it off somewhat the same as ordinary stairs, and fully describe the item. Curved seating should be taken off separately and also described. Aisle steps may be taken off separately by number: "Formwork for aisle steps 2–9 × 1–0 × 0–6 —74 each."

The concrete for straight and curved seating may be taken off in a single item; the small aisle steps, however, if poured separately should be taken off separately.

MISCELLANEOUS CONCRETE ITEMS

Roof fill is taken off in cubic yards. Care must be taken in determining the average depth of pitched roof fill. If the pitch is one way only (as from front to back or from both front and back to a parallel low line through the center) then the average depth is simply the average of the two thicknesses. In Fig. 3.8, for example, roof fill is 6 in. at the high point, 2 in. at the low point; the average thickness of fill for either A or B is 4 in.

Now consider Fig. 3.9, in which the roof fill pitches four ways, from 6 in. at the outside to 2 in. at the center. The average thickness will vary according to the roof dimensions. There is no *area* that is 2 in. thick—only the *point* at the center is 2 in. thick. The average thickness of the fill will be the thickness along the sides of the rectangle (dotted in Fig. 3.9) that encloses half of

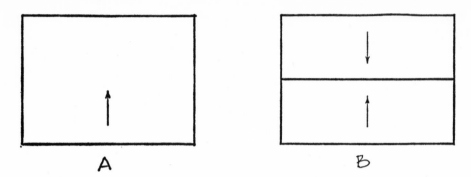

Fig. 3.8   Roof fill—one-way pitch

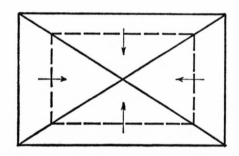

Fig. 3.9   Roof fill—four-way pitch

the roof area. The average thickness of roof fill for Fig. 3.9 would be $4\frac{3}{4}$ in. (The figure may be checked by laying out a sample roof.) For estimating purposes, the table shown will serve.

Roof Fill pitched as in Fig. 3.9

Pitch	*Fill — average thickness*
2 in.	Minimum $+\ 1\frac{1}{2}$ in.
3	Minimum $+\ 2$
4	Minimum $+\ 2\frac{3}{4}$
5	Minimum $+\ 3\frac{1}{2}$
6	Minimum $+\ 4\frac{1}{4}$
7	Minimum $+\ 5$

Note that from roof B in Fig. 3.8 to the roof in Fig. 3.9 the fill increases from 4 to $4\frac{3}{4}$ in.; fill pitched between those two extremes would vary accordingly, as shown in Fig. 3.10.

Slabs over paper-backed mesh must include additional concrete for keying to the mesh and for the sag in the mesh; this extra quantity will vary up to 20 per cent, according to the type of mesh and the free span.

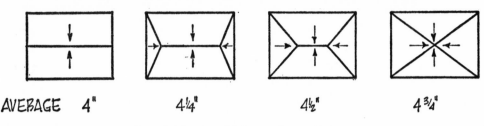

Fig. 3.10   Roof fill—various pitches

Lightweight concrete must be thoroughly investigated for yield. Some of the expanded vermiculite or foam-type lightweight concretes require a 10 per cent addition to the net volume.

For insulating concrete around underfloor ducts, measure the gross quantity of concrete and deduct the volume of the ducts. Side forms will probably be necessary; if so, take them off in square feet.

Concrete walks are taken off item by item: gravel bed in cubic yards; edge forms in lineal feet (curved forms separate from straight); concrete in cubic yards; finishing (float or trowel) in square feet; expansion jointing in lineal feet. If the walks are taken off with the site work, excavation for them could be taken off at the same time. It is generally best to include all site work items in the Excavation and Site Work part of the estimate. Both for the cost records and for comparing an estimate against previous estimates, it is best to have the items for the building proper segregated from the outside work.

Abrasive aggregate is taken off in pounds and fully described, or taken off in square feet with the quantity of abrasive per square foot of floor specified.

Granolithic pack for machine beds is taken off in square feet and the thickness stated.

Floor hardener is taken off in square feet and described; for example: "Magnesium fluosilicate floor hardener (2 coats)—........SF."

Cement fill for metal pan stairs is taken off item by item: "Cement fill (pan stairs) 1:1—........CY; Mesh for stair fill—........SF; Trowel finish stair fill—........SF; Set metal nosings (0–0 long)—........pcs."

Chimney caps (concrete) are best taken off as an item for lump-sum pricing of labor and material, although they could be taken off in detail. A building usually has only one chimney cap (or two at most), so that a lump-sum price is satisfactory.

Machine foundations may be taken off in the same way as concrete footings, but should be figured separately from the footings. Particularly if they are heavy foundations with especially heavy formwork and quantities of concrete, the formwork will be more expensive and the concrete probably cost less to place than for ordinary footings.

Heavy slabs—that is, floors over 12 in. thick—should be separated from slabs up to 12 in. thick, because of the lower labor cost of placing the concrete and the higher cost of screeds and stops.

Curbs may be taken off in lineal feet and described; or they may be measured in detail and described, with the formwork taken off as a separate item and all the finishing measured (the better of the two methods). In the case of exterior site curbs, which would be taken off with the site work, the excavation item would be taken off then too. The curb items would be kept together, and on the estimate they would read:

Curbs — excavation	....CY
Curbs — concrete (6 in. × 17 in.)	....CY
Curbs — forms	....SF
Curbs — rubbing	....SF

After having priced a few jobs that this item occurs in, you may be able to set up a lineal-foot price, and thereafter take the item off as "6-in. × 17-in. conc. curb (include exc., forms, etc.)—........LF."

Oil-tank mats are taken off the same as footings; concrete in cubic yards, forms in square feet. An additional item for "Setting oil-tank anchors" should be taken off and described if necessary.

Oil-tank manholes and oil-pipe trench (if concrete) may be taken off as one item. It is not necessary to make separate items of the bottom slab, sides, and top slab. Measure the various parts properly, but add them all into one total: "Oil-tank manholes and pipe trench, forms—........SF." Do the same for the concrete.

Concrete encasing ducts (electric or telephone): take off concrete in cubic yards (with duct volume deducted), and forms in square feet.

Hi-early cement for speeding up the setting of concrete must be allowed for in the estimate if it is to be used. Take off as an extra-cost item: "Extra for Hi-early cement—........CY."

Heated aggregate for cold-weather pours probably will not cost extra, but this must be checked with the ready-mix plant; if a charge *is* made, an extra-cost item should be carried for the anticipated quantity of concrete involved: "Extra for heated aggregate to concrete—........CY."

Locker bases and all similar bases: concrete taken off in cubic yards; edge forms in either lineal feet (if up to 12 in. high) or square feet (if over 12 in. high).

Curing slabs is taken off in square feet, and described if the curing method is specified. If burlap cover is called for, take it off, adding 10 per cent for laps and waste, and enter it as "Burlap, curing slabs—........SF"; if taped joints are called for, the item should be "Burlap (taped joints), curing slabs—........ SF."

Granolithic floor topping is taken off in a series of items: "Grano. floor topping (1 in.) 1:1:2—........CY; Screed for 1-in. topping—........LF; Trowel finish grano. floors—........SF."

Color admix for floors is taken off in pounds or gallons, depending on the type of color admix specified.

Cement base is taken off by sizes in lineal feet, and must be fully described; for example: "1 × 6 cement base, bullnosed (incl. mesh)—.......LF." Sometimes a small sketch of the base (in the left-hand margin of the estimate sheet) will prove helpful when pricing the item.

Waterproofing admix for concrete may be taken off in pounds or gallons, or for the quantity of concrete to be waterproofed—but always as an extra-cost item. Usually only particular areas are specified as requiring concrete to be waterproofed—they may be foundation walls, certain ground slabs, or perhaps pits. Do not separate the concrete items. Take off the concrete as usual (note the waterproofed items on the take-off sheet if it will help), and then take off a single extra-cost item—"Extra over concrete for waterproof admix—.......CY."—and describe the type of waterproofing specified. If you know the quantity of admix needed per cubic yard, the item may be expressed in pounds or gallons rather than in cubic yards.

Concrete tests are usually a lump-sum item on the estimate, so the take-off sheet may read simply "Concrete tests—L. S." If the specifications call for control of the concrete—with a testing engineer at the plant or at the site, or both—at the contractor's expense, and a price is quoted per cubic yard of concrete; then the item may be taken off as: "Testing and control of concrete—.......CY." If the requirements are more complex, the item should be marked with a reference to the applicable page in the specifications.

Precast concrete cannot be taken off to one set system; the method that is best for one item may not be suitable for other precast items. Simple precast lintels may be taken off by lengths, grouping the items together—3 ft to 4 ft, 4 ft to 5 ft, and so on—under the average length of each group, so that the estimate would simply show "Precast concrete lintels (0–4 × 0–8 × 3–6 long —.......pcs."; the following item might read "Ditto × 4–6 long—.......pcs."; and so on.

Precast concrete columns, beams, and copings must be taken off in such a way as to enable the items to be intelligently priced. As an example, consider precast concrete columns varying in both cross section and height. The concrete side of the take-off would list the items separately; they would each be measured and totaled, and the concrete quantity listed in cubic yards. The formwork side would show a cross-section sketch, the maximum length, and the number of columns of each type; there would be one formwork item for each type of column. The hardware (base plates, bolts, and the like) would be taken off and listed separately. An item for the erection would also be taken off, and could be carried as so many precast concrete columns at an average weight. As completed and transferred to the estimate, the precast concrete columns item might read as shown on the top of p. 76. The general idea, whatever method is used, is to make it possible to properly visualize the requirements of each item when pricing it.

Many precast concrete items will be taken off by cast-stone companies, and bid on as a delivered sub item. In that case, the general contractor's estimate

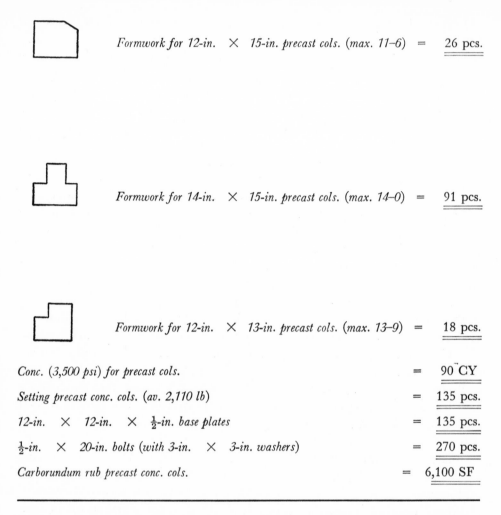

Formwork for 12-in. ✕ *15-in. precast cols. (max. 11–6)* =   26 pcs.

Formwork for 14-in. ✕ *15-in. precast cols. (max. 14–0)* =   91 pcs.

Formwork for 12-in. ✕ *13-in. precast cols. (max. 13–9)* =   18 pcs.

Conc. (3,500 psi) for precast cols.	=	90 CY
Setting precast conc. cols. (av. 2,110 lb)	=	135 pcs.
12-in. ✕ *12-in.* ✕ *½-in. base plates*	=	135 pcs.
½-in. ✕ *20-in. bolts (with 3-in.* ✕ *3-in. washers)*	=	270 pcs.
Carborundum rub precast conc. cols.	=	6,100 SF

would include only the items for unloading and setting. Especially heavy precast items or those that are to be set high above ground may require a crane item: "Crane setting precast items—........days." Similarly, if precast items will need considerable rigging or temporary guying, it may be advisable to include an additional item for that work. "Box up and protect precast concrete" is another item that should sometimes be taken off. For finished sills, steps, and the like, which are likely to be chipped after being set, a "Box up and protect" item is always necessary.

SUNDRY ITEMS TAKEN OFF WITH CONCRETE

Building paper or polyethylene under ground slabs is taken off in square feet with 8 to 10 per cent added for laps and waste.

Membrane or felt over slabs is also taken off in square feet with 8 to 10 per cent for laps and waste. If the membrane is to be mopped on, that fact should be noted. The same applies to any special requirements for felt, tar paper, and the like: always describe the requirements.

Perimeter insulation for foundation walls is measured in square feet. The waste may vary considerably, and will depend on the type of insulation and its depth. Usually a 10 per cent waste allowance is sufficient; some of the insulation board materials, however, come in standard 4-ft widths only, and cutting them to size may leave considerable waste—for instance, if 3 ft of insulation board is called for and "piecing up" is not allowed there will be 25 per cent waste. Often, even if it is permissible to piece up the insulation, it would not be economical to do so, because of the labor involved. The waste must be considered in conjunction with the labor factor, to determine whether it would be cheaper to piece up the material or to lose the waste and save labor by using only full-width material.

Waterstops of rubber or any of the synthetic materials are taken off in lineal feet by types and sizes. Copper waterstops are taken off in square feet and the weight stated; for example, "20-oz. copper waterstops—........SF".

Expansion jointing is taken off either in square feet with the thickness stated or in lineal feet with both the width and thickness stated. Some expansion material only comes ½ in. thick, so that for 1-in. expansion jointing the length or the area must be doubled and shown as ½ in. thick on the estimate sheet. Other expansion material comes in thicknesses up to 1 in.; the standard widths also vary. The method of taking off should properly describe the material specified. Liquid poured sealer for expansion joints is taken off in lineal feet.

METAL SUNDRIES FOR CONCRETE WORK

Dovetail the anchor slots and anchors for securing masonry to concrete, the slots are taken off in lineal feet and the anchors in thousands of pieces. Usually both the spacing and the required locations of dovetail slots are fully specified. If the spacing is not specified, allow one vertical dovetail anchor slot (that is, one continuous anchor slot) for every column face that has masonry veneer; and for spandrel beams, brick shelf, and the like, allow for the vertical placing of anchor slots full height on 2-ft centers. Unless spacing is specified, allow one anchor for every lineal foot of slot required.

Wedge inserts for securing steel lintels and the like to concrete are taken off in pieces of stated size. If spacing is not specified, allow 1 insert per 3 LF, plus "one for the end" for each lintel.

Ceiling inserts should be specified if required. Take them off in pieces, always allowing "one for the end." In laying out or taking off any item that is spaced out center-to-center, an extra piece will always be needed "for the end." Inserts on 4-ft centers on a ceiling 12 ft × 8 ft, would require 4 in one direction and 3 in the other—a total of 12 pieces.

Abrasive metal stair nosings are taken off by size in pieces, and described.

Light iron items to be supplied by a subcontractor but set in concrete by the general contractor should be taken off for setting. If *not* supplied by a subcontractor, they would have to be taken off item by item and fully described. For example:

4-in.   ×   *4-in.*   ×   *¼-in. angle-iron column guards 6–0 high*   =   22 pcs.

4-in.   ×   *4-in.*   ×   *¼-in. angle-iron column guards 7–4 high*   =   18 pcs.

½-in.   ×   *16-in. anchor bolts for cornice*   =   200 pcs.

Pipe sleeves 2-in. dia.   ×   *12 in. for fence posts*   =   132 pcs.

Set only 14-in.   ×   *14-in. col. base plate*   +   *1 pr. anchor bolts*   =   81 cols.

Set only 2-in.   ×   *2-in. angle-iron floor frame*   =   130 LF

Reference must be made to the structural-steel and miscellaneous-iron specifications to check which items are simply *set* by the general contractor and which are not included in the sublet sections and so must be both supplied and set by him.

Subcontract items generally must be checked to determine whether they are to be embedded in or secured to the concrete, in order to ensure that all the work required in the concrete section of the specifications is taken off. Discrepancies between the subcontractors' sections of the specifications and the concrete section must be clarified by the architect, or, if this cannot be done, agreed upon with the sub-bidder. If the item in question cannot be satisfactorily cleared, either it must be taken off or the sub-bid adjusted to include it.

CHAPTER 4 **Reinforcing Steel**

Taking off reinforcing steel may be either simple or complicated, depending on both the nature of the job and the purpose of the take-off. A general contractor will generally take off reinforcing steel to obtain the tonnage if no sub-bids have been received for the item. Even if prices for reinforcing steel have been received or promised, the general contractor may take off the item in order to have a check or control figure on the weight and price quoted by the supplier. If reinforcing steel is a major item in a bid, every effort should be made to ensure that sub-bids will be received, such as sending cards to prospective suppliers, with follow-up telephone calls.

In some districts labor agreements require reinforcing steel to be bent on the job rather than in the shop. The bending thus becomes part of the field setting, and must be considered even if the take-off is for setting only. Generally, the steel supplier's bid on reinforcing steel will include shop drawings, schedules, bending, and delivery. If shop bending is not permitted, then the bid will include everything except the bending, and the bars will be delivered in straight lengths (cut to size and tagged) for bending in the field. Steel suppliers' bids must be carefully checked, especially if the bid is on a unit-price basis. Sometimes the bid is given on a lump-sum basis, but more often it is quoted per 100 lb, with the estimated total weight given. The subcontractor's bid will define the terms and conditions of the quotation. It is especially important to check whether the weight is guaranteed, for there is no standard practice for this factor.

Also important is any escalator clause in a steel bid. It is common for steel suppliers to bid with a provision that the prices quoted are subject to increase should the mill price of steel increase after acceptance of the bid. Accessories must also be considered in evaluating reinforcing-steel bids. If the accessories are not included by the supplier, the general contractor must either take them off or make an allowance for them.

Reinforcing steel is taken off in lineal feet by sizes and then converted into weight—either pounds or tons (using the short ton of 2,000 lb). A take-off

Steel bars

Bar Size			
Old, size in inches	New, by number	Weight, in lb per LF	Lap (of 40 dia.), in ft
$\frac{1}{4}$ ϕ	2*	0.167	0–10
$\frac{3}{8}$ ϕ	3	0.376	1– 3
$\frac{1}{2}$ ϕ	4	0.668	1– 8
$\frac{5}{8}$ ϕ	5	1.043	2– 1
$\frac{3}{4}$ ϕ	6	1.502	2– 6
$\frac{7}{8}$ ϕ	7	2.044	2–11
1 ϕ	8	2.670	3– 4
1 ☐	9†	3.400	3–10
$1\frac{1}{8}$ ☐	10†	4.303	4– 3
$1\frac{1}{4}$ ☐	11†	5.313	4– 9

ϕ — round; ☐ — square.

* Plain round only (not "deformed").
† Round bars equivalent in weight to the 1-in., $1\frac{1}{8}$-in., and $1\frac{1}{4}$-in. square bars.

for supply and fabrication should include considerable detail. Separate totals are required for No. 2, 3, 4, and 5 bars; No. 6 to 11 may be lumped together. Base prices for reinforcing steel are adjusted by "size extra" costs—that is, the extra costs for sizes 2, 3, 4, and 5. The take-off must further designate steel bending by two categories: (1) light bending, and (2) heavy bending. Although it sounds contradictory, light bending is the more costly. It includes all stirrups and column ties (regardless of size), *all* bending for No. 2 and 3 bars, all bars bent at more than six places, all bars bent in more than one plane, and all bars with more than one radius bend (that is, a bend of 10-in. radius or greater). All other bending is classified as heavy bending.

Reinforcing steel is normally measured in 30-ft lengths, with allowance for laps. Laps are allowed for by adding 40 diameters of the bar for every 30 ft or fraction of 30 ft in length. Although the latest code permits laps of 30 diameters, many estimators continue to allow 40. In taking off top steel for slabs that are to have "one-way" reinforcing, the estimator should take off chair bars even if they are not shown on the drawings. High chairs are spaced at about 4-ft centers alongside the beams or at 30-ft intervals in the other direction, or both; a No. 5 bar is placed on each line of high chairs, and the top steel rests on these chair bars; otherwise, hundreds of high chairs would be needed. If temperature steel should run across the main steel, or the top steel should run in both directions, then chair bars would not be needed.

Such factors as waste and cutting do not concern the estimator in taking off reinforcing steel, except in special cases. Normally, no waste is allowed if there is a good set of drawings and specifications, and if a careful take-off has been made with allowances for laps. If the drawings are poor, however, and there is some doubt about the reinforcing-steel requirements, it might be prudent to add from 2 to 4 per cent to the total quantity.

If, as in the examples that follow, the reinforcing steel is to be taken off for setting, including job bending, then the final totals should separate the items to facilitate intelligent pricing. For this purpose, it is unnecessary to separate bars No. 2, 3, 4, and 5 (as is done in taking off for supply). In taking off reinforcing steel for setting, bars up to No. 4 may be lumped together, and bars No. 5 to 11 collected also. Bent bars should be separated into two items—light bending and heavy bending.

Any special reinforcing steel items must be considered separately. This classification would include such items as column spirals, prefabricated shear heads, all welded steel, and special dowels (greased and wrapped).

Wire mesh is sometimes taken off with the reinforcing steel, but it is simpler and more practical for the general contractor to take it off at the same time as the concrete items that it will be used for.

A table of steel bar data is shown at the top of p. 80.

TAKE-OFF FOR FOUNDATION (W. D. 3.1)

REINFORCING STEEL							*No. 3*	*No. 4*	*No. 5*	*No. 6*	*No. 8*
Ftgs.	A	No. 6	7 ×	8 ×	3–0					168 ft	
	B	No. 6	3 ×	4 ×	3–0					36	
		No. 6	3 ×	4 ×	4–6					54	
	C	No. 8	2 ×	6 ×	4–0						48 ft
		No. 8	2 ×	5 ×	5–0						50
Piers		No. 6		4 ×	74–0					296	
	(LB)*	No. 3	2 ×	12 ×	4–0		96 ft				
Wall ftgs.		No. 5		2 ×	325–0				650 ft		
Walls		No. 4		220 ×	7–0			1,540 ft			
		No. 4		220 ×	7–6			1,650			
		No. 4	2 ×	7 ×	325–0			4,550			
							96 ft	7,740 ft	650 ft	554 ft	98 ft
							×	×	×	×	×
							0.376	0.668	1.043	1.502	2.67
						(LB)	36 lb	5,170 lb	680 lb	832 lb	262 lb

Straight steel (up to No. 4) = <u>5,170 lb</u>

Straight steel (No. 5, 6, & 8) = <u>1,774 lb</u>

Light bending (No. 3) = <u>36 lb</u>

* Light bending

NOTES ON THE TAKE-OFF (W. D. 3.1)

The pier footing items are taken off at full length (although the actual bars as specified or called for on the drawings, would be about 4 in. shorter). The pier height is obtained from the concrete take-off (74 LF). The No. 3 stirrups are notated "LB" to signify light bending. The wall footings and the wall horizontal steel are both 315 LF net (see concrete take-off). Referring to W. D. 3.1, we find that 79–5 requires two laps, 60–4 two laps, 54–1 one lap, and 41–8 one lap, for a total of six laps at 1–8, or 10 LF. Thus, 315 LF plus 10 LF gives 325 LF total length for reinforcing steel.

The vertical wall steel quantities are obtained from the concrete sheet. There is a total of 2,232 SF of wall for the 314–10 perimeter of wall averaging 7 ft in height. For a perimeter of 315 LF with bars on 18-in. centers, 210 bars would be required; adding 1 for the end of each piece of wall, 210 plus 10 is 220 pieces total (for each face). The outside bars will be in two pieces with a 6-in. lap, so we carry 7–6 for the height of that face; that is, 220 pieces at 7–0 for the inside face, and 220 at 7–6 for the outside face.

TAKE-OFF FOR RETAINING WALL (W. D. 3.3)

Reinforcing steel (retaining wall)						No. 3	No. 4	No. 5
Ftg.	No. 4			9	×	54– 0		486 ft	
Ftg.	No. 3			52	×	4– 0	208 ft		
Ftg.	No. 5 (HB*)			52	×	6– 6			338 ft (HB)
Wall	No. 3	2	×	7	×	51– 9	725		
Wall	No. 4			42	×	6–10		287	
Wall	No. 4			42	×	9– 3		388	
						933 ft	1,161 ft	338 ft
						×	×	×
						0.376	0.668	1.043
						350 lb	775 lb	353 lb

Straight bars (No. 3 & 4) = 1,125 lb

Heavy bending (No. 5) = 355 lb

*Heavy bending

NOTES ON THE TAKE-OFF (W. D. 3.3)

The footing steel item is the measured total length of the footing plus the two 15-in. laps at the steps. The short steel is taken off at the wall length (50–6), which is 51 pieces (on 12-in. centers) plus 1 for the end. The wall height averages 6–10 (see concrete take-off, which shows 345 SF of wall area for 50–6 in length, or an average height of 6–10). The long vertical steel is 6–10 plus 1–5 plus 1–0, or 9–3.

TAKE-OFF FOR COLUMNS (W. D. 3.4)

REINFORCING STEEL								*No. 8*	*No. 6*	*No. 3* (LB)
Cols.	No. 8	10	×	4	×	11– 4		454 ft		
	No. 8	8	×	4	×	10–10 ⎫				
	No. 8	8	×	4	×	10– 5 ⎭		680		
	No. 6	18	×	4	×	10–10			780 ft	
	No. 6	26	×	4	×	9–11			1,032	
	No. 6	52	×	4	×	8–11			1,855	
	No. 6	30	×	4	×	11– 4			1,360	
	No. 6	32	×	4	×	10– 5			1,334	
	No. 6	80	×	4	×	9– 5			3,014	
Dowels	No. 6	264	×	4	×	3– 6			3,696	
								1,134 ft	13,071 ft	

LB ties	No. 3	61	×	12	×	3–8	=	732 ⎫		
		13	×	13	×	3–8	=	169 ⎬	1,083 × 3–8	= 3,971 ft
		13	×	14	×	3–8	=	182 ⎭		
		45	×	12	×	4–0	=	540 ⎫		
		18	×	13	×	4–0	=	234 ⎬	1,026 × 4–0	4,104
		18	×	14	×	4–0	=	252 ⎭		
		10	×	12	×	4–4	=	120 ⎫		
		17	×	13	×	4–4	=	221 ⎬	579 × 4–4	2,509
		17	×	14	×	4–4	=	238 ⎭		
		16	×	12	×	4–8	=	192 ⎫		
		10	×	13	×	4–8	=	130 ⎬	462 × 4–8	2,156
		10	×	14	×	4–8	=	140 ⎭		
		8	×	13	×	5–4	=	104 ⎫		
		8	×	14	×	5–4	=	112 ⎭	216 × 5–4	1,152
										13,892 ft

Straight bars (No. 6 & 8)

$$
\begin{array}{rcll}
1,134 \text{ ft} \times 2.67 &=& 3,028 \text{ lb} \\
13,071 \text{ ft} \times 1.502 &=& 19,633 \\
&=& 22,661 \text{ lb} \\
&=& 22,670 \text{ lb}
\end{array}
$$

Light-bent bars (No. 3)

$$
\begin{array}{rcll}
13,892 \text{ ft} \times 0.376 &=& 5,223 \text{ lb} \\
&=& 5,230 \text{ lb}
\end{array}
$$

TAKE-OFF OF STEEL FOR SUSPENDED SLAB (W. D. 3.5)

REINFORCING STEEL (susp. slabs & beams)				No. 3 LB	No. 4 LB	No. 6	No. 7	No. 8	No. 9	No. 10	No. 6 HB	No. 2
Span. bms. No. 8	3 ×	4 ×	324-0					3,888 ft				
No. 4 (LB)	3 ×	456 ×	5-0		6,840 ft							
Int. bms. No. 8	3 ×	4 ×	27-2					326 ft				
No. 3 (LB)	3 ×	37 ×	4-0	444 ft								
No. 8	6 ×	4 ×	68-0					1,632				
No. 3 (LB)	4 ×	83 ×	6-0	1,992								
No. 3 (LB)	2 ×	83 ×	5-0	830								
No. 10	6 ×	2 ×	42-0							504 ft		
No. 9	6 ×	2 ×	41-8						500 ft			
No. 4 (LB)	6 ×	57 ×	5-2		1,767							
No. 7	3 ×	4 ×	9-0				108					
No. 3 (LB)	3 ×	12 ×	3-8	132								
5-in. rib joists No. 6	3 ×	2 ×	26-0			156 ft						
No. 7	3 ×	26 ×	24-0				1,872					
No. 6 (HB)	3 ×	26 ×	30-8								2,392 ft	
No. 6	3 ×	13 ×	7-0			273						
No. 3	3 ×	38 ×	26-6	*No. 3* 3,021 ft								
No. 2	3 ×	10 ×	47-6									1,425 ft
Flat slabs No. 4	3 ×	124 ×	38-6		*No. 4* 14,322 ft							
No. 4	3 ×	63 ×	38-6		7,277							
No. 4	3 ×	32 ×	64-6		6,192							
No. 4	3 ×	57 ×	8-9		2,258							
No. 4	3 ×	29 ×	8-9									
No. 4	3 ×	77 ×	24-0		8,352							
No. 4	3 ×	39 ×	24-0									
No. 4	3 ×	19 ×	39-6		2,252							
No. 4	3 ×	8 ×	27-8		664							
Bent				3,398	8,607							
Straight				3,021	41,317	429	1,980	5,846	500	504	2,392 ft	1,425 ft

Straight bars (No. 2 to 4)

No. 2	1,425 ft	×	0.167	=	238 lb
No. 3	3,021	×	0.376	=	1,136
No. 4	41,317	×	0.668	=	27,600
					28,974 lb
				=	29,000 lb

Straight bars (No. 5 & up)

No. 6	429 ft	×	1.502	=	643 lb
No. 7	1,980	×	2.044	=	4,047
No. 8	5,846	×	2.67	=	15,609
No. 9	500	×	3.4	=	1,700
No. 10	504	×	4.303	=	2,169
					24,168 lb
				=	24,200 lb

Light bending

No. 3	3,398 ft	×	0.376	=	1,278 lb
No. 4	8,607	×	0.668	=	5,750
					7,028 lb
				=	7,030 lb

Heavy bending

| No. 6 | 2,392 ft | × | 1.502 | = | 3,593 lb |
| | | | | = | 3,600 lb |

NOTES ON THE TAKE-OFF (W. D. 3.5)

The take-off of the steel for the suspended slab in W. D. 3.5 illustrates the reinforcing needed in slabs and beams. Notice that the length of the rib steel is given on the longitudinal section through the rib. This is the *actual* total bar length (that is, the straight bar length before bending). The temperature steel in the top of the pan slab is tied with No. 2 bars every 5 ft. All the flat slabs have the same reinforcing: No. 4 on 6-in. centers in the bottom and No. 4 on 12-in. centers in the top, plus No. 4 on 16-in. centers temperature steel. Notice that W. D. 3.5 is for three slabs (including the roof).

If the lengths of the bars are specified or shown, those lengths are used for the take-off. Bar lengths not given are taken off at approximate lengths. Since it is not practical to lay out the entire reinforcing for the take-off, it must be expected that the final shop drawings will show some minor differences from the estimated quantities. For a three-floor building, the duplicated items would always be taken off either for one floor and multiplied by three, or as one of two similar items on a floor and multiplied by six. For example, in the corridor beams item: 1 beam is taken off, times 6 (2 per slab; 3 slabs).

The first item (spandrel beams) has a floor perimeter of 299–10; adding for 7 laps at 3–4 each, 299–10 and 23–4 gives 323–2, which is carried as 324–0. There are four No. 8 bars per beam for each of three floors, so the item is entered as $3 \times 4 \times 324$–0. The second item consists of the stirrups for the spandrel. All stirrups are measured as the beam perimeter—which in this case is twice the sum of 8 in. and 22 in., 5 ft—to allow for the hooks. A perimeter of 299–10 with stirrups on 8-in. centers will require 450 stirrups: adding one stirrup for every length of beam (that is, 6 extra) gives a total of 456 stirrups per floor. The take-off for interior beams proceeds in the same way, and is entered in the following order: the 10-in. × 14-in., 12-in. × 24-in., 10-in. × 20-in., 15-in. × 16-in., and finally 12-in. × 20-in. beams. Beams of a common length having the same reinforcing are combined for the longitudinal bars; but the stirrups are taken off separately by beam sizes. The pan slab is taken off next; it follows the detail section shown in W. D. 3.5. There are 12 pans; therefore there will be 13 joists, including the end joists at the beams. The flat-slab steel combines the two parallel slabs at the rear of the building (11–0 plus 27–6, or a 38–6 bar length).

In taking off each item, laps of 40 diameters have been allowed for every length of 30 ft or a fraction of 30 ft, and also one extra bar "for the end." For the item for temperature steel across the pan slab, the layout shown on the section through the joists is used; there are 19 bars on that section, so for both areas (only one of which is shown) there will be twice 19, or 38 bars.

CHAPTER 5   **Structural Steel**

Although structural steel is generally a subcontract item, it is often trouble-some to the estimator. The structural-steel section of the specifications may include items that the structural-steel companies do not bid on; or perhaps one steel company will exclude a certain item and a competing company include it. Many structural-steel firms will exclude standard open-web joists and long-span joists. There are a great many steel fabricators who specialize in those joists and will bid only on them—either standard open-web or long-span types, or both. On very large structural-steel jobs, major steel companies will bid "supply and erect"; on smaller jobs it is more customary for them to bid "furnish and deliver," so that the general contractor must either price the erection himself or obtain a price from a steel erection firm.

To further complicate structural-steel bids, the specifications for that section may have included items that none of the bidders will cover—such as loose lintels, wedge inserts, the setting of anchor bolts, corrugated metal roof decking, and closure plates at metal window walls.

These miscellaneous items, plus the possibility of separate sub-bids for steel joists, make it necessary for the estimator to know exactly what each sub-bid includes and what items are required to complete the entire structural-steel work as per drawings and specifications. It is also important to have the structural-steel requirements properly spelled out in the subcontracts. Thus it is often necessary for the general contractor's estimator to take off and schedule the work specified under structural steel.

In taking off the structural-steel requirements in order to check and properly evaluate steel bidders' quotations, the general contractor's estimator need not detail every item as he would if preparing a bid. He will first break the work up into separate items such as "Structural," "Standard steel joists," and "Roof decking," and then schedule the appropriate items under each such category. The roof decking may be taken off in square feet, and the structural steel and steel joists taken off by weight. Such a rough or approximate take-off should be reasonably complete, including all members listed and measured, but carrying an approximate percentage figure to allow for plates, gusset plates, angle connections, and similar items. This addition for connections should vary from 2 to 8 per cent of the total weight of the structural members, according to the type of job and the completeness of the structural-steel drawings. Simple one-story buildings and buildings that require steel framing for slabs may run 2 to 4 per cent for connections. Multiple-story buildings that are to be entirely steel-framed (that is, all columns and floors) will usually need an allowance of from 4 to 8 per cent for connections.

Working Drawing 5.1 shows the structural-steel framing for a small building. The work includes round prefabricated columns, steel beams, open-web steel joists, structural-steel lintels, and angle-iron loose lintels. The take-off will be done in detail and include all the steel items shown on the drawing.

TAKE-OFF FOR STRUCTURAL STEEL (W. D. 5.1)

H. D. Lally cols. 0–4 dia.   ×   *10–4 (top and bottom plate)*   =   <u>4 ea.</u>

H. D. Lally cols. 0–6 dia.   ×   *10–2 (top and bottom plate)*   =   <u>6 ea.</u>

Structural-steel framing

10 B 17	2	×	32–0	=	64–0	×	17 lb	=	1,088 lb
8WF 17	2	×	10–4	} 35–4	×	17	=	601
	2	×	7–4					
12WF 27	2	×	17–0	=	34–0	×	27	=	918
10WF 21	2	×	13–6	=	27–0	×	21	=	567

$$3,174 \text{ lb}$$

$$= \quad 1.6 \text{ tons}$$

Angle-iron lintels

5	×	$3\frac{1}{2}$	×	$\frac{5}{16}$	3/8 –0, 3/9 –0, 3/9 –0	=	78 ft	×	8.7 lb	=	679 lb
4	×	$3\frac{1}{2}$	×	$\frac{5}{16}$	3/5 –0, 3/6 –0	=	33 ft	×	7.7 lb	=	254

$$933 \text{ lb}$$

$$= \quad 940 \text{ lb}$$

Base plates & bearing plates

$\frac{1}{2}$ in.	8	×	8	=	8 pcs.	×	9.05 lb	=	73 lb
$\frac{1}{2}$ in.	8	×	9	=	4 pcs.	×	10.2	=	41
$\frac{1}{2}$ in.	9	×	9	=	6 pcs.	×	11.5	=	69

$$183 \text{ lb}$$

$$= \quad 185 \text{ lb (18 pcs.)}$$

Anchor bolts $\frac{3}{4}$ in.   ×   *18 in.*   =   <u>20 pcs.</u>

Anchor bolts $\frac{5}{8}$ in.   ×   *18 in.*   =   <u>16 pcs.</u>

Open-web steel joists

No. 147	2	×	14	=	28 at 26–6	=	742 ft	@	10.1 lb	=	7,494 lb
No. 124					13 at 17–4	=	226	@	6.0	=	1,356
											8,850 lb
										=	<u>4.45 tons</u>

$1\frac{1}{4}$-in.   ×   *$1\frac{1}{4}$-in.*   ×   *$\frac{1}{8}$-in. angle crossbracing*

$$2 \ \times \ 3 \ \times \ 13 \ \times \ 2 \ \times \ 4\text{–}0 \ = \ 624 \text{ ft}$$
$$2 \ \times \ 12 \ \times \ 2 \ \times \ 4\text{–}6 \ = \ 216$$
$$840 \text{ ft} \ @ \ 1.01 \ = \ \underline{850 \text{ lb}}$$

$\frac{3}{8}$-in. dia. rod ceiling extensions   =   <u>28 pcs.</u>

Bearing plates

$\frac{3}{8}$-in.   6 in.   ×   6 in.   =   28 pcs.   @   3.84 lb   =   <u>108 lb (28 pcs.)</u>

Anchor bolts $\frac{5}{8}$ in.   ×   *18 in.*   =   <u>28 pcs.</u>

1-in.   ×   *$\frac{1}{8}$-in.*   ×   *9-in. strap anchors*

$$4(8 \ + \ 6 \ + \ 8) \ = \ \underline{88 \text{ pcs.}}$$

NOTES ON THE TAKE-OFF (W. D. 5.1)

Notice that all of the sundries that are required for the open-web joists are taken off with those joists. This method will facilitate checking sub-bids that cover only either the structural or the joist items.

The round columns are a specialist item, and the majority of steel companies that would bid a job as small as this one would sublet the columns to a column manufacturer.

The loose lintels are kept separate from the structural steel items because they are simple "cut and deliver" items involving no fabrication nor erection. The setting of loose lintels should be carried in the masonry section of the estimate.

The structural members are listed by sizes and converted to weight. For drawings on which the items are given by size only, you would refer to any structural-steel data book for the weights. These data books are numerous and may be obtained free from most of the steel-manufacturing companies.

The base plates and wall-bearing plates are converted to weight, but the number of pieces is noted also, to facilitate pricing the item. In pricing base plate items, it is always useful to know how many pieces of plate will have to be fabricated, for the cutting will cost almost as much as the stock if the plates are small.

On the steel joist take-off, it is necessary to refer to a manufacturer's catalogue to obtain the weights of the specified items. The notations "No. 147" and "No. 124" refer to the type number, standardized by the steel manufacturers. The actual average weight per foot, however, varies for steel joists according to the manufacturer's detail, as there are variations in design among manufacturers. Two particular manufacturers may each make steel joists according to the standard code, yet for joist No. 147 one maker may list 9.3 lb per ft while the other maker's No. 147 weighs an even 10 lb per ft. This variation often accounts for the different total weights given on the quotations received from different joist companies.

MISCELLANEOUS IRON

There seems to be no limit to the variety of items that find their way into the miscellaneous-iron specifications. The first task of the general contractor's estimator is to separate the items that the steel bidders are not likely to cover. Those items should be listed separately on the sub-bid sheet of the estimate, and separate prices solicited from suppliers. Items that should be segregated from the miscellaneous iron might include: hollow metal doors and frames; kalamein work; metal toilet partitions; flagpoles; aluminum entrances; metal sash. Having listed such items separately, it is necessary to also make a checklist of the items that you expect to be covered by the miscellaneous-iron bidder. When your bid day arrives and the pressure is on, you will not be able to devote an hour simply to sorting out the miscellaneous iron items. At that time, you must have all the items segregated on your subsheet, in order to be able to quickly check and evaluate the various bids.

CHAPTER 6   **Masonry**

In a building that has masonry partitions and exterior walls, the half-dozen major masonry items are a relatively large part of the general contractor's own work; in fact, these items will often exceed in value any other six items that are taken off. It is therefore especially important for the estimator to know the masonry trade and to use his knowledge to obtain accurate and complete quantities. Masonry quantities seem to give estimators a considerable amount of trouble, yet if thoroughly understood and properly handled, they should be among the easiest items to take off.

In the first place, many estimators find masonry quantities difficult (or at least tedious) to compute. There may be exterior walls of different sections and heights, with the result that the quantity sheets can be somewhat complex if the take-off is not handled in an orderly manner. Interior partitions are often even more troublesome, particularly if there is to be glazed facing tile on one side of a partition and brick or cinder block on the other side, or perhaps three or four different types of facing tile, one or more of which extend to one dado height and others to another. Much of the trouble that such items give can be eliminated if the estimator proceeds methodically, making full use of the collection sheet. The examples in this chapter show how to take off the masonry items quickly and accurately, and are good illustrations of how the collection sheet can simplify the take-off.

In taking off brickwork, it is in converting the quantities from square feet (or cubic feet) to pieces that errors most commonly occur. Too many estimators rely on the multiplying factors that they pluck from a table or are handed by a superior, without knowing either for what purpose the factor was intended or how it was obtained. The most unsatisfactory of all multiplying factors for brick quantities are those that are all-inclusive; that is, those factors that have supposedly been calculated so as to include headers and waste. If such a factor is used, the take-off will not show the quantity of headers extending into the back-up area, a quantity that will be needed when the back-up material is being taken off.

Throughout the country, there are many different types of masonry materials, manufactured in a great variety of sizes. As an example, consider face brick: waterstruck brick will average $2\frac{1}{8}$ in. to $2\frac{1}{4}$ in. in height; shale face brick will average $2\frac{3}{8}$ in. in height; glazed brick in the standard nominal size of $2\frac{3}{8}$ in. $\times$ 8 in. is actually $7\frac{3}{4}$ in. long, with a "permissible variation" (according to the Facing Tile Institute; that is, the maximum difference or variation allowed between the smallest and largest units in any one order) of $\frac{3}{32}$ in. in the height and $\frac{3}{16}$ in. in the length. Some hardburned dense face bricks that are classified as standard size (8 in. $\times$ $2\frac{1}{4}$ in. $\times$ $3\frac{3}{4}$ in. nominal) will average $7\frac{5}{8}$ in. in length, while other standard-size face bricks will average 8 in. or even $8\frac{1}{16}$ in. In computing brick quantities, the height of the brick is not the questionable factor. The coursing (brick plus joint) is the governing factor, and (with rare exceptions) the vertical coursing will be given on the drawings or in the specifications. The length, however, of the brick or facing tile or back-up block, may also need to be checked before computing the masonry quantities, for an architect rarely lays out a building with regard to a particular horizontal lay-out. And it is in their length that clay products show the greatest variation. Standard bricks from different plants may vary $\frac{3}{8}$ in. or more in length. Manufacturers' technical data sheets show one manufacturer of Norman bricks listing his brick as $11\frac{3}{8}$ in. long, while from two other plants Normans would come $11\frac{1}{2}$ in. and $11\frac{5}{8}$ in. respectively. Common bricks, which are not culled out as are most face bricks, will vary considerably in size even in a single delivery. In addition to the length of the brick, the width of the end joint must be considered; this width will depend on not only the type of masonry material used, but also the size of the bed joint.

For over 30 years, people dedicated to the coordination and standardization of building materials and units of dimension have worked and argued to develop and promote the modular system of design and manufacture. The standard module is a 4-in. unit in all three dimensions—length, height, and thickness. Insofar as it affects masonry, the modular standard requires that brick and joint conform to the 4-in. unit; that is, bricks to be of a length that will lay 8 in. or 12 in. including the joint, and of a height that will provide a vertical rise of 8 in. for every 3 courses. The 5-in. facing tile in modular layout would course $5\frac{1}{3}$ in. (3 courses per 16 in.). Proponents of modular standards believe that the system reduces both cost and time, and of course that would certainly be true if modular standards were universally accepted.

The modular system has made great progress; today there are several brick manufacturers who are making modular-sized material exclusively. There are also hundreds of brick companies that have as yet shown no enthusiasm for converting their plants to the production of modular-sized material. Despite them, however, modular-sized brick and tile material is available in a great enough variety of types and colors to satisfy any architectural whim or preference anywhere in the country.

In the gradual conversion to modular standards, the architect is a key figure. No amount of standardization of materials will accomplish anything if the architect or engineer will not bring his design into conformity. At the first transition to modular layout, drafting costs will usually go up, and some architects are not inclined to persevere in the face of this factor, although in time the system would inevitably reduce drafting costs. Another reason why architects might not be keeping pace with manufacturers in the development of modular coordination is the simple fact that good architects are usually not conformists. Many architects simply don't want to be confined to 4-in. limits or any other limitations; they believe that it would restrict their design scope.

From all these facts and considerations, there emerges the conclusion that modular standards are not yet sufficiently common for masonry to be reduced to a few simple mathematical factors. There is still great variation in the size of "standard" brick and tile, and many different coursings and bonds to be considered as well; thus the estimator must be able to compute masonry quantities from first principles.

PRELIMINARY ANALYSIS

In computing any masonry quantities, certain factors must be determined before the square-foot area can be converted into pieces of brick, facing tile, cinder block, or whatever the masonry material happens to be. From the vertical and horizontal coursing, compute the net number of pieces per square foot, add the headers (where applicable), and then add the waste.

For common brick, which is sometimes taken off in cubic feet, the method is basically the same. For common-brick walls that are not to be left exposed, there may be leeway for the contractor (and the estimator) to utilize the brick and bond that will best serve them while still meeting the specified requirements. They may choose to use jumbo commons ($2\frac{5}{8}$ in. high), oversize commons ($3\frac{1}{2}$ in. high), or perhaps even double-sized commons (8 in. $\times$ 5 in. $\times$ $3\frac{3}{4}$ in.). Common brick backing up face brick does not offer the same leeway, except in the case of a cavity wall. If face-brick headers go through into the back-up area, then the back-up must course evenly with the face brick. Sometimes it is possible, however, to use jumbo or oversize commons as back-up for face brick; for example, with standard face brick having a header bond every fifth course, the four intermediate stretcher courses may be backed up with three courses of oversize commons.

As indicated above, the coursing is the important factor insofar as height is concerned; the height of the bricks themselves does not matter in figuring the quantities. If five courses are required in $13\frac{1}{8}$ in., then a coursing of

$2\frac{5}{8}$ in. must be used for estimating the brick quantities. Whether the brick to be used is $2\frac{1}{4}$ in., $2\frac{3}{8}$ in., or 2 in. high does not matter for the brick quantities, as the difference will be made up by the width of the joint. The size of the brick may be a factor in estimating mortar quantities or the probable number of bricks laid per day, but it is the coursing that must be used in computing quantities of brick.

The length of the bricks must be known. As we have seen, it is not uniform; there may be a considerable variation. The temperature at which the bricks are baked and the nature of the clay used in them cause the variation in size that is found when a kiln is emptied. Underburned bricks will be the largest and overburned bricks the smallest; their color will vary from salmon to dark purple. Thus, if a considerable color variation is required, the length of the bricks will usually vary greatly; some dense, hard-burned bricks (nominally 8 in.) are very short, as short as $7\frac{5}{8}$ in. Because of these variations, you should always examine a sample strap of the proposed bricks before becoming committed to them. For estimating, if you are not familiar with the face brick specified, either see a few samples or get sufficient information from the supplier—the size, the weight, the density, and the price.

A difference of $\frac{1}{4}$ in. between the average length of one type of brick and that of another (for bricks nominally 8 in. long) would mean a difference of 3 per cent in the quantity to buy and lay.

The bond is very important in computing brick quantities. Not only are headers an addition to face-brick quantities, but they also affect the back-up. It is important to understand what is involved in using certain bonds. In figuring a wall that has 4 in. of face brick with a header bond and 8 in. of common-brick back-up, the part of the face-brick header that extends 4 in. into the back-up area becomes a deduction from the back-up quantity. A 12-in. wall that has 4 in. of face brick with a header bond and 8 in. of cinder-block back-up will require some common-brick or cinder-brick fillers between the headers in the center 4 in. of the wall (unless the header course is made up entirely of headers).

Waste is an item that varies—it may be anything from 3 to 6 per cent. For a building that has long stretches of straight walls with headers but very few openings, 3 per cent waste would probably suffice; if the walls were cut up by numerous openings and piers that would necessitate cutting the bricks, waste could be as high as 6 per cent. Snapped headers (that is, headers that are only half-bricks and do not bond) might be cut without trouble from whole bricks, but they also might snap badly and cause considerable waste. Usually, for a snapped-header bond, the waste will be around 5 per cent. A plain running-bond job, in which no spalled (chipped) stretchers could be hidden in the wall, would also carry a greater waste percentage— say, 5 per cent.

ESTIMATING BRICK QUANTITIES

We will consider face brick first, since that is the most costly and usually involves some kind of bond. The take-off (which is in square feet) will be shown in the examples later in this chapter. To show how the face brick item is computed, we will consider total net area of 13,006 SF for a 12-in. wall—4 in. of face brick and 8 in. of common-brick back-up, for which: coursing is $2\frac{5}{8}$ in.; brick plus joint measures $8\frac{1}{8}$ in. ($7\frac{3}{4}$ in. plus $\frac{3}{8}$ in.) for both face and back-up; and the face brick is laid with a Flemish-header bond every sixth course. The number of bricks per square foot would be:

$$\frac{12 \times 12}{8\frac{1}{8} \times 2\frac{5}{8}}$$
$$= 12 \times 12 \times \frac{8}{65} \times \frac{8}{21}$$
$$= \frac{9,216}{1,365}$$
$$= 6.75 \text{ per SF}$$

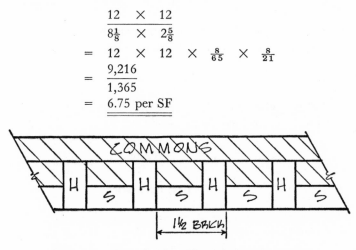

Fig. 6.1 Face brick—Flemish-bond course

The Flemish-bond course is shown in Fig. 6.1. Consider a panel $1\frac{1}{2}$ bricks wide and 6 courses high: there would be 9 bricks on the face, plus half of the header that extends into the back-up space. That is, $9\frac{1}{2}$ face bricks show 9; therefore the allowance for headers in the back-up space should be $\frac{1}{2}$ in 9 for this bond, or $\frac{1}{18}$ of the net face quantity. The items would read as follows:

Exterior face brick

Total area		$=$	13,006 SF
$8\frac{1}{8} \times 2\frac{5}{8} =$	6.75 per SF	$\times$	6.75
			87,790 pcs.
	$+$ Headers $\frac{1}{18}$		4,877
			92,667
	$+$ Waste 3%		2,780
			95,447 pcs.
		$=$	**95.5 M**

Common-brick back-up

Total area					=	13,006 SF
8 in.	2	×	6.75	= 13.5 per SF	×	13.5
						175,581 pcs.
				Less Headers		4,877
						170,704
				+ Waste 3%		5,121
						175,825 pcs.
					=	176 M

Alternatively, the common-brick back-up item may be figured by taking off the entire 12-in. wall quantity and deducting the face brick:

Common-brick back-up

Total wall area (12 in.)					=	13,006 SF
12 in.	3	×	6.75	= 20.25	×	20.25
						263.371 pcs.
				+ Waste 3%		7,901
						271,272
				Less Face brick		95,447
						175,825 pcs.
					=	176 M

Note that the final number of pieces is rounded off, the adjustment being slight considering the total quantities involved.

The coursing used for face brick was $2\frac{5}{8}$ in. vertically and $8\frac{1}{8}$ in. horizontally; with face-brick headers, the back-up brick would have to maintain that vertical coursing. Horizontally, however, the mason might increase the end joint to $\frac{1}{2}$ in., so that the back-up would have a brick-plus-joint length of $8\frac{1}{4}$ in. The estimator who knows his masons and is alert to getting the bid down to tight but still practical figures, might compute the

---

Common-brick back-up

Total area (as before)					=	13,006 SF
8-in. wall	2	×	6.65	= 13.3 per SF	×	13.3
						172,980 pcs.
				Less Headers		4,877
						168,103
				+ Waste 3%		5,047
						173,150 pcs.
					=	173.15 M

back-up using that length. If the common brick is to be exposed and pointed on the inside face, the architect might not accept a ½-in. joint; but assuming there is no such objection, the back-up brick in the previous example could be taken off as shown on the bottom of p. 96 (with the common brick coursing 8¼ in. × 2⅝ in., or 6.65 pieces per SF).

Coursing 2¾ in., with brick plus joint 8¼ in., the conversion factor would be:

$$12 \ \times \ 12 \ \times \ \frac{4}{11} \ \times \ \frac{4}{33} \ = \ \frac{2,304}{363}$$

$$= \ \underline{\underline{6.35 \text{ per SF}}}$$

Or, coursing 2½ in., with brick plus joint 8 in.:

$$12 \ \times \ 12 \ \times \ \frac{2}{5} \ \times \ \frac{1}{8} \ = \ \frac{36}{5}$$

$$= \ \underline{\underline{7.2 \text{ per SF}}}$$

Note that although all these three examples are for the standard American brick (nominally 8 in. × 2¼ in. × 3¾ in.) the number of bricks per square foot varies from 6.35 to 7.2, due to the differences in the vertical and horizontal coursings.

Full Flemish bond, with header and stretcher alternating in every course, takes 2 bricks (1 header and 1 stretcher) to cover the area of 1½ bricks on the face, so the addition for headers is ½ brick in 1½, or ⅓. Add for headers: one-third.

Full English bond, with stretcher and header courses alternating, in 2 courses 1 brick wide take 3 bricks to show* 2, an addition of 1 brick in 2, or ½. Add for headers: one-half.

Full header course every fifth course (consider a panel 1 brick wide with 4 courses of 1 stretcher and 1 course of 2 headers—Fig. 6.2) takes 6 bricks to show 5, an addition of 1 in 5, or ⅕. Add for headers: one-fifth.

Flemish header every fourth course, with 3 stretcher courses to 1 course of header and stretcher alternating, in a 4-course panel 1½ bricks wide, takes 6½ bricks to show 6, an addition of ½ in 6, or ½₁₂. Add for headers: one-twelfth.

The requirements for any bond may be computed in the same way. It is simply a question of how many bricks are laid and how many show in the face area. The addition for headers is the quantity of face brick within the back-up area expressed as a fraction of those that show on the face. The total

---

* The expression "to show" means the number of stretchers that would fill an equivalent area on the face of the wall; in this example, 4 stretchers and 2 headers "show" the equivalent of 5 stretchers.

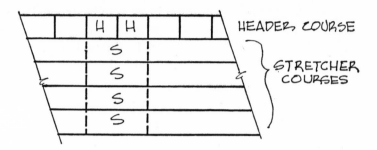

Fig. 6.2   Face brick—full header bond every fifth course

back-up area is usually different from that of the face, and so the actual number of pieces of face brick within the back-up area has to be computed in order to make the proper deduction of face brick from the gross back-up brick quantity and obtain the actual back-up brick quantity. How this can be done by those using an all-inclusive multiplying factor is a mystery.

CINDER-BLOCK BACK-UP

Backing up with material other than common brick was mentioned in the initial paragraph on the bond (p. 94). To elaborate on those remarks, and also to show the importance of knowing the number of face-brick headers extending into the back-up area for all types of back-up material, let us consider two examples:

1. A 12-in. wall, with 4 in. of face brick (Flemish header in the sixth course) and 8 in. of cinder-block back-up (Fig. 6.3).

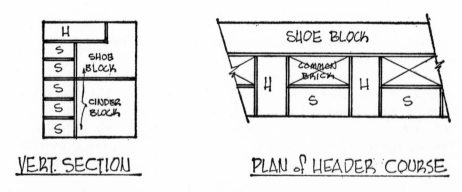

Fig. 6.3   Face brick—Flemish bond every sixth course

The cinder-block shoe block (sometimes called a header block) is recessed to receive the headers. Cinder blocks come 16 in. or 18 in. long, so where brick headers occur the entire block course must be made up of shoe blocks. Because of their shape, the recessed blocks leave spaces in the center 4 in. of wall between the headers. That space must be filled with either cinder brick

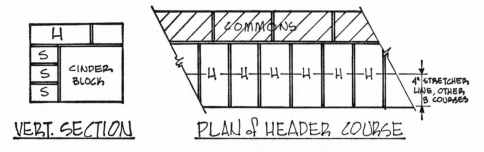

Fig. 6.4   Face brick—full header bond every fourth course

or common brick. As may also be seen, there would be one common-brick filler required per header—that is, twice as many common bricks as were added to the face brick item for headers in the back-up area.

2. A 12-in. wall with 4 in. of face brick (full header course every fourth course) and 8 in. of cinder-block back-up, with common brick back-up in the header course (Fig. 6.4).

The header bricks would take up the entire center 4 in. of the wall in the header course, with common bricks backing up the remaining (inner) 4 in., so the quantity of common bricks required would be the same as the quantity of face brick added for headers. The cinder-block area would be 75 per cent of the face-brick area. Sometimes deductions must be made in computing the back-up item from the face-brick area, such as for face brick against a concrete wall that will not require any masonry back-up. For the cinder block item, take the total face-brick area and deduct those areas that will not be backed up (brick shelf at concrete walls; concrete columns and spandrel beams that have face-brick veneer). The concrete take-off is set up to have available the items required in taking off masonry (p. 52—brick shelf; p. 61 —concrete column; p. 63—spandrel beams).

A SINGLE-STORY BUILDING

Working Drawing 6.1 shows a simple masonry building, with 12-in. masonry exterior walls, a brick shelf at the foundation walls, and concrete spandrel beams. The masonry take-off is straightforward, yet it contains almost everything that would be found in any major building. A multistory building hundreds of feet long would be only slightly different, having perhaps concrete columns, several sizes of window openings, and spandrel beams of varying depths. Once the basic methods of taking off have been mastered, the size of the job should be of no consequence; the system is the same no matter how large the figures involved.

The area of the brick shelf and the concrete spandrel beams would be shown on the concrete take-off, and so they are provided here: brick shelf— 156 SF; spandrel face area—165 SF.

THE TAKE-OFF (W. D. 6.1)

MASONRY

Ext. waterstruck face brick			*Outs*			
Shelf	=	156 SF	Drs.	2/3–6 × 7–0	=	49
132–0 × 9–7	=	1,265	Wind.	3/6–0 × 4–2	=	75
		1,421				124 SF
	–	124				

$$\text{Net Area } 1,297 \text{ SF}$$
$$8\tfrac{1}{8} \times 2\tfrac{1}{2} = 7.09 \text{ per SF} \times \underline{7.09}$$
$$9,195 \text{ pcs.}$$

Headers on
$$976 \text{ SF} \quad \tfrac{1}{18} \times 6,920 \quad + \quad \underline{385}$$
$$9,580$$
$$+ \text{ Waste } 4\% \quad \underline{383}$$
$$9,963 \; = \; \underline{\underline{10 \text{ M}}}$$

Common-brick back-up
$$2 \quad \times \quad 385 \text{ pcs.} \quad = \quad 770 \text{ pcs.}$$
$$+ \quad \text{Waste } 4\% \quad \underline{30}$$
$$800 \text{ pcs.} \quad = \quad \underline{\underline{0.8 \text{ M}}}$$

8-in. cinder-block back-up

Total face area			=	1,297 SF
Less Shelf	156 SF		}	321
Spandrel	165			
				976 SF
16 in. × 7½ in. = 1⅕ per SF	+	⅕		195
				1,171 pcs.
	+	Waste 4%		49

$$1,220 \text{ pcs.} \quad \underline{\underline{(8 \quad \times \quad 16)}}$$
$$(\text{Note—}7\tfrac{1}{2}\text{-in. coursing})$$

Wash down face brick = $\underline{1,297 \text{ SF}}$

Ext. scaffold = $\underline{1,500 \text{ SF}}$

Int. scaffold
$$125\text{–}4 \quad \times \quad 8\text{–}4 \quad = \quad \underline{1,044 \text{ SF}}$$

Clean and point cinder block = $\underline{920 \text{ SF}}$

NOTES ON THE TAKE-OFF (W. D. 6.1)

The face-brick take-off starts with the brick-shelf area, which would be obtained from the concrete sheets. The 132–0 perimeter is (33–7 plus 28–8 plus 3–9), or 66–0, doubled. (Having taken off the long dimension to the outside of the face brick (33–7), the other dimension is taken to the inside— that is, 29–4 less twice 0–4.) The openings are then deducted and the net face-brick area found. The brick coursing works out at 7.09 pieces per SF, so 9,195 pieces is the net quantity of face brick required for the face of the wall. There are no headers to add for the areas with concrete backing, so the net face-brick area for headers is 1,297 SF less the sum (156 SF and 165 SF)—that is, 976 SF, or 6,920 pieces. Flemish headers in the sixth course add half a brick in nine, or one-eighteenth the net face-brick area requiring headers. With some snapped headers required, 3 per cent waste would be tight; 4 per cent is a more likely figure.

A Flemish-header course would need common-brick fillers between the headers—a full common for every half header; that is, twice as many commons as the number of face bricks added for headers.

The cinder-block area is the same as the area of face brick requiring backing up. The actual back-up area is less than the face-brick area by the difference in the four corners, but in figuring cinder-block back-up the corners are not deducted, as the waste on the blocks is considerable due to their length. The cinder blocks are nominally 16 in. long, although some manufacturers make an 18-in. block. The blocks in our example must course $7\frac{1}{2}$ in. (for 3 brick courses), which means using $7\frac{1}{8}$-in. blocks (probably a special-order block from some plants). Cinder blocks are made to fit various coursings, the most common being a $7\frac{5}{8}$-in. block, which works with 3 brick courses to every 8 in. In our example, taking the block-plus-joint dimensions as 16 in. × $7\frac{1}{2}$ in., one block would cover 120 sq. in., or $\frac{5}{6}$ SF. Thus there would be $1\frac{1}{5}$ blocks per SF, so the square-foot area should be increased by $\frac{1}{5}$ to convert to pieces. Note that wherever it is convenient to do so, the waste item is adjusted slightly so as to round out the final total. Shoe blocks would be shown separately only if they differed in price from ordinary blocks, or if the take-off was for purchasing rather than estimating purposes.

Cinder blocks 16 in. long (with joint) and coursing 8 in., would cover 128 sq in., or $\frac{8}{9}$ SF. Thus there would be $1\frac{1}{8}$ blocks per SF, and $\frac{1}{8}$ should be added to the square-foot area to convert to pieces.

The wash-down area for face brick is the net face-brick area.

The exterior-scaffolding area is the gross face-brick area plus an allowance for the distance between the ground and where the brickwork starts.

The interior-scaffolding area is the interior perimeter times the height from the floor to the underside of the spandrel beam.

The clean and point cinder block item is the interior-scaffolding area less the "outs"—that is, 1,044 SF less 124 SF.

The conversion from square feet to pieces in the cinder block item may be worth a little extra attention, since it seems to chronically give trouble and cause arguments. If the block plus joint is 16 in. long by $7\frac{1}{2}$ in. high, then it covers 120 sq. in. One SF (144 sq. in.) equals one-fifth more than 1 block, so add one-fifth to convert from square feet to pieces. To convert from pieces to square feet, however, one-*sixth* would be deducted, not one-fifth. To demonstrate:

	500 SF		600 pcs.
$+ \frac{1}{5}$	100	Less $\frac{1}{6}$	100
	600 pcs.		500 SF

The principle is elementary, yet it invariably gives trouble. It is the same as for percentages "on and off"; if 25 per cent has been added for waste, then the gross quantity must be reduced by 20 per cent (that is, 25 in 125) to arrive at the net.

Several conclusions emerge from the masonry take-off for W. D. 6.1: (1) the value of saving the figures for the concrete items that will be deductions from the masonry; (2) the accuracy of step-by-step calculation of the total quantity of face brick by applying basic principles; (3) the way that such calculation aids in the computation of the common brick and cinder block items.

Further examples will elaborate the method used for the exterior-masonry take-off, but the entire basic outline has been given in this example.

COMMON-BRICK BACK-UP

Consider the building in W. D. 6.1 if the back-up was to be 8 in. of common brick. The face-brick quantity, of course, would be unchanged; the back-up-brick take-off would be as follows:

Common-brick back-up

8 in.	128–0 $\times$ 8–4	=	1,067 SF
Less Outs		=	124
			943 SF
		$\times$	14.18
			13,372 pcs.
	Less Headers		385
			12,987
	+ Waste 4%		513
			13,500 pcs.
		=	13.5 M

For common-brick back-up, the four corners are deducted. Each corner is 1 ft less than the face brick (Fig. 6.5), so the common-brick perimeter is 132–0 (see face-brick take-off) less 4 times 1 ft. The common-brick height is 9–7 less the spandrel beam depth. The openings must be deducted from the area, the same as for face brick. The common-brick area could also have been obtained by deducting the four corners from the back-up face area:

$$976 \text{ SF} - (4/ \; 1\text{–}0 \times 8\text{–}4) = 976 \text{ SF} - 33 \text{ SF} = 943 \text{ SF}$$

The common brick is 8 in. thick, so (using the conversion factor found for face brick) it is two times 7.09 pieces per SF, or 14.18 pieces per SF. The headers were added on the face brick item to the net quantity before waste, so they must be deducted from the commons total before figuring waste.

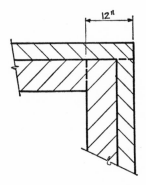

Fig. 6.5   Back-up brick at corners

A FOUR–STORY BUILDING

Working Drawing 6.2 shows a four-story building in outline. The first- and second-floor exterior walls are 16-in. masonry; the third and fourth floors have 12-in masonry walls. Additional information that would come from the drawings is the following:

Schedule of openings

Heating louver					
(1st & 2nd)	1 at 32 SF			*Brick shelf* =	1,807 SF
Doors (1st & 2nd)	3 at 6–8 × 7–3½				
Doors (1st & 2nd)	7 at 3–6 × 7–3½		Concrete		
				columns 1st	560 SF
Sash A (1st)	4 at 18–2 × 5–4		Concrete		
				columns 2nd	536
Sash B (1st & 2nd)	28 at 4–3 × 4–7		Concrete		
				columns 3rd	500
Sash C (1st)	20 at 4–3 × 5–4		Concrete		
				columns 4th	410
Sash D (2nd)	20 at 4–3 × 3–8				
Sash E (1st)	2 at 10–6 × 5–4		Concrete		
				spandrels 2nd	1,610 SF
Sash B (3rd)	28 at 4–3 × 4–7		Concrete		
				spandrels 3rd	1,610
Sash E (3rd)	16 at 10–6 × 5–4		Concrete		
				spandrels 4th	1,042
Sash D (4th)	36 at 4–3 × 3–8		Concrete		
				spandrels roof	744

Shale face brick — $2\frac{3}{4}$-in. coursing; full header course every 3rd course.
Cinder block back-up — shoe blocks throughout (for headers in 3rd course).

COLLECTION SHEET FOR EXTERIOR MASONRY

		Drs.	Outs Sash	Conc. (SF) Cols.	Span.
Ext. masonry — face brick		10–0 × 9–2	4/18–2 × 5–4	560	1,610
	23–10				
4-in. face	281–4	3/6–8 × 7–3½	28/ 4–3 × 4–7	536	1,610
+	67–2	7/3–6 × 7–3½	20/ 4–3 × 5–4	1,096	3,220
12-in. blocks	40–2		20/ 4–3 × 3–8		
	53–0		2/10–6 × 5–4		
2/26–6	441–8				
	2				
	883–4				

			Outs Sash	Conc. (SF) Cols.	Span.
4-in. face	10–6½	10–6½	28/ 4–3 × 4–7	500	1,042
+	281–4	204–4	16/10–6 × 5–4	410	744
8-in. blocks	93–0	66–6	36/ 4–3 × 3–8	910	1,786
	26–6	270–10			
	400–10	2			
	2	541–8			
	801–8				
	(1,343–4)		Shelf 1,807		
			Cols. 2,006		
			Span. 5,006		
			8,819 SF		

For a building of this size, a collection sheet would be used, as shown.

The perimeter is taken off for each of the three floor plans; at the first, the third, and the fourth floors. The 16-in. wall goes up two floors, for a height of two times 11–11, or 23–10.

The perimeter is: the long side (281–4), plus the sum of the two widths that make up the widest part of the building (67–2 and 40–10) less twice the wall width (2 × 0–4) plus twice the 26–6 setback—all multiplied by two. The perimeter is actually the perimeter of the rectangle (281–4 × 108–0) plus 4 times 26–6 (Fig. 6.6). The third-floor perimeter is quickly checked; it should be the first-floor perimeter less twice 40–10; that is, 883–4 less 81–8, or 801–8. The fourth-floor perimeter is a simple rectangle.

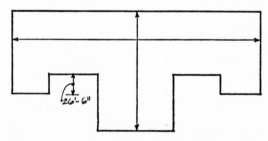

Fig. 6.6   Perimeter for exterior masonry

The 12-in. wall items could have been collected by taking them off in another way—taking off the third-floor plan at the end wings 10–6½ high, the center portion (which goes all the way up) at 21–1, and the fourth-floor ends again at 10–6½. This method would provide the same total as the method used, only there would be more computations.

THE TAKE-OFF (W. D. 6.2)

EXTERIOR MASONRY

Ext. shale face brick   *OUTS*

	Shelf	=	1,807 SF	Heating louver	=	32 SF

$$
\begin{array}{lrll}
(4 + 12) & 883\text{–}4 \times 23\text{–}10 & = & 21,053 \\
(4 + 8) & 1,343\text{–}4 \times 10\text{–}6\tfrac{1}{2} & = & 14,161 \\
\hline
& & & 37,021 \\
& & - & 4,169 \\
\hline
\text{Net area} & & & 32,852 \text{ SF}
\end{array}
$$

OUTS
Heating louver = 32 SF
Drs. 3/ 6–8 × 7–3½ ⎫
Drs. 7/ 3–6 × 7–3½ ⎬ 325
Sash 4/18–2 × 5–4 ⎫ 16-in.
Sash 20/ 4–3 × 5–4 ⎬ 953 wall
Sash 2/10–6 × 5–4 ⎭ 2,167
Sash 28/ 4–3 × 4–7 = 545
Sash 20/ 4–3 × 3–8 = 312
Sash 28/ 4–3 × 4–7 ⎫ 1,106 12-in.
Sash 36/ 4–3 × 3–8 ⎬ wall
Sash 16/10–6 × 5–4 = 896
4,169 SF

$$
\begin{array}{lrll}
8\tfrac{1}{4} \times 2\tfrac{3}{4} = 6.35 \text{ per SF} & \times & 6.35 \\
\hline
& & 208,610 \text{ pcs.} \\
+ \text{ Headers } \tfrac{1}{3} \times 152,610 & = & 50,870 \\
32,852 & & 259,480 \\
- 8,819 & + \text{ Waste } 4\% & 10,380 \\
\hline
24,033 & & 269,860 \text{ pcs.} \\
\times 6.35 & = & 270 \text{ M} \\
\hline
152,610
\end{array}
$$

12-in. cinder-block back-up

Total face area	=	21,053 SF
Less Opgs. 2,167 SF ⎫		
Cols. 1,096 ⎬	6,483	
Span. 3,220 ⎭		
	14,570 SF	
16 × 8¼ = 1 1/11 per SF + 1/11	1,325	
	15,895 pcs.	
+ 4%	635	
	16,530 pcs. (8 × 16)	

8-in. cinder-block back-up

Total face area	=	14,161 SF
Less Opgs. 2,002 ⎫		
Cols. 910 ⎬	4,698	
Span. 1,786 ⎭		
	9,463 SF	
+ 1/11	860	
	10,323 pcs.	
+ 4%	417	
	10,740 pcs. (8 × 16)	

Wash down face brick   =   32,852 SF

Exterior scaffold   =   37,100 SF

Interior scaffold

$$2 \quad \times \quad 879\text{--}4 \quad \times \quad 10\text{--}1 \quad = \quad 17{,}733 \text{ SF}$$

$$\left.\begin{array}{ccc} 797\text{--}8 & \times & 9\text{--}2 \\ 537\text{--}8 & \times & 9\text{--}2 \end{array}\right\} \quad 12{,}241$$

29,974 SF

Clean & point cinder block   =   24,033 SF

NOTES ON THE TAKE-OFF (W. D. 6.2)

With the collection sheet properly prepared, the take-off should give no trouble and is quickly done. The 16-in. walls are separated from the 12-in. walls; the two floors at 10–6½ are added together to simplify the brick calculations. Note that on the collection sheet the brick-against-concrete areas are added together for a total area of 8,819 SF of face brick that will not be backed up. Deducting that 8,819 SF from the total face-brick area leaves 24,033 SF to be backed up with cinder block. Headers required against the concrete will be snapped. A full course of headers every three courses takes 4 bricks to show 3 on the face—an addition of 1 in 3, or one-third, for headers.

The "outs" are set out to reduce the computations by keeping together items that have a common dimension. The doors 7–3½ high are an example: 3 at 6–8 plus 7 at 3–6 equals 44–6, which multiplied by 7–3½ gives 325 SF.

Computation of the cinder-block area starts with the face-brick area taken from the face brick item; for the 12-in. cinder block, that area is the original, gross face-brick area—21,053 SF (see second line of face-brick quantities). Deduct from that the outs, the concrete columns, and the concrete spandrel beams—the result is the net area of 12-in. cinder block. The brick courses 2¾ in., which is 8¼ in. for three brick courses (one cinder block). Block plus joint will run 16 in. × 8¼ in., or 132 sq in., so that 1 SF of area will contain 1$\frac{1}{11}$ blocks; thus one-eleventh must be added to the square-foot area to convert it to pieces. Not all cinder-block plants make a 12-in. header block; in areas where 12-in. header blocks are not available, the take-off would have to be for 8-in. header blocks and 4-in. standard blocks.

The exterior-scaffolding area is the gross brick area (37,021 SF) plus a small allowance for the distance from the ground to the bottom of the brickwork. If the grade around the building is low, with a considerable height of foundation wall showing, the item for rubbing exterior foundation walls would provide this additional area to be allowed in computing the exterior scaffolding.

The interior-scaffolding area is the gross inside perimeter times the brick height from the floor to the underside of the spandrel for each floor.

The cinder block will be exposed throughout; therefore an item for cleaning and pointing is required. If the cinder block was to be exposed only in certain areas, the item could be priced to include the extra cost of laying as well as the cleaning and pointing; exposed blockwork must be good, clean work without any rough filler pieces or chipped blocks.

For W. D. 6.2 with solid common-brick back-up, the face-brick quantity would be as before, and the back-up take-off would read as follows:

Common-brick back-up

12-in.	Face area		=	21,053 SF			
Less	Opgs.	2,167	⎫				
	Cols.	1,096	⎬	6,483			
	Spand.	3,220	⎭				
				14,570 SF	× 12 in.	=	14,570 CF

8-in.	Face area		=	14,161 SF			
Less	Opgs.	2,002	⎫				
	Cols.	910	⎬	4,698			
	Spand.	1,786	⎭				
				9,463 SF	× 8 in.	=	6,309

$$
\begin{aligned}
&&& 20,879 \text{ CF} \\
&& \times & \quad 19.05 \\
&&& 397,745 \text{ pcs.} \\
\text{Less Headers} &&& \quad 50,870 \\
&&& 346,875 \\
+\ \text{Waste } 4\% &&& \quad 13,875 \\
&&& 360,750 \text{ pcs.} \\
\\
&& = & \quad 360.75 \text{ M}
\end{aligned}
$$

Cinder-block back-up will not often work out as neatly as it did in the take-off shown for W. D. 6.2. Such items as pipe chases, radiators, and window sills will usually necessitate the use of smaller-sized blocks—4-in. and 6-in. ones most commonly, although 2-in. blocks might be required in some places. In taking off 12-in. cinder-block back-up, it is often advisable to take off a relatively small quantity of 8-in. and 4-in. blocks. For 8-in. block back-up, some 4-in. blocks should also be taken off to fit around irregularities. If the interruptions were shown on the drawings, the quantities for the smaller-size blocks could be measured; but even if not shown on the drawings, they will inevitably occur and should be allowed for. For the cinder block taken off for W. D. 6.2—if you should decide to carry 1,000 pieces of 8-in. block and 1,000 pieces of 4-in. block within the 12-in. block areas, and 500 pieces of 4-in. block within the 8-in. block areas—the adjustment (starting with the totals on the take-off) would be:

12-in. cinder-block back-up

$$
\begin{array}{ll}
 & 16,530 \text{ pcs.} \\
\text{Less 4-in. \& 8-in.} \quad = & \underline{1,000} \\
 & 15,530 \text{ pcs.}
\end{array}
$$

8-in. cinder-block back-up

$$
\begin{array}{ll}
 & 10,740 \text{ pcs.} \\
+ \quad \text{At 12-in. block} \quad = & \underline{1,000} \\
 & 11,740 \\
\text{Less 4-in. block } \tfrac{1}{2} \times 500 = & \underline{250} \\
 & 11,490 \text{ pcs.}
\end{array}
$$

4-in. cinder-block back-up

$$
\begin{array}{lll}
\text{At 12-in.} & = & 1,000 \text{ pcs.} \\
\text{At 8-in.} & = & \underline{500} \\
 & & 1,500 \text{ pcs.}
\end{array}
$$

It should be noted that 1,000 pieces of 8-in. block and 1,000 pieces of 4-in. block replace 1,000 (not 2,000) pieces of 12-in. block.

Special cinder blocks such as bullnosed sill or jamb blocks should be taken off as "Extra for bullnosed jamb blocks" (or whatever description applies) and the item priced *only* for the extra cost over standard material. It is not advisable to try to separate special types in taking off the back-up.

GLAZED FACE BRICK

Glazed brick will be glazed only on the side or sides to be exposed, and so the costs of the various pieces will differ according to their function. Consequently the different types, such as stretchers and headers, should be taken off separately. Stretchers are glazed only on the face; quoins on the face and one end; headers on one end only; double-ended headers are glazed on both ends, kerfed for splitting, and used where snapped headers are required; head-and-sill pieces are glazed on the face and one bed-surface. There are many other specials available, such as for bullnosed sills, bullnosed jambs, miters, and radius walls. A complicated glazed-brick job will necessitate your using the manufacturer's catalogue to identify the various specials required.

Working Drawing 6.2 may be used to show how glazed face brick (ceramic, shade No. 104) is taken off, although in practice glazed face brick does not usually course as much as 2¾ in. Let us say that examination of the drawings shows the following, in addition to the normal quoins: the door jambs have bullnosed brick, the windows bullnosed jambs, and the A and E windows (only) bullnosed sill stretchers; no specials are required at any door or window heads, nor at any sill (except the A and E windows). The brick shelf may be presumed to be 9 courses.

The face brick would be taken off exactly as in the original example—except that having arrived at the total of 269,860 pieces, the item would be left open until the specials had been taken off, so that the total number of specials could be deducted to obtain the number of stretchers. The take-off is shown, starting with the face-brick total quantity.

THE TAKE-OFF (W. D. 6.2)

Ceramic glazed face brick (Shade No. 104)

(See previous take-off)	Stretchers	=	269,860 pcs.
	Less 1,420		
	6,950		
	410		
	44	} 134,014	
	105,800		
	19,400		
		=	135,846 pcs.
		=	135,850 pcs.

Square quoins

Shelf			8	×	9c	=	72 pcs.
1st–2nd	2	×	8	×	52c	=	832
3rd			6	×	46c	=	276
4th			4	×	46c	=	184
							1,364
					+ 4%		56
							1,420 pcs.

Bullnosed jamb quoins

Doors (7–3½)	2	×	10	×	32c	=	640 pcs.
Sash (5–4)	2	×	42	×	24c	=	2,016
Sash (4–7)	2	×	56	×	20c	=	2,240
Sash (3–8)	2	×	56	×	16c	=	1,792
							6,688
				+ 4%			262
							6,950 pcs.

Face brick summary

4 S	135,850 pcs
4 S 2	1,420
4 S 4	6,950
4 S 20	410
4 S 31 (L & R)	44
2 S 80	105,800
2 S 80 D kerfed	19,400
	269,874 pcs

Sill stretcher bullnosed

$$
\begin{array}{llrcrl}
\text{A sash (18–2)} & 4 & \times & 27 & = & 108 \text{ pcs.} \\
\text{E sash (10–6)} & 18 & \times & 16 & = & 288 \\
& & & & & \overline{396} \\
& & & + \ 4\% & & 14 \\
& & & & & \overline{410} \text{ pcs.}
\end{array}
$$

Still miters

$$
2 \ \times \ 22 \ = \ 44 \text{ pcs.}
$$

Headers (standard)

$$
\begin{array}{rr}
& 152,610 \text{ pcs.} \\
+ & 50,870 \\
\hline
2\,) & 203,480 \\
\hline
& 101,740 \\
+ \ 4\% & 4,060 \\
\hline
& 105,800 \text{ pcs.}
\end{array}
$$

Double-ended headers (kerfed)

$$
\begin{array}{rcrcl}
\tfrac{1}{3} & \times & 56,000 & = & 18,666 \text{ pcs.} \\
& + \ 4\% & & & 734 \\
& & & = & \overline{19,400} \text{ pcs.}
\end{array}
$$

NOTES ON THE TAKE-OFF (W. D. 6.2)

The slight difference (only 14 pieces) between the total glazed-brick quantities and those in the previous shale-brick take-off is due to the slight adjustments made on the various waste allowances. The identifying numbers and letters shown against the items in the summary are the standard Facing Tile Institute designations for those items. The "4S" designates a face-brick series; the "2S" signifies headers in a face-brick series.

The quoin and jamb items are figured according to their various heights for a 2¾-in. coursing. The bullnosed sill stretchers are 8-in. pieces. The sill miters (4S 31) are required at the junction of sill and jamb. They are designated "L" and "R" for left-hand and right-hand; as shown, they would be ordered as 22L and 22R.

The standard headers occur in the backed-up areas. The item starts with the total backed-up face-brick quantity, 152,610 pieces (see the original take-off for W. D. 6.2), to which is added the header item of 50,870 pieces, giving the gross total of face brick that is backed up. This area has two headers to every two stretchers, so the headers are 50 per cent of the total.

The kerfed headers are glazed on both ends to be snapped into two half-headers (for the 4-in. bricks against the concrete). There being 8,819 SF of concrete area at 6.35 pieces per SF, the face-brick total quantity is 56,000 pieces. Every two stretchers have two half-headers (that is, *one* double-ended header), so one-third of the total is double-ended headers. If kerfed double-ended headers are not available from the brick supplier, ordinary double-ended headers should be ordered in the same quantity, except with more waste allowed—say, 6 per cent.

If the glazed brick was quoted for rail delivery, it would be necessary to add an item "Truck and stack glazed brick—........tons." The weights of the various items can be obtained from the brick suppliers.

EXTERIOR WALLS WITH PREFORMED WATERPROOFING

There are several waterproofing companies producing preformed fabric waterproofing for use in exterior walls. Figure 6.7 shows a typical exterior wall with preformed waterproofing. The back-up area will consist of 50 per cent 8-in. blocks and 50 per cent 4-in. blocks with common-brick fillers. The common brick item will be 50 per cent of the backed-up area, less the add for face-brick headers extending into the back-up area.

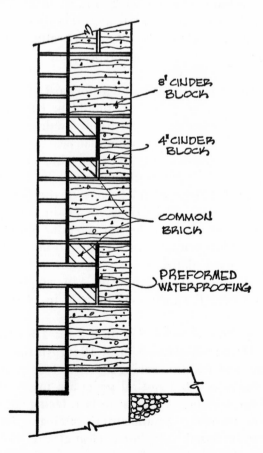

Fig. 6.7   Section through exterior wall with preformed waterproofing

INTERIOR MASONRY PARTITIONS

Masonry partitions may be any one of many materials: brick, cinder block, gypsum block, clay tile block, or structural facing tile. Unless the drawings show otherwise, all partitions should be taken off to the underside of the slab or beam. For a large building that has several types of partitions of varying heights, it is advisable to mark the partition information on the plans. First mark the heights of the partitions that vary from the predominant height (for the floor being taken off) alongside each one on the plan, and then mark that predominant height clearly in colored pencil—for example, "Ptns. 9–6 except noted." Next, in the applicable rooms, mark the materials that vary from the predominant material. If all interior partitions were to be of cinder block except a few of structural facing tile, then it would only be necessary to mark the areas requiring facing tile.

When all the required information has been transferred onto the floor plans, then the partitions can be taken off without having to turn from one sheet of the drawings to another and then back to the floor plans. Such constant referring to the various drawings and room schedules while trying to take off a particular floor would waste a great amount of time. If all floor plans are properly notated before the take-off is begun, it should be possible to see where materials and room layouts repeat, and so save time by making the repeating items work for you.

Interior partitions generally are straightforward items, and except for structural glazed material no difficulties should be encountered. The most common masonry materials used for partitions are described below.

Cinder block and concrete block—nominal face sizes 8 in. × 16 in. and 8 in. × 18 in. (in thicknesses of 2 in., 3 in., 4 in., 6 in., 8 in., 10 in., and 12 in.). The actual length and width are approximately $\frac{3}{8}$ in. less than the nominal dimensions. The block height would be one of the following (rising one block to three brick courses): $7\frac{1}{8}$-in. block for $7\frac{1}{2}$-in. coursing; $7\frac{1}{2}$-in. block for $7\frac{7}{8}$-in. coursing; and $7\frac{5}{8}$-in. block for modular 8-in. coursing. Not all manufacturers make blocks of all three heights, so the requirements should be checked with the local plants.

Gypsum block—12 in. × 30 in. (2 in., 3 in., 4 in., and 6 in. thick).

Load-bearing clay tile (T. C. tile)—12 in. × 12 in. (4 in., 6 in., 8 in., and 12 in. thick).

Structural facing tile—4S series, $2\frac{3}{8}$ in. × 8 in; 4D series, 5 in. × 8 in.; 6T series, 5 in. × 12 in.; 8W series, 8 in. × 16 in. All sizes are nominal face dimensions (height and length). Facing-tile stretchers come in 2-in., 4-in., 6-in., and 8-in. thicknesses, but not all series are made in all thicknesses. There are also numerous special shapes; in fact, facing tile cannot be taken off properly without using the manufacturer's catalogue. Facing tile is made in several finishes: unglazed, salt-glazed, clear-glazed, and ceramic-glazed.

Glazed cinder block (a cinder-concrete masonry block with a glazed face)—

sizes and thickness the same as ordinary cinder blocks, except that the 3-in. and 10-in.-thick blocks are not standard glazed items. Specials include bull-nosed jamb and head pieces, coved-base blocks, square quoins, and miter blocks. As for facing tile, a manufacturer's catalogue should be used to identify the various specials.

WORKING DRAWINGS 6.3 AND 6.4

Working Drawings 6.3 and 6.4 show the interior masonry partitions and the room finish schedules. A considerable amount of information is given, much of it descriptive matter that would ordinarily be given on other drawings or in the specifications. Some of the notations on the plan are our markings; such as the "G.F.T." notations, the window sizes, and the partition heights. Note that where a 6-in. partition requires a glazed-facing-tile dado with plaster above, the facing tile has a bullnosed cap and the partition above is 4 in. thick. These requirements are necessary because the 6-in. facing-tile partition will measure 5¾ in. and the 4-in. block 3¾ in.; thus the partition, plastered on both sides, will be 5 in. wide (3¾ in. plus 1¼ in.), and ⅜ in. of bullnose will be exposed. The alternative construction would be a 4-in. partition with a full inch of plaster on each side, so that the plaster would be flush with the facing tile. (The collection sheet is on p. 114.)

The collection sheet is done by taking off the facing-tile areas first and progressively adding the cinder block items to complete those walls, and then afterwards taking off the walls that are entirely cinder blocks. The facing tile is measured as if it was all stretchers, and the specials are taken off as extra-cost items. The facing-tile specials are taken off by group regardless of type, because all pieces in a particular group will be the same price (they run from Group 1 to Group 6). You will need a manufacturer's booklet in order to follow the facing tile take-off—any catalogue of 5-in. × 12-in. (6T series) facing tile will do.

The "outs" for doors was taken off simply as "Singles" or "Pairs." In estimating masonry partitions, door openings should be deducted at 18 SF for a single door and 35 SF for a pair, unless the openings are abnormally large. In buildings (such as hospitals) that have a considerable number of 4-ft single doors, the 4-ft doors should be taken off separately and deducted at 25 SF per single opening.

Window openings in the 2-in. furring tile for the exterior walls, are deducted at the nearest tile multiples (even feet for the length and the tile coursing for the height) less than the openings; that is, a 21-ft 9-in. opening would be deducted at 21 ft, not 22 ft.

In Room 2 (Fig. 6.8): for the window wall, 2-in. glazed facing tile is taken off at 36 ft long, with an "out" of 21 ft × 10 courses for the window. The 8-in. west wall (26–6) and on around the corner to the corridor (3–6) is 30–0 in length less an "out" of 1 door for 22 courses of 2-in. glazed facing tile with 6-in. cinder-block backing 9–8 in height; above this, the wall

COLLECTION SHEET FOR INTERIOR MASONRY

G.F.T. 4-in. (clear)

22c	12c	20c	Outs	
32–8	32–8	41–0	Drs. S	1✓
✓	21–0	✓		
	12–0		Drs. pr.	1✓
	33–0			
	33–0		Drs. 25 SF	1✓
	26–0			
	41–0		Drs. 14 SF	2
	31–0			1
	229–8			2
	✓			✓5 =

Opg. 1/6–0 × 5–3✓

G.F.T. 2-in. (clear)

22c	12c	20c	Outs
36–0	41–6	22 ft	Sash
30–0	41–4	19	21–0 × 10c✓
5–6	15–6	41 ft	17–0 × 10c✓
21–0	98–4	= ✓	
92–6	✓		Drs. 1 + 1✓
✓			Dr. pr. 25 SF✓
	Opg.	6 × 7 ft = 1✓	
	Dr.	14 SF = 1	
			3
			4✓ =

4-in. cinder block

9–8	1–6	6–0	11–2	Out	
5–6	21–0	12–0	14–6	Dr. S	1
✓	✓	41–4	12–6		3
		31–0	21–0		2
		✓84–4	48–0✓		1
					7✓ =

2–4	3–0	8–9	5–3
10–0	26–0	19–0	41–4
16–0	✓	✓	✓
10–0			
36–0✓			

G.F.T. 4-in. G2F

12c	16c
9 ft✓	8 ft✓

Clear G.F.T. specials

1	2	3	4
22	21	8	4
32	21	11	4
24	14	6	2
48	17	15	4
24	17		2
22			
172	{ 66	42	6
Base	{ 33	45	10
	{ 41	38	8
	{ 83	144	14
Cap	{ 60		6
	{ 227		14
	600	309	74
	✓	✓	✓

3-in. cinder block

4–4	3–0	3–6
32–8	26–0	41–0
21–0	✓	✓
53–8✓		

6-in. cinder block

9–8	1–6	11–2	Out	
30–0	32–8	41–6	Drs. 1	
✓	5–6	38–0		1
	38–2	79–6		2✓ =
	✓	✓		

6–0	2–5
33–0	41–0
✓	19–0
	60–0✓

Ceram. F.T. 4-in.

19c
10–0
16–0
26–0✓

Ceram. F.T. 2-in.

19c	Out
26 ft✓	Drs. 2✓

Ceram. F.T. 4-in. G2F

19c
10–0✓

8-in. cinder block

1–6	11–2
30–0✓	16–0✓

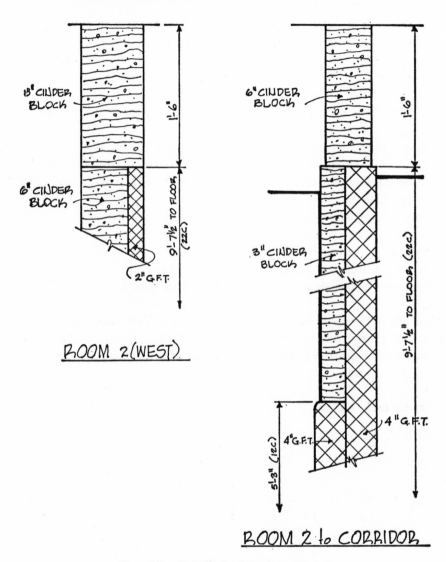

Fig. 6.8   Details for interior masonry

requires 8-in. cinder block 1–6 high, taken off at the full 30–0 in length. The south wall of Room 2 to the corridor is 32–8, with 4-in. glazed facing tile on both sides: 22 courses high on the room side and 12 courses on the corridor side; 1 pair of doors (marked "C") is deducted from the room side, and for the corridor side the same door is deducted at 25 SF. Above the 12-course facing tile on the corridor side is cinder block—3-in. cinder block 4–4 high at 32–8 in length. This completes the take-off for the wall up to 9–7½ (22 courses) in height, so we take off 6-in. cinder block—1–6 high at 32–8—to pin up to the slab.

The take-off continues item by item, clearing one area of facing tile before proceeding to another area. After all walls requiring facing tile have been completed, the facing tile specials are taken off.

The Group 1 items are: window jambs—for Room 2 (2 times 11 pieces) 22 pieces, for opening E (2 times 16 pieces) 32 pieces plus (2 times 12 pieces) 24 pieces, for Room 13 (2 times 11 pieces) 22 pieces. Quoins—for corridor (4 times 12 pieces) 48 pieces, for door "X–1" (2 times 12 pieces) 24 pieces. Total: 172 pieces.

Group 2 items are the window sills and heads, the head at opening E, the 2-in. coved base, and the dado caps.

Group 3 items are the 4-in. double-bullnosed caps for the low partitions (each 1 piece less than the full partition length), the double-bullnosed jamb pieces for the low partitions (each 1 piece less than the full height), and the 4-in. coved base.

Group 4 items are: 4 miter pieces at the window in Room 2; the same for Room 13; 2 corner pieces of 2-in. thickness for each low partition; 4 miters for opening E; internal and external corners for the coved bases; internal and external miters for the bullnosed cap at dado height.

There are no specials required for the ceramic glazed facing tile in Rooms 7 and 8.

Note that doorways are deducted at *less* than their full area where the deduction is from dado-height facing tile. With a 12-course dado a single doorway (2–8 × 5–3) is deducted at 14 SF, and double-door openings are deducted at 25 SF.

THE TAKE-OFF (W. D. 6.3, 6.4)

INTERIOR MASONRY

Clear glazed facing tile 5 × 12 2-in.

					OUTS					
93 ft	×	22c	=	2,046 pcs.	Drs.	2	×	18 SF	=	36 SF
99	×	12c	=	1,188		1	×	25	=	25
41	×	20c	=	820		4	×	14	=	56
				4,054	Opg.	6–0	×	7–0	=	42
		Less		724	Sash	21–0	×	4–2½	}	156
				3,330 pcs.		17–0	×	4–2½		
	+	Waste 4%		130						315 SF
				3,460 pcs.	@	2.3 per SF			=	724 pcs.

4-in. G1F

					Drs.	1	×	18 SF	=	18 SF
33 ft	×	22c	=	726 pcs.		1	×	35	=	35
230	×	12c	=	2,760		1	×	25	=	25
41	×	20c	=	820		5	×	14	=	70
				4,306	Opg.	6–0	×	5–3	=	32
		Less		414						180 SF
				3,892						
	+	4%		158	@	2.3 per SF			=	414 pcs.
				4,050 pcs.						

4-in. G2F

9 ft	×	12c	=	108 pcs.
8	×	16c	=	128
				236
+ 4%				9
				245 pcs.

Extra for Group 1 = 180 pcs.

2 = 625 pcs.

3 = 320 pcs.

4 = 78 pcs.

Ceramic glazed facing tile 5   ×   12

2-in.

| 26 ft | × | 19c | = | 494 pcs. |
| Less Drs. | 2 | × | 41 pcs. | = | 82 |

412

+ 4%   18

430 pcs.

4-in. G1F   26 ft × 19c = 494 pcs.

+ 4%   21

515 pcs.

4-in. G2F   10 ft × 19c = 190 pcs.

+ 4%   10

200 pcs.

Wash down facing tile

3,330 pcs.

3,892

236

412

494

190

8,554 pcs.

= 3,720 SF

Truck facing tile   2-in.   3,890 × 7 lb = 27,230 lb

4-in.   5,010 × 12 = 60,120

87,350 lb

= 43.7 tons

8-in. cinder-block ptns.

| 30–0 | × | 1–6 | = | 45 SF |
| 16–0 | × | 11–2 | = | 179 |

224 SF

Coursing 8 in. × 16 in. = $1\frac{1}{8}$ per SF + $\frac{1}{8}$ 28

252 pcs.

+ 4%   10

262 pcs. (8 × 16)

6-in. cinder-block ptns.

30–0	×	8–8	=	290 SF
38–2	×	1–6	=	58
79–6	×	11–2	=	888
33–0	×	6–0	=	198
60–0	×	2–5	=	145

OUTS

Drs. 2 × 18 = 36 SF

30–0 × 8–8 = 290 SF
38–2 × 1–6 = 58
79–6 × 11–2 = 888
33–0 × 6–0 = 198
60–0 × 2–5 = 145
———
1,579 SF
+ ⅛   198
———
1,777 pcs.
+ 4%   73
———
1,850 pcs. (8 × 16)

4-in. cinder-block ptns.

5–6 × 9–8 = 54 SF
21–0 × 1–6 = 33
84–4 × 6–0 = 506
48–0 × 11–2 = 536
36–0 × 2–4 = 84
26–0 × 3–0 = 78
19–0 × 8–9 = 166
41–4 × 5–3 = 217
———
1,674
−   126
———
1,548 SF
+ ⅛   193
———
1,741 pcs.
+ 4%   69
———
1,810 pcs. (8 × 16)

Drs. 7 × 18 = 126 SF

3-in. cinder-block ptns.

53–8 × 4–4 = 232 SF
26–0 × 3–0 = 78
41–0 × 3–6 = 144
———
454 SF
+ ⅛   57 pcs.
———
511
+ 4%   19 pcs.
———
530 pcs.

NOTES ON THE TAKE-OFF (W. D. 6.3, 6.4)

The facing tile items are rounded off to even feet when transferred from the collection sheet. The deductions are changed from square feet to pieces before the total is transferred to the other side of the take-off sheet. The tile lays 12 in. long and 5¼ in. high—that is, 2.3 pieces per SF.

Waste of 4 per cent (plus or minus) is allowed for all partition items. The waste for extra-cost specials is added mentally when transferring the items from the collection sheet.

On the 2-in. ceramic facing tile item, the deduction is made in one step, using 41 pieces for a single door—18 SF times 2.3 pieces per SF, or 41 pieces.

For washing down, the total quantity of all 2-in. and 4-in. tile is converted into square feet.

The item for trucking tile from the nearest railway siding to the job is figured by totaling the weight of the 2-in. material (allowing 7 lb per piece) and adding that of the 4-in. material (allowing 12 lb per piece). The weight of glazed facing tile varies, but can be obtained from the supplier.

The cinder block is all plastered, and so can be figured to course 8 in. (the most common coursing), which would require 9 blocks to cover 8 SF, or 1⅛ blocks per SF.

MASONRY—MISCELLANEOUS ITEMS

Interior scaffolding, if required, is taken off in square feet. This item is the gross area of the interior partitions. The item should be taken off after the masonry take-off has been completed, when the total area of the partitions is available.

Mortar is taken off in cubic yards of a stated mix (more detailed information can be found on p. 121).

Brick anchors and ties are taken off per thousand (M) and described.

Metal reinforcing for block partitions is taken off in lineal feet of stated width. The spacing requirements are usually specified. If they are not, the wall reinforcing should be figured for every second course.

Angle-iron lintels set by masons are taken off at the number of pieces.

Arch bricks are taken off in pieces, either separately from the rest of the brick or as an extra-cost item. Usually flat splayed arches require splayed bricks, which must be specially made to a pattern but are sometimes ground or cut on a brick saw on the job.

Face brick laid in special patterns should be taken off as an extra-cost item, measured in square feet. For example, "Extra cost for face brick laid herringbone—........SF."

A molded-brick course should be taken off in pieces, either as a separate brick item or an extra-cost item.

Roman bricks are 11½ in. long by 1½ in. high, and usually lay 11⅞ in. brick plus joint. The vertical coursing would be as shown on the drawings.

Norman bricks are 11½ in. × 2¼ in., and usually lay 11⅞ in. brick plus joint: the vertical coursing would be as shown on the drawings.

Oversize bricks are any bricks that are greater in height than the usual 2¼ in. to 2⅜ in. Usually, oversize face bricks will course 3 oversize bricks per 4 standard-size.

Fire-clay flue lining is measured per lineal foot of stated size.

Glass blocks are measured in pieces of stated size (6 in. × 6 in., or 8 in. × 8 in., or 12 in. × 12 in.). Expansion material and reinforcing are usually included in the quotation for the glass blocks; thus those items are normally not taken off.

Glazed facing tile: The comparative cost of various facing-tile walls is a constant topic of discussion among masonry men. The most commonly occurring consideration, which should be examined by everyone who has to estimate masonry, is the comparative cost of laying 5-in. × 8-in. facing tile and 5-in. × 12-in. tile. We are concerned here only with job costs—with determining which material is cheaper to handle. The costs of the materials themselves are about the same; if a particular 5 × 8 piece costs $0.20, the same piece in 5 × 12 material will cost about $0.30. Those who favor 5 × 8 tile claim that it is a more flexible size and can be laid with considerably less cutting than is possible with the 5 × 12 size. While this may be true, it hardly seems a strong enough argument. The cutting of facing tile is admittedly expensive, but the actual amount of cutting required for a given quantity of tile would be relatively little. The main argument in favor of the 5 × 12 material is that there is little difference between the two sizes in the rate of laying—that is, a mason will lay about as many pieces of 5 × 12 tile as 5 × 8 tile in a day; thus a considerable saving in labor can result from the use of 5 × 12 tile. This question would have to be decided should the specifications allow either 5 × 8 or 5 × 12 tile at the contractor's option.

Another facing-tile problem is how to take off composite walls if the various items are not specifically detailed—such as an 8-in. partition with facing tile on one side and cinder block on the other, or perhaps a 12-in. bearing partition of brick with facing tile on both sides. In general, 2-in. facing tile will prove less expensive than 4-in. tile in its effect on the over-all cost of a composite wall; that is, a 12-in. wall as described above should be taken off as 2-in. facing tile plus 8 in. of brick plus 2-in. facing tile rather than as 4-in. tile both sides. An 8-in. partition consisting of 6-in. cinder block (or 6-in. clay tile) plus 2-in. facing tile would be less expensive than one of 4-in. pieces of each. An 8-in. partition with facing tile on both sides, however, would be less expensive as 4-in. facing tile back-to-back than as a combination of 2-in. facing tile, 4-in. block, and 2-in. facing tile.

Mortar is an item that costs considerably more than many people realize. The theoretical quantity of mortar required to lay a given amount of masonry material is not difficult to compute, but the actual amount of mortar used will be much greater than that theoretical quantity. Standard face brick with ⅜-in. joints requires (theoretically) 9 to 10 CF of mortar per 1,000 bricks, but on the job that would not be nearly enough. "Where does the mortar go?" is a question often asked. The answer is that some of it stays in the mixer, some spills out of the barrow, some sticks to the barrow, some sticks to the mortar board, some slops off the trowel, and some is left at the end of the day's work; in addition, a few cement and lime bags are sure to burst; and finally, much of the extra mortar goes into the wall for slushing up brick batts or cut bricks. Whatever does happen to it, it should be clear that theoretical quantities are not reliable guides for the estimator. The quantities suggested below are the results of many years of checking the mortar quantities used on major jobs, yet for this problematical item, they must be regarded as approximate only.

Masonry material				*Mortar*
Standard face brick or common brick		$\frac{1}{4}$-in. joints		16 CF per 1,000 pcs.
Standard face brick or common brick		$\frac{3}{8}$-in. joints		18 CF per 1,000 pcs.
Standard face brick or common brick		$\frac{1}{2}$-in. joints		20 CF per 1,000 pcs.
Cinder concrete blocks	8 in. × 16 in.	4 in.		5 CF per 100 pcs.
Cinder concrete blocks	8 in. × 16 in.	6 in.		6 CF per 100 pcs.
Cinder concrete blocks	8 in. × 16 in.	8 in.		8 CF per 100 pcs.
Cinder concrete blocks	8 in. × 16 in.	10 in.		9 CF per 100 pcs.
Cinder concrete blocks	8 in. × 16 in.	12 in.		10 CF per 100 pcs.
Clay tile partition blocks	12 in. × 12 in.	4 in.		4 CF per 100 pcs.
Clay tile partition blocks	12 in. × 12 in.	6 in.		5 CF per 100 pcs.
Clay tile partition blocks	12 in. × 12 in.	8 in.		6 CF per 100 pcs.
Clay tile partition blocks	12 in. × 12 in.	12 in.		7 CF per 100 pcs.
Glazed facing tile		2 in.		4 CF per 100 SF
Glazed facing tile		4 in.		6 CF per 100 SF
Gypsum tile (Gypsum mortar) tile		3 in.		3 CF per 100 SF
Gypsum tile (Gypsum mortar) tile		4 in.		4 CF per 100 SF
Gypsum tile (Gypsum mortar) tile		6 in.		5 CF per 100 SF
Fire brick — thin joint	fire clay			350 lb per 1,000 pcs.
Fire brick — ordinary work	fire clay			550 lb per 1,000 pcs.

Computing the total quantity of mortar (in cubic yards) and carrying it as a separate item in the estimate is a much better practice than adjusting the unit prices of masonry items to allow for the mortar. This "juggling" method is very hit-and-miss, being perhaps the addition of $8 or $10 per M to the face-brick price and a penny or so to the unit price for back-up blocks. Some examples of mortar mixes and costs are given on p. 232.

STONEWORK

Stonework may be taken off in various ways, depending on the most satisfactory unit of measurement for pricing. The standard unit of measurement used by cut-stone suppliers is cubic feet. The total quantity of stone shown on the bid from the stone company will often be considerably greater than the total on your estimate. Such a difference does not necessarily indicate that one of the two quantities is wrong, because stone companies usually take off the items at the sizes of the stone blocks from which the finished material would be cut.

Stonework features for exterior face-brick walls (such as sills, plinth courses, band courses, and trim around openings) should be taken off on the face-brick collection sheet. Where applicable, the stone quantity would be included in the "outs" from the face brick item on the take-off sheet. Deductions for stonework would usually be from the face brick item only; thus the back-up area would be the net face-brick area plus the "outs" for stonework.

If any appreciable quantity of stonework is involved, the requirements for stone anchors, dowels, cramps, and the like must be examined and may have to be taken off. Stone anchors and dowels are often specified in materials and sizes that sound as though they are simple enough items, and yet prove very expensive. Bronze, brass, or hot-dipped, galvanized dowels might have to be made to order at a cost that could be $0.10 or more per piece. Two actual recent examples can be cited: a small job with $4,000 worth of polished-marble exterior features for which the stone anchors and dowels cost about $200; and a major seven-story building with granite facing throughout, for which the cost of granite was $240,000 and the cost of stone dowels, cramps, and anchors $3,500.

Boxing up and protecting stonework may be necessary or even specified; if so, an item should be taken off for it (usually as a lump sum). Such an item is frequently carried as a "protection" item under carpentry.

Working Drawing 6.5 shows a granite base course and limestone features for the building shown in W. D. 6.2. In taking off the stonework, W. D. 6.2 is used only for the plan layout and the windows; that is, the plan dimensions and the window schedules used are from W. D. 6.2.

THE TAKE-OFF (W. D. 6.2, 6.5)

STONEWORK

4-in. granite base course

$$883\text{–}4 \quad \times \quad 2\text{–}9 \quad = \quad \underline{2{,}430 \text{ SF}}$$

9-in. × *5½-in. limestone sills*

A	4	×	18–8	=	75 ft
E	18	×	11–0	=	198
B, C, D	132	×	4–9	=	627
					<u>900 LF</u>

$3\frac{3}{4}$-in. $8\frac{1}{4}$-in. *limestone band*   =   542 LF

15-in.   ✕   *6-in. limestone coping*   =   1,102 LF

Wash down stonework

Granite				=	2,430 SF
Sills	900–0	✕	1–3	=	1,125
Band	542–0	✕	0–9	=	407
Coping	1,102–0	✕	2–6	=	2,755
					6,717 SF

Box up & protect stone sills   =   900 LF

Truck stone from siding to job

2,155 CF   ✕   180 lb   =   194 tons

$\frac{5}{8}$-in.   ✕   *3-in. galv. dowels*

Coping   293   ✕   2   =   586 pcs.

Galv. strap anchors (twisted)

Band   140   ✕   1   =   140 pcs.

Galv. dovetail anchors (split)

Base course   265   ✕   2   =   530 pcs.

Nonstain cement mortar

2,155 CF conc. ✕ 7 CF per 100 CF conc.	=	151 CF
	=	6 CY

NOTES ON THE TAKE-OFF (W. D. 6.2, 6.5)

The perimeter of the granite base course is the same as that of the face brick at the first floor. The limestone sills are taken off from the window schedule in W. D. 6.2, except that the stone should be 6 in. longer than the window opening. The band course item is the fourth-floor face-brick perimeter. The coping item is the sum of all the perimeters at roof level, and is made up of:

Roof at 3rd floor	95–2	+	39–10	+	39–10	=	174–10
Roof at 4th floor	2 (93–8	+	37–6	+	37–6	+ 25–6) =	388– 4
Main roof	2 (204–4	+	65–2)			=	539– 0
							1,102– 2
						=	1,102 LF

The washing-down area includes all of the exposed stone surfaces: the granite area, plus the sills, (allowing for approximately two faces), plus the band course (measured to the nearest inch—9 in.), plus the coping (the sectional perimeter less the 12-in. bed: 2 times the sum of 15 in. and 6 in., less 12 in.—2 ft 6 in.).

Protection will be needed only for the window sills. The item for trucking from the railway siding would be required only if the stone was shipped by rail. The items are reduced to cubic feet and the weight computed at 180 lb per CF (a figure that is only approximate and can be replaced by a more accurate figure if the actual density of the stone is known).

The dowels and anchors are taken off to show what those items might amount to; whether you should carry a lump-sum item or take off each item separately would depend on the particular job being figured. In taking off those items, one extra stone must be allowed for every straight run; as an example, consider the dowels for the copings: 1,102 LF of coping in 4-ft lengths is 278 stones, but as there are 15 straight runs (3 runs at the third floor, 8 at the fourth, and 4 at the main roof), there would be 293 stones in all, each requiring 2 dowels.

The nonstain cement mortar item allows 7 CF of mortar per 100 CF of stone—a reasonable average allowance for stonework that is mostly in large pieces.

Stonework in general is taken off as follows:

Veneer or facing stone up to 8 in. thick—in square feet of stated thickness.

4-in and 8-in. "in and out" courses (that is, alternating 4-in. and 8-in. courses)—in square feet, "average 6-in. thickness."

Trim, feature panels, and the like, over 12 in. in the smallest face dimension—in square feet of stated thickness.

Trim, sills, jambs, and the like (except as above)—in lineal feet of stated width and thickness.

Steps, buttresses, entrance walls—in cubic feet.

Special features (such as round columns or corner stones)—in pieces, fully described (for example, "Circular fluted limestone cols., 20-in. dia. × 11-4 —8 pcs.").

Flagstone paving—in square feet of stated thickness.

Rubblestone walls—in cubic feet.

CHAPTER 7 **Carpentry**

Many estimators confine their take-off for carpentry to rough carpentry work, and carry the millwork, doors, and windows on the subcontract sheet, pricing the labor for setting those sub items at a percentage of the sub-bid. This is a very haphazard way of handling carpentry labor, and is not recommended. The majority of finish items also involve some other part of the estimate, so that much of the information used for the take-off of finish carpentry would already have been collected; consequently, that take-off would be neither too difficult nor very time-absorbing. The doors and windows would be deducted as "outs" from the masonry; blocking and furring would be taken off for cabinets, paneling, and closets; eaves nailers and roof blocking items would provide the figures to be used in taking off fascia boards, soffit boards, gutters, and the like.

Carpentry is not usually a major item in modern first-class construction; in fact, with the exception of houses, apartment buildings, and schools, carpentry work is relatively easy to take off. The carpentry in hospitals, office buildings, and industrial buildings generally is confined to such items as protection work, guard rails, roof nailers, furring and grounds, blocking for casework; and wood doors, shelving, and cabinets. Except for wood-framed buildings, carpentry work consists of many relatively small items, each of which has to be taken off piece by piece or item by item—a somewhat tedious job.

Framing lumber, continuous blocking, grounds, furring, and studding must all be measured either in multiples of even feet or to be cut from such multiples. Lumber in lengths of 18 ft or more will usually cost more than the standard prices, so 16 ft is generally taken off as the maximum standard unit. Items up to 7 ft long may be measured in the odd-foot length—two 7-ft pieces for example, could be cut from a 14-ft length—but a 9-ft piece would have to come out of a 10-ft length. Short-length material—items up to 3 ft long—may be measured as shown in the drawings. Such pieces can be readily cut from long lengths, and might even be obtained from the cuttings that accumulate on most jobs.

The specifications must be checked for any special requirements and such requirements noted on the take-off sheets. Framing lumber is usually dressed on all four sides, and so is only nominally of the given dimensions. For example, 2-in. × 4-in. D4S is actually 1⅝ in. × 3⅝ in., and 1-in. boarding is nearer ¾ in. when dressed. Should the specifications call for finish sizes, care must be taken to check those sizes against what would be standard and what would be special. As an example, consider a job that calls for roof boarding of ⅞-in. finish (D2S). That material would not come out of a 1-in. rough board—it would have to come out of 1¼-in. material; thus the material price should be checked with a supplier. An item for full-dimension lumber specified as rough, must allow for both its material price and the labor costs of its handling.

The preservative treatment required for wood should be carefully checked, and the requirements described on the take-off sheet. Pressure treatment of lumber is expensive, in fact it is often more costly than the lumber itself; material costing $120 per 1,000 BF originally, might cost another $160 per 1,000 BF for pressure preservative treatment. Moreover, should the job be in an area that contains no facilities for pressure treatment of lumber, the material might have to be trucked 50 miles to the pressure tanks and 50 miles back, all of which must be included as part of the cost of the item. A specification calling only for "wood preservative treatment," however, would be quite a different matter—then a simple dipping or a brush coat would serve.

The take-off examples cover: (1) simple blocking and furring for a masonry building with wood doors and double-hung wood windows, (2) typical classroom requirements for a school, and (3) the majority of the carpentry for a wood-framed two-family house.

EXTERIOR CARPENTRY

Working Drawing 7.1 shows the exterior-wall carpentry details for the building shown in W. D. 6.2; W. D. 6.2 should be used in conjunction with W. D. 7.1 for the carpentry items. The carpentry take-off includes all the rough and finish items shown. Additional information taken from the specifications: Exterior wood blocking at roof, eaves nailers, and cants to be pressure "wolmanized"; rough bucks for doors to have 3 galvanized anchors ⅛ in. × 1¼ in. × 8 in. per jamb. Exterior doors to be 3 ft × 7 ft, 2-in. solid pine, 6-panel; the pair of doors to have 2-in. molded, beveled astragals (one for each leaf). Ceiling height to vary from 8 ft 6 in. to 9 ft 4 in.; all exterior trim to be clear pine, all interior trim birch. Ends of window stools to be notched and returned; window frames and sashes to be white pine; all doors, door frames, window frames, and sashes to be primed at the mill; all other millwork and trim to be back-primed before erection. Total number of rooms: 112.

THE TAKE-OFF (W. D. 6.2, 7.1)

ROUGH CARPENTRY

3 × *12 eaves nailers (pressure wolmanized)*

3rd	96–0	+	42–0	+	42–0		=	180 ft
4th	2(94–0	+	40–0	+	40–0	+ 28–0)	=	404
Main	2(206–0	+	68–0)				=	548
								1,132 LF
							=	3,396 BF
							=	3,400 BF

1 × *6 eaves nailer (pres. wolm.)*   =   1,140 LF

4-in. roof cants (pres. wolm.)

$$96\text{–}0 \ + \ 68\text{–}0 \ + \ 68\text{–}0 \ = \ 232 \text{ LF}$$

$\frac{1}{2}$-*in.* × *12-in. bolts for conc.*

1,132 at 1 per 3 ft	=	378	pcs.
+ 1 per run	=	15	
		393	pcs.
Say,		400	pcs.

Window blocking

Head	2	×	6	4/20	+	18/12	+	132/ 5	=	956 ft	}	2,468 BF	
Jambs	2	×	6	84/ 6	+	112/ 5	+	112/ 4	=	1,512	}		
Sill	2	×	4	16/12	+	64/ 5			=	512	=	342	
Sill	2	×	8	4/20	+	68/ 5	+	2/12	=	444	=	592	
												3,402 BF	
											=	3,400 BF	

1 × *4 blocking at mullions*

A	4	×	3	×	6–0	}	288 ft
E	18	×	2	×	6–0	}	
						=	290 LF

1 × *2 wall furring for plaster*

1st & 2nd	2(877	+	12)	=	1,778 pcs.			
3rd	795	+	8	=	803			
4th	535	+	4	=	539			
					3,120 pcs.	×	10 ft =	31,200 LF
Add 1 length per room				112		×	10 =	1,120
								32,320 LF

$\frac{3}{4}$-in.   ×   4-in. ground for metal base

$$880\text{--}0 \quad + \quad 880\text{--}0 \quad + \quad 800\text{--}0 \quad + \quad 540\text{--}0 \quad = \quad \underline{3,100 \text{ LF}}$$

2   ×   8 rough bucks for door frames

$$
\begin{array}{rcrcl}
3 & \times & 24\text{--}0 & = & 72 \text{ ft} \\
7 & \times & 20\text{--}0 & = & 140 \\
& & & & \overline{212 \text{ LF}} \\
& & & = & \overline{\underline{284 \text{ BF}}}
\end{array}
$$

$\frac{1}{8}$ × $1\frac{1}{4}$ ×   8 galv. anchors

$$10 \quad \times \quad 2 \quad \times \quad 3 \quad = \quad \underline{60 \text{ pcs.}}$$

MILLWORK (SET ONLY)

Wood window frames (white pine, primed)

$$18\text{--}2 \quad \times \quad 5\text{--}4 \quad = \quad \underline{4 \text{ fr.}}$$

$$10\text{--}6 \quad \times \quad 5\text{--}4 \quad = \quad \underline{18 \text{ fr.}}$$

$$4\text{--}3 \quad \times \quad 5\text{--}4 \quad = \quad \underline{20 \text{ fr.}}$$

$$4\text{--}3 \quad \times \quad 4\text{--}7 \quad = \quad \underline{56 \text{ fr.}}$$

$$4\text{--}3 \quad \times \quad 3\text{--}8 \quad = \quad \underline{56 \text{ fr.}}$$

D.H. sashes (spiral balances)

$$
\begin{array}{rcrcl}
4 & \times & 3 & = & 12 \\
18 & \times & 2 & = & 36 \\
& & & & 132 \\
& & & & \overline{\underline{180 \text{ pairs}}}
\end{array}
$$

Ext. wood door frame 2 in.   ×   *9 in., 3 ft*   ×   *7 ft*   = $\underline{7 \text{ fr.}}$

Ext. wood door frame 2 in.   ×   *9 in., 6 ft*   ×   *7 ft*   = $\underline{3 \text{ fr.}}$

2-in. pine ext. doors 3 ft   ×   *7 ft*   = $\underline{13 \text{ dr.}}$

2-in. Astragal 7 ft long   = $\underline{6 \text{ pcs.}}$

Clear pine staff bead 3 in.   ×   *2 in. (back-primed)*   = $\underline{2,468 \text{ LF}}$

Clear pine mullion trim 1   ×   *$3\frac{1}{2}$ (back-primed)*   = $\underline{290 \text{ LF}}$

Birch window trim (back-primed) 1 $\times$ *4 cover mold* = <u>2,468 LF</u>

Birch window trim (back-primed) 1-in. scotia = <u>2,468 LF</u>

Birch window trim (back-primed) 1 $\times$ *8 stool (notch & return)*

$$
\begin{array}{rcrcr}
4 & \times & 20\text{-}0 & = & 80 \text{ ft} \\
68 & \times & 5\text{-}0 & = & 340 \\
2 & \times & 12\text{-}0 & = & \underline{24} \\
& & & & \underline{444 \text{ LF}}
\end{array}
$$

Birch window trim (back-primed) 1 $\times$ *12 stool (notch & return)*

$$
\begin{array}{rcrcr}
16 & \times & 12\text{-}0 & = & 192 \text{ ft} \\
64 & \times & 5\text{-}0 & = & 320 \\
& & & & \underline{512 \text{ LF}}
\end{array}
$$

Birch window trim (back-primed) $\frac{3}{4}$ $\times$ *4 apron* = <u>956 LF</u>

Birch window trim (back-primed) 1 $\times$ *2$\frac{1}{2}$ mullion trim* = <u>290 LF</u>

1 $\times$ *4 door casing (birch, back-primed)* = <u>284 LF</u>

Set finish hardware = <u>L. S.</u>

Rough hardware = <u>L. S.</u>

Temporary doors = <u>10 opgs.</u>

NOTES ON THE TAKE-OFF (W. D. 6.2, 7.1)

The eaves nailer item collects the roof dimensions in the nearest even-foot multiples: the front roof at the third floor is actually 95 ft 2 in. $\times$ 40 ft 10 in., for which we take off 96 ft plus 42 ft plus 42 ft. Continuous nailers in long runs, such as these, do not require any waste allowance unless the specifications require the joints to be half-lapped. For all items—such as eaves nailers or sill plates—that call for lapped joints, an allowance should be made of 6 in. for every 14 ft, and the total quantity increased accordingly. If the eaves blocking had been specified as requiring lapped joints, the total length in lineal feet would have been 1,132 LF plus 42 LF, or 1,174 LF. The total quantity is converted from lineal feet to board feet. One BF of lumber is 1 LF times 12 sq in. in section; thus a 3 $\times$ 12 is 3 BF per LF.

The 1 $\times$ 6 nailer has the same length as the 3 $\times$ 12, but is rounded out from 1,132 LF to 1,140 LF. Notice that the 1 × 6 is *not* converted to board feet. For members not more than ½ BF per LF the lineal-foot measure is better for pricing; since small-section items are usually relatively costly to handle, they should be left in lineal feet rather than lumped in with the larger-section items carried in board feet.

There should be an extra bolt added for the end of each run of wall. Many estimators do not take off anchor bolts, yet there is no excuse for omitting them. They are required, their take-off is simple, and they cost up to $0.30 each; so why deliberately leave them out of the estimate?

The window blocking follows the window schedule, with even-foot multiples taken off for everything over 7 ft and odd-foot multiples for lengths under 7 ft. The first item of 2 × 6 at the head is for the A-type windows: 4 windows at 18 ft 2 in. long require 4 pieces at 20 ft each of the 2 × 6 blocking. Notice that the sill blocking is 2 × 4 for the third and fourth floors, but 2 × 8 for the first and second floors. The two sill totals, added together, check the head item (512 ft plus 444 ft—956 ft).

The item of 1 × 4 blocking at the mullions would probably not be needed. It would not be required if the window frames were completely mill-assembled; it *would* be required, however, if the big windows were to be delivered with the mullion material bundled for job assembly.

To determine the required amount of the 1 × 2 furring (or "strapping" as it is sometimes called), we take off the perimeter at each floor, and add one (10-ft) piece for each run of wall, plus an additional piece for every room. The first-floor inside perimeter is 876 ft 8 in., for which we take off 877 ft, adding 12 lengths of wall to allow an extra piece of furring at every corner. This gives 889 pieces of furring (1 piece per LF) for each of the first two floors—1,778 pieces total for two floors. Repeating this method for the third and fourth floors, the total of 3,120 pieces at 10 ft each gives 31,200 LF. (The furring is taken off at 10 ft per piece because the ceiling heights vary from 8 ft 6 in. to 9 ft 4 in. and so 10-ft lengths are required throughout.) Finally, there are 112 rooms in the building, each of which will break up the furring and require an extra piece at the corner; therefore we add 112 additional pieces. (Given a full plan layout, we would count the rooms involved to determine this last allowance.) It should be noted that in taking off the wall furring, no allowance has been made for window openings. Unless such openings are either predominantly very large or very small, it is not necessary to allow for them in the wall furring item. It is usually found that the furring required around the perimeter of the openings will offset that deducted from the straight-run vertical material. Calculating the window openings in this example would show that the adjustment for windows would amount to an additional 40 LF of furring, which would not be significant in a total of 32,000 LF. This calculation is worth considering in detail:

18–2 × *5–4 window*

Deduct	17	×	6–0	⎫				
Add	2	×	18–0	⎬ Deduct	56–0	×	4	=	224 ft
Add	2	×	5–0	⎭				

10–6 × *5–4 window*

Deduct	9	×	6–0	⎫ Deduct	22–0	×	18	=	396
Add	2	×	16–0	⎭				−	620

4–3 × *5–0 average window*

Deduct	3	×	5–0	⎫ Add	5–0	×	132	=	660
Add	4	×	5–0	⎭		Net	+	40 LF

If the wall furring is to be spaced on 14-in. or 16-in. centers, an additional amount of furring will probably be required for the windows; in other words, the deductions from the straight runs would be less than the additions required around the openings.

The item of grounds for the metal base is simply the sum of the floor perimeters slightly rounded out. The other rough carpentry items are self-explanatory. It should be noted that at the very end of the take-off (following the millwork) there are two items that properly belong with the rough carpentry: rough hardware and temporary doors. Those items would be entered on the estimate sheet with the rough carpentry; they are shown where they are only because they were missed when the rough carpentry items were taken off.

The wood doors, windows, and millwork have been taken off for setting only. This procedure presumes that those items will be supplied by a sub-contractor. In taking off millwork for setting only, it is not necessary either to describe the items in great detail nor to break them down by sizes. Since job-cost records will not separate the costs of (for example) hanging sashes or hanging doors according to their various sizes, there is no advantage in breaking down the various sizes on the take-off—unless there is something unusual about the items. Triple and double window frames should be separated from the single ones, and very large doors ($3\frac{1}{2}$ ft wide and over) separated from the more usual 3-ft and under sizes. Should you be pricing the doors, windows, or millwork for supply, however, then the take-off must describe the items completely.

The take-off of wood window frames, sashes, and doors is straightforward. All the single window frames would probably be priced at the same unit cost for setting; in fact, they could be taken off as: "Single window frames average 4–3 × 5–0—132 fr." Notice that the door frames are measured at the *door* sizes, not the masonry-opening sizes.

The window trim items follow the quantities taken off for the blocking. The staff-bead length is the same as that of the 2-in. × 6-in. blocking at heads and jambs; referring to the blocking take-off, it would be 956 ft plus 1,512 ft, or 2,468 LF. The same procedure applies to all the window trim items: the quantities come from the blocking take-off.

An item for setting the finish hardware is included. If the hardware was scheduled in the specifications, it could be taken off directly from there. Very often the finish hardware is to be an allowance item for supply, so that the setting labor has to be priced as a lump sum at a percentage of the allowance amount. That method, however, is not very satisfactory. A better way for handling the setting of finish hardware would be to price the applicable item so as to include the setting labor for its hardware. Doors, for example, might be taken off as: "Set 2-in. wood ext. doors and hardware—13 drs."

A CLASSROOM

Working Drawings 7.2 and 7.3 show the plan and details for a typical classroom of a school that is to have 12 such rooms in all. The take-off will include all rough carpentry, the setting of all millwork and casework, the setting of door frames and doors, and the supply and setting of all chalkboard and tackboard material and the resilient flooring, base, and linoleum.

THE TAKE-OFF (W. D. 7.2, 7.3)

1 × 2 wall furring

$$
\begin{array}{rclr}
16 & \times & 7\text{--}0 & = & 112 \text{ ft} \\
13 & \times & 4\text{--}0 & = & 52 \\
4 & \times & 4\text{--}0 & = & 16 \\
10 & \times & 6\text{--}0 & = & 60 \\
\hline
& & & & 240 \text{ ft} \times 12 \\
& & & = & 2{,}880 \text{ LF}
\end{array}
$$

1 × 3 grounds for casework

Teacher's closet	3	×	10–0	=	30 ft
Sink cab.	2	×	6–0	=	12
Window cab.	2	×	30–0	=	60

$$
\begin{array}{rcl}
& & 102 \text{ ft} \times 12 \\
& = & 1{,}224 \text{ LF}
\end{array}
$$

Blocking for cabinets

$$2 \ \times \ 4 \quad \begin{matrix} 2 & \times & 6\text{--}0 \\ 2 & \times & 30\text{--}0 \end{matrix} \left. \right\} \quad \begin{matrix} 72 \text{ ft} \\ \times \ 12 \\ \overline{864 \text{ LF}} \\ = \ \underline{\underline{580 \text{ BF}}} \end{matrix}$$

$\frac{3}{8}$-*in. plywood behind chalk and tack bds.*

$$\begin{matrix} 12 & \times & 12\text{--}0 & \times & 6\text{--}0 \\ 12 & \times & 36\text{--}0 & \times & 4\text{--}6 \end{matrix} \left. \right\} \ = \ 12 \ \times \ 234 \text{ SF} \ = \ 2,808 \text{ SF}$$

$$+ \ \text{Waste } 10\% \quad \underline{\ \ 282 \ \ }$$
$$\underline{\underline{3,090 \text{ SF}}}$$

$\frac{3}{8}$-*in. plywood GlS to wall dado*

$$\begin{matrix} & 12 & \times & 19\text{--}6 & \times & 6\text{--}6 & = & 1,521 \text{ SF} \\ \text{Less} & 12 & \times & 16\text{--}0 & \times & 4\text{--}6 & = & \underline{\ \ 864 \ \ } \\ & & & & & & & 657 \\ & & & & + & 10\% & & \underline{\ \ 63 \ \ } \\ & & & & & & & \underline{\underline{720 \text{ SF}}} \end{matrix}$$

$\frac{1}{4}$-*in. cork tackboards*

$$\begin{matrix} & 12 & \times & 12\text{--}0 & \times & 1\text{--}4 & = & 192 \text{ SF} \\ 12 & \times & 3 & \times & 4\text{--}0 & \times & 4\text{--}0 & = & \underline{\ \ 576 \ \ } \\ & & & & & & & 768 \\ & & & & & + & 5\% & \underline{\ \ 38 \ \ } \\ & & & & & & & \underline{\underline{806 \text{ SF}}} \end{matrix}$$

$\frac{1}{8}$-*in. porc. steel chalkboards (cemented to ply)*

$$\begin{matrix} 12 & \times & 36\text{--}0 & \times & 4\text{--}0 & = & 1,728 \text{ SF} \\ & & & + & 5\% & & \underline{\ \ 82 \ \ } \\ & & & & & & \underline{\underline{1,810 \text{ SF}}} \end{matrix}$$

Rough hardware $\ = \ \underline{\underline{\text{L. S.}}}$

MILLWORK ETC. TO SET

Int. H. M. door frames $\ = \ \underline{\underline{24 \text{ ea.}}}$

Int. H. M. door & hardware $\ = \ \underline{\underline{24 \text{ ea.}}}$

Teacher's closet 2–6 $\times$ *2–0* $\times$ *9–0* $= \ \underline{\underline{12 \text{ ea.}}}$

Sink counter 6–0 $\times$ *2–0* $\times$ *2–4* $= \ \underline{\underline{12 \text{ ea.}}}$

Window counter 30–0 ✕ 2–0 ✕ 2–4 = <u>12 ea.</u>

Hang cabinet doors (2 ft ✕ 2 ft) & hardware

$$12 \quad \times \quad 14 \quad = \quad \underline{168 \text{ drs.}}$$

1 ✕ 6 backboard over counters

$$12 \quad \times \quad 36 \text{ ft} \quad = \quad \underline{432 \text{ LF}}$$

1 ✕ 4 chalk tray

$$12 \quad \times \quad 36 \text{ ft} \quad = \quad \underline{432 \text{ LF}}$$

1 ✕ 4 trim at C.B. & T.B.

$$\left.\begin{array}{l} 12 \quad \times \quad 52 \text{ ft} \\ 12 \quad \times \quad 20 \\ 12 \quad \times \quad 56 \\ 12 \quad \times \quad 46 \end{array}\right\} \quad 12 \quad \times \quad 174 \text{ ft}$$

$$= \quad \underline{2,088 \text{ LF}}$$

$\frac{3}{8}$ ✕ $\frac{1}{2}$ trim at C.B. & T.B.

$$\left.\begin{array}{l} 12 \quad \times \quad 60 \text{ ft} \\ 12 \quad \times \quad 16 \\ 12 \quad \times \quad 48 \\ 12 \quad \times \quad 40 \end{array}\right\} \quad 12 \quad \times \quad 164 \text{ ft}$$

$$= \quad \underline{1,968 \text{ LF}}$$

$\frac{3}{4}$ ✕ 2 trim at C.B. & T.B.

$$\left.\begin{array}{l} 12 \quad \times \quad 52 \text{ ft} \\ 12 \quad \times \quad 20 \\ 12 \quad \times \quad 56 \\ 12 \quad \times \quad 20 \end{array}\right\} \quad 12 \quad \times \quad 148 \text{ ft}$$

$$= \quad \underline{1,776 \text{ LF}}$$

$\frac{1}{8}$-in. lino. to counter tops

$$12 \quad \times \quad 36\text{–}0 \quad \times \quad 2\text{–}0 \quad = \quad \underline{864 \text{ SF}} \text{ (net)}$$

$\frac{1}{8}$-in. lino. to 6-in. backboard = <u>432 LF</u> (net)

4-in. rubber tile coved base

$$12 \quad \times \quad 102 \text{ ft} \quad = \quad \underline{1,224 \text{ LF}} \text{ (net)}$$

9-in. ✕ 9-in. ✕ $\frac{1}{8}$-in. asphalt-tile floor (2 colors)

$$12 \quad \times \quad 30\text{–}0 \quad \times \quad 24\text{–}0 \quad = \quad \underline{8,640 \text{ SF}}$$

NOTES ON THE TAKE-OFF (W. D. 7.2, 7.3)

The first wall furring item is for the 19-ft 6-in. wall, which has plywood 6 ft 6 in. high; that is, 15 pieces of 1 × 2 on 16-in. centers plus 1 for the end, a total of 16 pieces each 7 ft long. The other items are for the 16-ft combination of chalkboard and tackboard, the 4-ft tackboard, and the 12-ft chalkboard (which will have tackboard above it). The length of furring for one room is multiplied by 12 for 12 rooms.

The grounds and blocking for the casework are straightforward items. The plywood backing is taken off first at elevation A for the 4-ft-high chalkboard and 1-ft 4-in. tackboard above it. That plywood will be exactly 6 ft high, as shown on the section. The other boards are all 4 ft high (with 4-ft 6-in. plywood backing), so they are combined into one item—4 ft plus 16 ft plus 16 ft, or 36 LF. A waste allowance of 10 per cent is added for cutting.

The exposed plywood is separated from the backing plywood because they are different materials; the dado plywood must have one good face for a paint finish, and greater care will be required in setting it.

The tackboard and chalkboard are taken off at the full sheet sizes, 4 ft (the 1-ft 4-in. item will cut three pieces evenly from a 4-ft sheet). Only a 5 per cent waste allowance is needed for those items, as there will be no waste in the width of the material.

The casework and trim items are straightforward. The trim is measured for the total quantities in even feet per board (chalk and tack): first the board on Elevation A, then the 4-ft tackboard, then the combination 4-ft plus 8-ft plus 4-ft board, and finally the 16-ft chalkboard. In taking off the board on Elevation A, since the 4-in. trim around the board is to be mitered, a 12-ft piece would be too short to cover a 12-ft board; thus the top and bottom trim must each be taken off at 14 ft, although the 12-ft length will do for the intermediate horizontal piece. The sides are 6 ft each. This calculation gives a total of 14 ft plus 12 ft plus 14 ft plus 6 ft plus 6 ft, or 52 LF per board. Notice that although 14 ft is taken off for a net 12-ft board in the length, the height is taken off at the net 6 ft, not at 7 ft. That is because it should be possible to cut one miter without waste, but in order to cut and fit another miter to it, a longer length will be needed.

The resilient flooring, base, and counter tops are measured net—a procedure that is perfectly satisfactory, providing the fact is clearly notated. The asphalt-tile floor is measured to the face of the continuous window cabinet (26 ft less 2 ft), but the small cabinet and closet are *not* deducted.

WOOD-FRAMED BUILDINGS

Working Drawings 7.4–7.9 show a wood-framed duplex house, such as might be found in private home construction or a large government housing project. If you can take off a single building such as this accurately, you can with very little additional effort take off an entire project of 2,000 dwelling

COLLECTION SHEET FOR WOOD-FRAMED BUILDINGS

Bldg. type	Dwelling units		Perimeter		Area		Fire walls		
			1 bldg.	Total	1 bldg.	Total	1st	2nd	Roof
	Bldgs. D. U.								
A	25 × 4 =	100	179–4	4,483 ft	1,503 SF	37,575 SF	550 ft	600 ft	600 ft
B	24 × 4 =	96	210–0	5,040	1,904	45,696	541	552	552
C	12 × 4 =	48	199–8	2,396	1,963	23,556	308	308	308
D	1 × 6 =	6	292–2	292	2,886	2,886	45	45	45
		250		12,211 ft		109,713 SF	1,444 ft	1,505 ft	1,505 ft

Bldg. type	Bast. sash		Entrance doors		Windows			
	1	2	A	B	1	2	3	4
A	25	25	100	100	400	400	300	400
B	24	24	96	96	576	480	288	384
C	18	6	36	60	288	192	192	192
D	2	1	—	12	24	24	12	24
	69	56	232	268	1,288	1,096	792	1,000

units. In taking off a large housing job that consists of many identical buildings, it is perfectly permissible to take off one building, price it, and multiply the total by the number of buildings. This procedure, however, will usually apply only to the work above ground, as the foundation depth and excavation required will very likely vary from building to building. The multiplication procedure then becomes somewhat complex, and must be handled carefully; all the steps involved should be very clearly shown on the estimate sheets.

More often than not, a housing project will include several types of buildings; if it does, it is best to take off the entire job progressively, item by item. Each item should be taken off by measuring its quantity for one type of building, multiplying that figure by the number of buildings of that type, and repeating the procedure for the next type of building—finally arriving at the total quantity required of that item for the entire job. Such a method has its advantages: it reduces the paper work in the take-off; it reduces the estimate itself to a normal straightforward set of sheets; it provides the actual total quantities for each item; and it gives the actual buying quantities, which will probably enable you to obtain much more accurate quotations.

Much combining of repetitive items or items of similar design can be done in taking off a housing project in which the several types of buildings repeat such items. In taking off houses that are of similar exterior wall design, you can combine the various types of buildings to obtain such figures as a total perimeter and the total number of entrance porches of this and that type. All such information can then be collected in a single recapitulation that will greatly simplify your take-off. A typical collection of several items is shown for an actual case—a job of 250 dwelling units taken off some years ago.

Collecting the information shown above not only saved hours of estimating time, but also, by simplifying the subsequent calculations, decreased the probability of errors considerably. Basically, the take-off for this $2,800,000 project was the same as that shown for the single building in the example that follows.

Working Drawings 7.4–7.9, showing a two-story duplex dwelling, are taken off in two parts: first, the rough carpentry framing (walls, partitions, roof framing, boarding, and exterior-wall finish boarding, roof shingles, and gutters); and second, the interior furring, grounds, blocking, plyscore, stairs, millwork, and finish carpentry.

THE EXTERIOR

The following items and description of materials supplement the drawings: wall studding to be 2 × 4 on 16-in. centers unless otherwise indicated. (Sill bolts may be considered as having been previously taken off.) Sills and girts to be lapped at joints and corners; fire-stopping of the same depth as joists required at first- and second-floor exterior walls; all boarding to be 1-in. × 8-in. (laid diagonally for walls and subfloors); exterior wall finish to be ¾-in. × 8-in. bevel siding, 6¾ in. to weather, with 15-lb felt underneath. Asphalt shingles for roof to be 3-tab, 12 in. × 36 in., 5 in. to weather; cedar shingles to be used in starter course at eaves; 30-lb felt to roof. Soundproof partitions to be two 2 × 4 stud partitions with offset studs and 4-in. blanket insulation woven between the studs. Ceiling under roof to have 2-in. blanket insulation, with vapor-barrier paper on the underside. Lay 15-lb felt over all subflooring. Gutters to be 4-in. × 3-in. redwood, twice primed, with joints half-lapped with lead insert, set in white lead. (The Lally columns supporting the beam at the first floor may be considered as having been previously taken off.)

The small check marks on the various drawings were made as the items were being taken off; they are shown there to demonstrate how items are checked off as they are cleared.

THE TAKE-OFF (EXTERIOR—W. D. 7.4–7.9)

4 × 6 sill

$$2 (50 \text{ ft} + 24 \text{ ft}) = 148 \text{ ft}$$
$$= \underline{300 \text{ BF}}$$

Floor frmg.

1st 2 × 8 (half of floor)	23	×	16–0	=	368 ft
	24	×	10–0	=	240
	4	×	4–0	=	16

$$\overline{624 \text{ ft}} \times 4 = 2,496 \text{ ft}$$
$$= \underline{3,328 \text{ BF}}$$

4 × 6 beam

$$50 \text{ ft} = \underline{100 \text{ BF}}$$

1 × 3 cross bridging

$$4 \times 42 \times 2\text{--}6 = \underline{420 \text{ LF}}$$

4 × 4 posts

$$2 \times 3 \times 10\text{--}0 = \underline{80 \text{ BF}}$$

Joist hangers (for 2 × 8) $= \underline{8 \text{ pcs.}}$

Joist hangers (for double joist) $= \underline{8 \text{ pcs.}}$

Ceiling joists 2 × 6

$$4 \times 19 \times 14\text{--}0 = \underline{1,064 \text{ BF}}$$

Roof frmg.

Hips	2 × 10–0	4 × 20–0	=	80 ft
Ridge	2 × 10–0	26–0	=	26

$$\underline{106 \text{ ft}}$$
$$= \underline{180 \text{ BF}}$$

Rafter 2 × 8

	23 × 14–0	=	322 ft
8 × 8 × 7–0		=	448

$$= \overline{\underline{770 \text{ ft}}}$$
$$= \underline{1,030 \text{ BF}}$$

Collar ties 2 × 6

$$21 \times 8\text{--}0 = \overline{\underline{168 \text{ ft}}}$$
$$= \underline{170 \text{ BF}}$$

Hangers 1 × 6

$$21 \times 2 \times 5\text{--}0 = \underline{210 \text{ LF}}$$

1 × 6 cont. bridging

$$2 \times 50\text{--}0 = \underline{100 \text{ LF}}$$

Wall frmg. 4 × 6 girt

$$148 \text{ ft} = \underline{300 \text{ BF}}$$

Wall frmg. 4 × 6 posts

$$
\begin{array}{rcrcl}
7 & \times & 8\text{–}0 & = & 56 \text{ ft} \\
7 & \times & 10\text{–}0 & = & \underline{70} \\
& & & & \overline{126 \text{ ft}} \\
& & & = & \overline{\underline{252 \text{ BF}}}
\end{array}
$$

Wall frmg. 2 × 4

Head			2	×	148–0	=	296 ft
1st	2	×	47	×	8–0	=	752
2nd	2	×	47	×	10–0	=	940
Wind. V	2	×	26	×	4–0	=	208
Door	2	×	4	×	1–0	=	8
Door head	4	×	2	×	4–0	=	32
Wind. H & S	6	×	4	×	6–0	=	144
Wind. H & S	14	×	4	×	5–0	=	280
Wind. H & S	2	×	4	×	4–0	=	32
Bracing			8	×	8–0	=	64
Bridging	2	×	61	×	1–3	=	154

$$
\begin{array}{rcl}
& & \overline{2{,}910 \text{ ft}} \\
& = & \overline{\underline{1{,}940 \text{ BF}}}
\end{array}
$$

2 × 8 firestopping

$$
2 \ \times\ 2 \ \times\ 50\text{–}0 \ =\ \underline{270 \text{ BF}}
$$

1 × 8 T. & G. subflooring

$$
\begin{array}{lrcrcrcl}
& 2 & \times & 47\text{–}6 & \times & 22\text{–}4 & = & 2{,}122 \\
\text{Less} & 4 & \times & 9\text{–}0 & \times & 3\text{–}8 & = & \underline{132} \\
& & & & & & & \overline{1{,}990 \text{ SF}} \\
& & & + & \text{Waste } 20\% & & & \underline{400} \\
& & & & & & & \underline{2{,}390 \text{ BF}}
\end{array}
$$

15-lb felt over subflooring

$$
\begin{array}{rcl}
& & 1{,}990 \text{ SF} \\
+ \ 10\% & & \underline{200} \\
& & \underline{2{,}190 \text{ SF}}
\end{array}
$$

1-in. × 8-in. roof bdg. (T. & G.)

$$
\begin{array}{rcrcrcl}
2 & \times & 48\text{–}2 & \times & 14\text{–}0 & = & 1{,}349 \text{ SF} \\
& & + & \text{Waste } 15\% & & & \underline{201} \\
& & & & & & \underline{1{,}550 \text{ BF}}
\end{array}
$$

30-lb roofing felt

$$\begin{array}{r} 1,349 \text{ SF} \\ +\quad 10\% \quad \underline{135} \\ \hline 1,484 \text{ SF} \\ =\quad \underline{1,500 \text{ SF}} \end{array}$$

Cedar shingle starter course

$$\begin{array}{r} 142\text{--}4 \text{ at } 0\text{--}4 \quad = \quad 427 \text{ pcs.} \\ +\quad \text{Waste} \quad \underline{23} \\ \hline \underline{450} \text{ pcs. (4 in.} \quad \times \quad 16 \text{ in.)} \end{array}$$

Asphalt shingles, 3 tab, 12 in. $\times$ *36 in., 5 in. to weather*

$$\begin{array}{r} 1,350 \text{ SF} \quad = \quad 13.5 \text{ sqrs.} \\ +\quad \text{Waste } 7\% \quad \underline{1.0} \\ \hline \underline{14.5} \text{ sqrs. (to cover)} \end{array}$$

4-in. $\times$ *3-in. redwood gutter (twice-primed)*

$$2 \ (52 \text{ ft} \ + \ 26 \text{ ft}) \ = \ \underline{156 \text{ LF}}$$

Half-lapped joints $+$ *lead insert* $=$ $\underline{14 \text{ jnts.}}$

2-in. blanket insulation over clg. $=$ $\underline{2,200 \text{ SF}}$ ($+$ vapor barrier 1 side)

Alum. foil insulation to ext. walls.

	139–8	$\times$	17–4			$=$	2,422 SF	
Door	4 $\times$	20 SF			$=$	80	
Sash A	4 $\times$	6–0	$\times$	4–0	$=$	96	
B	8 $\times$	4–6	$\times$	4–0	$=$	144	
C	6 $\times$	4–0	$\times$	4–0	$=$	96	480
D	2 $\times$	3–0	$\times$	4–0	$=$	24	
E	2 $\times$	5–0	$\times$	4–0	$=$	40	

$$\begin{array}{r} 1,942 \\ +\quad 10\% \quad \underline{198} \\ \hline 2,140 \text{ SF} \end{array}$$

1 $\times$ *8 T. & G. wall sheathing*

$$\begin{array}{r} 142\text{--}4 \quad \times \quad 18\text{--}4 \quad = \quad 2,610 \text{ SF} \\ \text{Less Opgs.} \qquad\qquad = \quad \underline{480} \\ \hline 2,130 \text{ SF} \\ +\quad 20\% \quad \underline{430} \\ \hline \underline{2,560 \text{ BF}} \end{array}$$

15-lb felt to walls

$$
\begin{array}{r}
2{,}130 \text{ SF} \\
+ \quad 10\% \quad \underline{220} \\
\hline
2{,}350 \text{ SF}
\end{array}
$$

¾-in. × 8-in. bevel siding (6¾ in. to weather)

$$
\begin{array}{r}
2{,}130 \text{ SF} \\
+ \text{ Waste } 28\% \quad \underline{600} \\
\hline
2{,}730 \text{ SF}
\end{array}
$$

Int. stud ptns. 2 × 4

1st Sill and head	3	×	118–0		=	354 ft
Studs	112	×	8		=	896
+ Cupb.	2	×	20		=	40
2nd Sill and head	3	×	188		=	564
Studs	175	×	8		=	1,400
+ Cupb.			40		=	40
Low ptns.	2	×	2	× 6	=	24
Low ptns.	2	×	6	× 4	=	48
Bridging	310–0				=	310
Add for doors	10	×	16		=	160
						3,836 LF
					=	2,560 BF

4-in. blanket insulation to ptns.

1st	29–0	×	8–2	=	237 SF
2nd	24–0	×	8–0	=	192
					429
		+ 15%			66
					495 SF
				=	500 SF

NOTES ON THE TAKE-OFF (EXTERIOR—W. D. 7.4–7.9)

The exterior sill item, taken off at 50-ft and 24-ft lengths, allows sufficient material for both laps and 2-ft multiples. The floor joists are added up from the framing plan (and checked off there), taking off half of one floor and then multiplying that figure by four to obtain the total for the two floors. The cross bridging item allows 2 ft 6 in. for 2 pieces of 15 in. each for each joist spacing. Joist hangers are taken off for the framing at the stairwells.

The hip is laid out on the roof plan (see the lightly dotted line). This is done by setting up the rise square off the hip in plan, then projecting the full dimensions of the hip on the plan so that it appears as it would if flopped over to rest on the roof. In this particular roof, the hipped ends are at the same pitch as the main roof line; therefore the hips form a right angle on the plan; and so the rise is laid out on one hip and the hip length measured along the dotted line. Since it measures 17 ft 6 in. with a long cut at each end, an 18-ft length would be doubtful, and the hip is taken off at 20 ft.

The main rafters scale 13 ft 6 in., so a 14-ft length is used. The hip rafters must average half the main rafters (7 ft), so 8 hip rafters for one side of each hip gives eight at 8 times 7 ft. The collar ties and hangers are scaled from the drawing.

The 4 × 6 girt is the same length as the 4 × 6 sill. The 4 × 6 posts are 8 ft for the first floor, but the second floor—from girt to plate—is slightly more than 8 ft 4 in. high, and so those posts are taken off at 10 ft.

The exterior 2 × 4 framing is added up from the wall-framing drawing. For the under- and over-window studs, 4 ft is allowed (to cut both pieces). The window sill and head plates follow the window items (window A is 6 ft long, and there are 6 windows, with double 2 × 4 for head and sill of each; that is, 6 times 4 times 6 ft).

The 2 × 8 firestop runs only along the front and rear walls, across the open ends of the joists. The item is taken off at the full length of the building: 50 ft, for a 48-ft 2-in. length.

The subflooring runs to the inside face of the exterior studding, a distance twice 4 in. less than the outside dimensions. An 8-in. board with tongue and groove will lay 7¼ in.; that is, a loss of ¾ in. in 8 in., or 9½ per cent. To include cutting, a total waste allowance of 20 per cent is carried. The felt over the subfloor is the same area as the boarding.

With a 45-degree hip, a hipped roof has the same area as the roof would have with gable ends—a simple calculation of twice the length times the slope. The roof boarding is not to be laid diagonally; therefore a 15 per cent waste allowance should be enough. The cedar-shingle starter course item is measured *in pieces*, not in squares. The asphalt shingles are in squares of *area to cover*. In ordering asphalt shingles, the size and the exposure are given; one square calls for enough shingles to cover 100 SF. One square of 3-tab 12-in. × 36-in. shingles, 5 in. to weather, would consist of 80 pieces (80 times 3–0 times 0–5 gives 100 SF). The same shingle with 4 in. to weather would have 100 pieces per square.

The redwood gutter is measured with allowance for the half-lapped joints. The expensive joint with lead insert is measured as a separate item: there are 4 joints along each of the front and back gutters, 1 joint on each end run, and 4 corner miters—a total of 14 joints.

The ceiling insulation item is the same area as the flooring. The wall insulation is measured inside the studding, with the openings deducted and waste added. The area of the exterior-wall sheathing is the exterior perimeter measured from the bottom of the sill to the top of the eaves (0–4 plus 0–8 plus 8–10 plus 8–6, a total of 18–4), with openings deducted—the same as for the previous item—and 20 per cent waste added, to allow for diagonal laying as specified. The felt item is the sheathing area plus waste. The bevel siding measured 7¼ in. but will lay 6¾ in.—a loss of 1¼ in. in an 8-in. board, or 16 per cent. Allowing another 12 per cent for cutting and fitting, the total waste is 28 per cent.

The stud partitions are measured directly from the plan (in even-foot lengths). Taking off the first floor: there are 60 LF of partition (14 ft plus 6 ft plus 20 ft plus 6 ft plus 14 ft), and 58 LF for the double partition (8 ft plus 7 ft plus 14 ft, all doubled), totaling (60 LF plus 58 LF) 118 LF. For a single sill plate and a double head, the item is 3 times 118 LF. The studs are on 16-in. centers, so:

	118–0 at 16 in. c–c	=	89 studs
+	11 walls, 1 for each end	=	11
+	Closet studs, 2 at 6 each	=	12
			112 studs

40 LF is added for the sills and plates at the two closets. The second floor is similarly treated. The low 4-ft partitions follow the above calculations, with an allowance of 310 LF of bridging (for 306 LF of partition). An extra 16 LF of studding will also be needed for each doorway; 16 LF of additional material is a good average to allow for framing around ordinary door openings.

The blanket insulation is slightly different in height on the two floors, being 8–10 less 0–8 for the first and 8–6 less 0–6 for the second. The 15 per cent waste allows for weaving the material snake-like around the double studding.

THE INTERIOR

The finish carpentry and miscellaneous rough carpentry for the building shown in W. D. 7.4 and 7.5 was taken off according to the following specifications: Ceilings to be furred with 1-in. × 2-in. spaced at 12-in. centers; ⅝-in. × 1-in. plaster grounds required for base in all rooms except bathrooms, and around all door and window openings. 2 × 4 continuous nailers required for kitchen cabinets, and 1 × 2 grounds on 14-in. centers behind kitchen cabinets. Plyscore (⅝-in.) to be laid over subfloor. Exterior doors to be 4-panel pine, 2 ft 8 in. × 7 ft × 2 in. with 1¾-in. pine frame, double rabbeted; 2-in. staff bead required for exterior door and window frames, to be caulked. Interior doors to be 1⅜-in., solid-core, flush; interior door frames of 1⅝-in. pine. Door casings to be ¾ in. × 3½ in., and base ¾ in. × 4 in. in all rooms except baths and closets; window casings ¾ in. × 3 in., stool 1 in. × 4 in.; apron ¾ in. × 3 in. Windows to have ponderosa-pine frames, double-hung wood sashes with spiral balances. Basement stairs to have 2 × 10 treads, 3 × 4 newels, and 2-in. × 2-in. handrails with 2-in. × 2-in. posts (5 per handrail); handrails on both sides; open risers. Main stairs to have 2 × 12 carriages; risers and treads of oak, framed and glued; oak balusters, newels, and handrails. Kitchen cabinets prefabricated. Closet folding doors to be fabric type, 2 ft 6 in. × 6 ft 6 in., with necessary track. A shelf 12 in. wide, a hanging pole, and 1-in. × 6-in. bearers required for each closet. Oak thresholds 1 in. × 3 in. required for exterior doors. Eaves fascia to be 1 in. × 6 in.; corner boards 1 in. × 5 in. and 1 in. × 6 in.; drip mold 1½ in. × 1½ in. over all windows. Combination storm and screen doors of aluminum; aluminum window screens to be "half" screens.

THE TAKE-OFF (INTERIOR—W. D. 7.4, 7.5)

1 × 2 ceiling furring

Floor area						=	1,990 SF
+ Over stairs	2	×	9–0	×	3–8	=	66
							2,056 SF
	1	×	2 at 12 in. c-c			=	2,056 LF
+ 4	×	48 ft				=	192
							2,248
						=	2,250 LF

$\frac{5}{8}$*-in.* × *1-in. plaster grounds*

Base	=	524 ft
Doors 42 × 20–0	=	840
Window-stool	=	118
Window casings	=	336
		1,818 LF
	=	1,820 LF

1 × 2 grounds for kitchen cabinets

$$2 \times 3 \times 14\text{–}0 = 84 \text{ LF}$$

2 × 4 blocking for kit. cabinet

$$2 \times 2 \times 14\text{–}0 = 56 \text{ LF}$$

$\frac{5}{8}$*-in. plyscore to floor*

As subflr.	=	1,990 SF
+ 10%		200
		2,190 SF
	=	2,200 SF

2 × *10 cut stair stringer 12 ft long* = <u>6 pcs.</u>

2 × *10 stair treads 4 ft long* = <u>24 pcs.</u>

3 × *4 newel posts 3 ft long* = <u>4 pcs.</u>

2-in. × *2-in. stair balusters 2 ft long* = <u>20 pcs.</u>

2-in. × *2-in. handrail 4* × *12 ft* = <u>48 LF</u>

Rough hardware = <u>L. S.</u>

Temporary doors = <u>4 each</u>

Set only

  Ext. wood door frame (2 in.) = <u>4 ea.</u>

  Int. wood door frame ($1\frac{5}{8}$ in.) = <u>10 ea.</u>

  Ext. wood door 2–8 × *7–0 (2 in.) and hardware* = <u>4 ea.</u>

  Int. flush ($1\frac{3}{8}$ in.) wood door and hardware = <u>10 ea.</u>

  Fabric folding closet door 2–6 × *6–6* = <u>10 ea.</u>

  Wood window frame (av. 18 SF) = <u>22 fr.</u>

  Wood D.H. sashes and hardware = <u>22 prs.</u>

  Comb. storm and screen door (alum.) = <u>4 ea.</u>

  Window screen (alum. $\frac{1}{2}$-screens) = <u>22 ea.</u>

  Eaves fascia 1 in. × *6 in.*

        2 (50 ft + *24 ft)* = <u>148 LF</u>

1 × *5 corner boards*

        4 × *18 ft* = <u>72 LF</u>

1 × *6 corner boards* = <u>72 LF</u>

Window drip mold $1\frac{1}{2}$ $\times$ $1\frac{1}{2}$ = __118 LF__

Staff bead 2 in. (*caulked*)

Drs.	4 $\times$ 20 ft	=	80 ft
Windows			=	336
				416 LF

1-in. $\times$ *3-in. oak threshold 3 ft long* = __4 pcs.__

Window trim		Stool			Casing		
A	4 at 6–0 $\times$ 4–0	4/7 ft	=	28 ft	4/16 ft	=	64 ft
B	8 at 4–6 $\times$ 4–0	8/5	=	40	8/16	=	128
C	6 at 4–0 $\times$ 4–0	6/5	=	30	6/14	=	84
D	2 at 3–0 $\times$ 4–0	2/4	=	8	2/14	=	28
E	2 at 5–0 $\times$ 4–0	2/6	=	12	2/16	=	32
				118 LF ✓			336 LF ✓

Stool 1 in. $\times$ *4 in.* = __118 LF__

Apron and window casings $\frac{3}{4}$ *in.* $\times$ *3 in.* = __454 LF__

$\frac{3}{4}$-*in.* $\times$ $3\frac{1}{2}$-*in. door casings* = __840 LF__

$\frac{3}{4}$ $\times$ *4 base*

Living	2 $\times$	50 ft
Dining	2 $\times$	30
Kitchen	2 $\times$	24
Bedr. 3	2 $\times$	48
Bedr. 1	2 $\times$	48
Bedr. 2	2 $\times$	40
Passage	2 $\times$	22
		262 LF $\times$ 2
	=	524 LF

Main stair 3–8 wide (14R) *complete including newels and rail* = __2 sets__

Kitchen counter cabinets 12 LF = __2 ea.__

Closet shelf & pole = __10 sets__

1 $\times$ *6 shelf bearer* (*8 LF average*) = __10 ea.__

NOTES ON THE TAKE-OFF (INTEROR—W. D. 7.4, 7.5)

The ceiling furring is on 12-in. centers; that is, 1 LF of furring per SF of area. The ceiling area is the floor area plus the second-floor area over the two stairs. One length of furring is added for each side of the partition (two at 48 ft) for each floor. Each room *could* be measured separately—a tedious and unnecessary method that would yield about the same total as is obtained by this quicker and simpler one.

The plaster grounds items are first listed without quantities, and then *after* the various millwork items have been figured, the totals are entered in the grounds items. The grounds item for around the doors includes both sides of all interior doors except the door to the basement (which is taken off for one side only), both sides of the cupboard doors, and one side of the exterior doorways.

The basement stair is not a millwork item, and so is taken off with the rough carpentry for labor and material. The lengths given for the various items are reasonably accurate for a stair about 8 ft high.

The items for rough hardware and temporary doors were not specified, but they will be needed; these items should, in fact, always be included in the carpentry take-off. The rough hardware item provides such things as nails, screws, sandpaper, glue, and bolts for all the carpentry work in the entire building.

The door and window items are straightforward. It is not necessary to list the windows separately by sizes. Reference to the exterior take-off provides the essential information: 22 window openings—400 SF; an average of 18 SF per opening.

The various trim items for the windows are computed by totaling the requirements for each size window, and adding them to arrive at the totals for stools and casings; those totals will then provide the quantities for other window items. The stool quantity is also the exterior drip-mold figure, while the casing quantity equals that of the staff beads; the combined stool-and-casing total is used for the plaster grounds.

The door casings item is the same as the door grounds and staff bead. For all normal-sized doors (up to 3 ft wide) it can be taken off as 20 LF of casing (two 8-ft lengths and one 4-ft). The wood base is added up for each room either by measuring around the walls and keeping a running total, or by jotting down the various lengths from the plan dimensions and then totaling them. Again, take off in even feet only for long lengths (8 ft and over), but use one-foot multiples for short pieces up to 7 ft.

The main stairs are taken off at a lump-sum price for setting, a price that will include everything—carriages, treads, risers, skirt board, balustrading, newels, and handrail. If the millwork bid "excludes" the carriages, they will have to be taken off as rough carpentry and some extra setting labor allowed, because then the stair materials will be shipped in pieces for job assembly.

The kitchen counters will be prefabricated and each kitchen unit delivered in two pieces.

In general, millwork and casework are not described in great detail on the take-off unless the general contractor himself has a mill and bids the work for complete supply and setting. And even in that case, the contractor's millwork department would often make its own take-off, and then simply provide a lump-sum price for the main estimating department to use.

MISCELLANEOUS ROUGH CARPENTRY

Framing lumber is always measured in board feet. Unless otherwise stated in the take-off, the framing will be D4S. If rough lumber is specified for framing, this fact should be stated in the take-off; rough framing material is more costly to handle than dressed stock. The specified dimensions must always be checked to ensure that you are figuring exactly what is called for. If the roof boarding is to be a 1-in. finish thickness, then 1¼-in. board is called for; if the boarding is to be a 1-in. nominal thickness, it can come out of 1-in. stock.

Boarding for floors, roofs, and wall sheathing should have an allowance for cutting and waste added according to the type of board, its width, and whether it is to be laid straight or diagonally. Tongued and grooved boarding (T. & G.) lays ¾ in. less than its nominal width, so a 1-in. × 6-in. T. & G. board would lay only 5¼ in.; the loss in a 1 × 6 board then, would be ¾ in. in 6 in., or 14 per cent. Square-edged boarding would lay ⅜ in. to ½ in. less than its nominal width. The amount of waste involved in cutting and fitting will vary according to how much cutting the job required. Exterior sheathing for walls with many openings will require more cutting waste than subflooring. Cutting waste will vary from 7½ to 12½ per cent.

Hips and roof rafters can be set up on the plan as shown in W. D. 7.7. The rise is set up square off the hip in plan and the hip drawn in at what would be its flopped-over position. Allowance must be made for both the eaves overhang and the long bottom cut. The hip length could also be obtained by calculation: the square of the hypotenuse equals the sum of the squares of the two sides. Two calculations, however, would be involved: the first to determine the hip length in plan, and the second to obtain the actual hip length.

Laminated wood arches are prefabricated timber arches made by wood-engineering companies and shipped to the job paper-wrapped for job erection. They should be taken off in pieces fully described, with a sketch if it will aid in pricing the estimate.

Laminated wood beams, purlins, and the like are made and shipped as are the arches. The take-off should be in pieces, by sizes. Usually the sub-bid for supply and delivery of laminated wood framing will include the necessary bolts, angles, plates, and the like, but this must not be presumed; the sub-bids should be checked to ensure that the rough hardware is not omitted. The various laminated wood framing items may be entered on the estimate in separate items for pricing, they may be converted into board feet and combined in one item, or converted into weight and combined in a single tonnage item. If they are combined in a single item using tonnage as the estimating unit, the laminated wood would be priced somewhat like the setting of structural steel. In any case, no matter which way the items are shown in the estimate, the setting of laminated wood framing will probably require a crane, which will have to be figured either within the unit price or as a separate item. The cost of loading the laminated framing at the railway siding, trucking it to the job, and unloading it, would also have to be allowed for if not included in the sub-bid.

Roof trusses of wood that have to be fabricated on the ground must be taken off for both material and fabrication, with still another item for hoisting and setting. The fabrication item should include all the timber connectors, washers, and bolts. The hoisting and setting item should include the crane required for lifting and also any rigging or guys that might be needed.

Stud framing is usually reduced to board feet, although it is probably better to leave miscellaneous minor items of studding in lineal feet if not larger than 2 × 3 stock. The cost of a few hundred board feet of 2 × 3 stud framing made up of many small items will be much greater than the figure that might first come to mind in pricing an item that says simply "2 × 3 framing for cupboards—460 BF." If the item is listed in lineal feet, that will act as a warning to the estimator pricing the sheets.

Wall boarding such as plaster board, pressed hardboard, and asbestos-cement board is measured in square feet, with care being taken to consider the waste. If a composition board is to be covered by some other finish material, the waste should not be too great, and a 10 per cent allowance will probably suffice. For finish material, however, the waste may be a serious factor. Panels in window walls, for example, might be specified as 1½-in. asbestos-cement board, a material that comes only in sheets 4 ft wide. Panels slightly more than 2 ft in both dimensions, then, would involve a waste of almost half of each sheet. Cutting 4-ft × 8-ft sheets of asbestos-cement board for panels 2 ft 3 in. wide, would mean wasting 1 ft 9 in. out of 4 ft. The result is a considerable quantity of material left over—material that may not be used for years and will cost money to truck to the yard, where it will take up space.

MISCELLANEOUS FINISH CARPENTRY

Moldings are taken off in lineal feet, with each member measured separately. Some estimators take off multiple-member pieces as one item, as for instance, "Eaves cornice, 4-member." This is not a very satisfactory procedure, however, unless the various pieces and their sizes are noted. If there were too many pieces to list individually, it would be prudent to write the item up as "Eaves cornice, 4-member, see Drg. ...." Trim that is curved or polygonal in shape should be taken off separate from ordinary moldings. It will be expensive to fit moldings that do not meet at a true miter.

Paneling is measured in square feet, separating the items into paneling up to 4 ft high, that over 4 ft and up to 6 ft, and that over 6 ft high. The low dado paneling will cost more to set per square foot than similar paneling 6 ft high. Paneling to be built up on the wall is measured in separate items—plywood, cover strips, and moldings. Prefabricated paneling, on the other hand, is measured in square feet of finished panel, with only the base and cap mold separately measured. First-class hardwood paneling should be carefully described so as to present an item that can be properly evaluated and priced. Paneling of narrow width should be kept separate from the main-run wall paneling. (A narrow width may be considered to be up to 15 in. wide—such panels as might occur at window reveals or beams, or around isolated columns.)

Cabinets and casework are usually taken off in items of stated size. Long storage cabinets may be measured in lineal feet of a stated width and height. Casework that cannot be preassembled should be kept separate from casework that will arrive on the job completely assembled. It would be foolish to price casework that will be too large to go into the building preassembled, as a simple setting-up item. Library stacks, for example, would be shipped broken down, as would any casework that had to be fitted tightly into a recess without filler pieces. It is entirely a matter of using some common sense in taking off the various items, so as to separate the preassembled casework from the items that will involve a considerable amount of job labor.

Cut-outs in counter tops must be taken off as labor items, unless it is certain that the mill will make the cut-outs. Usually a sink cut-out will have to be made on the job while the counter is being set up; radiator grilles, also, may have to be cut into counter tops on the job. Those cut-outs should be considered as extra over the normal cost of setting the cabinets, and should be taken off as additional-cost items.

Window walls are taken off in square feet, fully described. Any trim items that are not part of the window sub work must be taken off separately. Sometimes it is best to take off the window walls in square feet for the setting of window frames, take off all the trim and cover molds separately, and take off the sashes for setting in yet another item. There are many types of wood window walls—some are prefabricated units, and others are simple job-constructed posts and frames. The take-off should employ whatever method will be best according to the details shown on the drawings.

Glazed wood partitions and screens are measured in square feet, like window walls; preassembled partitions are taken off in a unit item, and job-assembled partitions in separate items. All stud framing, blocking, and backing material for job-assembled partitions should be taken off as rough carpentry.

CHAPTER 8   **Alteration Work**

Alteration work should always be taken off separately from the new building in estimating a job that involves alterations and additions. There are two reasons for this: (1) The alteration work will be more costly than new work of the same type. Face brick for filling in several isolated openings will cost much more per brick to lay than face brick for an entire new wing. As another example, patching the wood base in existing rooms would cost much more for labor in proportion to the amount of material used than setting a wood base in a new building. (2) The alteration work must be examined when you visit the site; thus the items involved should be clearly set out so that they may be identified and evaluated as you go through the building. The best way to set out such items is according to an orderly progression through the building room by room. Identify each item by noting its location on the left-hand side of the take-off sheet, and then transfer that notation to the estimate sheet.

Architects do not always show the alteration work in full detail on the drawings, as will be evident when you visit the building and find, perhaps, that what appeared as a dotted line on the drawings, notated simply "remove partition," is in fact a 12-in. brick wall plastered on both sides and also a load-bearing wall for the two floors above it. Such conditions will present shoring problems and require compressor work that could not possibly be inferred from the drawings. Sometimes the drawings show only the revised layout and details, with a simple note to "remove present walls, floors, etc. as necessary." Moreover, some alterations might be too complex for all the work involved to be shown on the drawings. If for one reason or another the drawings do *not* show all the removal work, it may be necessary to visit the site and take off some of the items right there and then, measuring and describing the various items as you see them.

When going through a building looking at removal and alteration work, there is nothing to be gained by rushing through the rooms. This is one time that speed is definitely *not* the most important consideration. There are usually many factors to consider for a given item, and all kinds of conditions and considerations that do not show on the drawings will be seen on the job by an observant estimator. The finish materials to be patched—and matched—may be materials not easily obtained. Wood moldings, for instance, might have to be custom-made to match those that have been in place for many years.

Removal work can be considerably more difficult than the drawings would show or could be seen by a casual observer. In addition to the actual work involved in demolition, the rubbish must be removed and, equally important, working conditions may present problems. Cutting and patching in buildings that the owner intends to occupy while the work is being done can be very expensive, involving dust partitions around small areas, interrupted work, and perhaps night or overtime work. Alterations in the main business area of a bank that was going to continue transacting business during the construction work, for example, would pose several problems for the estimator. Many special problems, such as security, protecting the public, dust partitions, and overtime work, would have to be considered.

Every alteration job will present its own problems, which must be given some thought either before taking off the work or before pricing the estimate. The take-off should spell out the items and describe the work in such a way that the estimate can be properly priced. If you must do the take-off without having seen the site, then list doubtful items with query marks. It is better to have an item listed, even if it is later decided that it is not required, than it is to miss an item that might cost a considerable amount of money. As an example, if there was nothing on the drawing to show which walls were load-bearing, then a shoring item should be included for the removal of *any* basement walls. The item might simply be: "Shore first floor for removal of 8-in. wall below—24 LF." Without more detailed information, the item could then be evaluated fully when the building was visited.

Alteration work will often necessitate using many lump-sum items in the take-off, either for work that cannot be taken off in detail or for removal work that must be priced by on-the-job evaluation of the labor and equipment required for the operation. Overtime work may have to be priced as a lump sum, consisting of the estimated number of Saturdays and Sundays that would have to be worked for certain phases of the alterations. Trucking away of rubbish is another item that cannot always be measured. Examples of items that might have to be priced as a lump sum while actually looking at them are: entrance steps or windows to be removed; sash cords to be replaced "as necessary." Any information available concerning such an item should be included in the take-off description. If a retaining wall to be removed is clearly shown on the drawings so that it can be measured, then it should be measured and the quantity indicated in the item: "Remove concrete retaining wall—182 CF." If the windows are all shown on the drawing, then an item for a requirement to "replace sash cords as required" should indicate the number of sashes: "Replace sash cords as necessary—82 prs. sashes."

UNDERPINNING

Working Drawing 8.1 shows an extension to a present building. The floor of the new basement is to be at grade 82–9; the present basement floor is at grade 86–7. The end wall of the present building is to be underpinned as shown, in lengths of 3 ft with 6 ft between the areas that are open at any one time. Excavation, except as required for underpinning, may be considered as having been previously taken off. The bulk excavation, however, would not have been taken off all the way up to the old wall for the full depth, because it would be unsafe to do so. The machine excavation should include the entire space up to the old wall down to about 2 ft above the present floor and then step out to about 3 ft away from the old wall, leaving the ground supporting the end wall undisturbed. The amount left—from grade 88–7 at a width of 3 ft for the entire 36-ft length—would have to be carefully excavated in sections to enable the underpinning to proceed. The specific method of excavation would depend on job conditions, the firmness of the ground, the amount of water present, and the condition of the old wall.

THE TAKE-OFF (W. D. 8.1)

UNDERPIN END WALL

Excavate adjacent to end wall (part machine)

$$36\text{–}0 \quad \times \quad 3\text{–}0 \quad \times \quad 6\text{–}10 \quad = \quad \underline{\underline{738 \text{ CF}}}$$
$$= \quad \underline{28 \text{ CY}}$$

Hand exc. for underpinning (in 3-ft lengths)

$$36\text{–}0 \quad \times \quad 1\text{–}2 \quad \times \quad 3\text{–}6 \quad = \quad \underline{\underline{147 \quad \text{CF}}}$$
$$= \quad \underline{5\tfrac{1}{2} \text{ CY}}$$

Conc. 3,000 psi (Hi-Early) in underpinning (3-ft sections)

								FORMS (one face only)
36–0	×	1–2	×	3–6	=	147 CF		126 SF
36–0	×	0–6	×	0–6	=	9		
						156 CF		
								End stops
					=	6 CY		1–2 × 3–6 = 13 pcs.

$\tfrac{5}{8}$-*in.* × *12-in. dowels to foundation walls* = 12 pcs.

Cut off footing projection 6 in. × *12 in.* = 36 LF

NOTES ON THE TAKE-OFF (W. D. 8.1)

The excavation adjacent to the wall is notated "part machine" so that it will be priced to include some hand work. The item would be evaluated (probably after one had seen the site), and priced accordingly. Let us assume that the excavation would be 70 per cent machine work and 30 per cent hand work, and that the machine work is worth $1.40 per CY and the hand work $6.25 per CY. The item would then be priced as follows:

Machine	70%	×	$1.40	=	$0.98
Hand	30%	×	$6.25	=	1.87
				=	$2.85 per CY

If machine excavation is an item usually given to an excavation contractor, then the pricing would be entered as $1.87 per CY on the labor side of the estimate and $0.98 per CY on the material side. If it would be done by the general contractor's own crew, however, the machine item would be broken down into labor and material, perhaps in the ratio of 1 to 3—25 per cent labor and 75 per cent equipment and fuel. This procedure would split the machine item into $0.24 for labor and $0.74 for material, so that the entire excavation item would be priced at $2.11 per CY for labor and $0.74 per CY for material—a total of $2.85 per cubic yard.

Hand excavation of the underpinning is taken off at 1–2, *not* at the neat 1–0 that is shown on the drawing. It would be difficult and costly to excavate under an old wall to an exact line; therefore it is necessary to allow a little additional width for both excavation and concrete to obtain realistic quantities.

The formwork is notated "one face only" to serve notice that this will be expensive formwork to hold in place. The end stops are to stop off the concrete at each 3-ft length of formwork.

The concrete item includes the small 6-in. × 6-in. offset. The items for cutting off the footing projection and for dowels for the old wall are as shown on the drawing.

EXCAVATION AND CONCRETE FOR PIPING WORK

Working Drawing 8.2 shows new sanitary drainpipe for a present building. The piping itself may be considered as part of the plumbing work; the general contractor's work will consist of breaking out the concrete floor, excavating, backfilling, replacing the floor, and removing the rubbish.

THE TAKE-OFF (W. D. 8.2)

EXCAVATION, ETC. IN PRESENT BAST. FOR MECH. TRADES

Hole through foundation wall for 4-in. soil pipe & make good = 1 ea.

Cut conc. floor (4 in.) before breaking out

2 (28–0 + 43–0 + 7–0 + 6–0) = 168 LF

Break out 4-in. conc. floor

$$84\text{--}0 \quad \times \quad 3\text{--}0 \quad = \quad \underline{252 \text{ SF}}$$

Exc. gravel bed (& stockpile)

$$84\text{--}0 \quad \times \quad 3\text{--}0 \quad \times \quad 0\text{--}6 \quad = \quad \underline{5 \text{ CY}}$$

Exc. for plumber

$$84\text{--}0 \quad \times \quad 3\text{--}0 \quad \times \quad 2\text{--}8 \quad = \quad 672 \text{ CF}$$
$$= \quad \underline{25 \text{ CY}}$$

Backfill (compacted)   = $\underline{25 \text{ CY}}$

Replace gravel bed   = $\underline{5 \text{ CY}}$

Concrete patching floor

$$252 \text{ SF} \quad \times \quad 0\text{--}4 \quad = \quad \underline{3 \text{ CY}}$$

Float & trowel floor   = $\underline{252 \text{ SF}}$

Remove rubbish   = $\underline{\text{L. S.}}$

Clean up basement   = $\underline{\text{L. S.}}$

NOTES ON THE TAKE-OFF (W. D. 8.2)

The items themselves are simple enough; the example is probably most useful in showing how to set out the requirements in an orderly manner. The hole through the foundation wall includes the cost of making it good afterwards. The cutting and excavation items allow 1 ft extra on the long 42-ft run for working space. This run, taken off at 3 ft wide, will also provide the working space necessary for the other three runs. The excavation of the gravel is taken off separately, because that material will have to be piled separately to be available for the backfilling.

An item for removing rubbish is needed, as is an item for cleaning up the floor after the work is completed.

This work is a good example of the general contractor's work that is found on the mechanical drawings. It is always necessary to examine the mechanical drawings for items that might have to be done by the general contractor. The specifications should also be checked to ascertain which work is to be done by the mechanical trades and which by the general contractor. The allocation of responsibility might be spelled out in the various mechanical-trade sections of the specifications, it might be found in the general conditions, or it might be described in some other section such as excavation or concrete. Each and every section of the specifications that *could* apply must be examined before deciding who is responsible for items required to complete a given trade's work, yet not strictly part of that trade.

REMOVING WALLS (SHORING)

Working Drawings 8.3 and 8.4 show two walls of a building that is to be enlarged. Part of the end wall (Elevation 1–1) and part of the front wall (Elevation 2–2) are to be removed; new lintels, beams, and columns are to be installed to support the floor and roof load and connect the structural-steel framing of the addition. A new doorway is to be cut through at the basement level. The windows to be removed from the basement are not to be reused; the openings are to be bricked up with common bricks (12 in. thick). The windows on the main floor are all semicircular-headed; there are four such windows (4–4 × 9–6) with wooden frames and sashes, all of which are to be used in the new wing.

The structural-steel contractor is to supply all the steel shown, erect all the columns, and erect the 10 WF 49 shown on Elevation 1–1. The general contractor is to erect lintels A, B, C, D, and E, set the base plates and anchor bolts for the columns, and set the bearing plate for the 10 WF 49. The dry pack over the lintels is to be nonshrink-cement grout packing. The two fireproofed beams shown on column line F9 are framing coming in from the new wing and are not part of the alteration work.

Before work is begun on the alterations, a dustproof partition is to be installed in the present building, extending from the floor at grade 286–0 to the ceiling, a height of 22 ft, running from line H to line F on the drawing. A similar partition 11 ft high is to extend from line F around the corner to line 11. In addition, the building must be protected from the weather by covering up the outside face where necessary while the walls are open.

THE TAKE-OFF (W. D. 8.3, 8.4)

ALTERATION WORK

2 × 4 frmg. temp. partition

End	3	×	26 ft	=	78 ft	
	2	×	24	=	48	
	21	×	12	=	252	
	21	×	10	=	210	
Front	2	×	24	=	48	
	20	×	12	=	240	
					876 LF	
				=	585 BF	

⅜-in. plywood to temp. ptn. (taped joints)

$$25\text{--}8 \ \times \ 22\text{--}0 \ = \ 565 \ SF$$
$$23\text{--}0 \ \times \ 11\text{--}0 \ = \ 253$$
$$\overline{818}$$
$$+ \ \text{Waste } 10\% \ \ \ 82$$
$$\overline{900 \ SF}$$

Scaffolding for removing walls

$$26\text{--}0 \ \times \ 30\text{--}0 \ = \ 780 \ SF$$
$$26\text{--}0 \ \times \ 22\text{--}0 \ = \ 572$$
$$\overline{1,352 \ SF}$$

Remove bast. window 4–4 × 2–9 = 3 ea.

Remove window sashes (approx. 4–0 × 3–6) & store for reuse = 4 prs.

Remove wood window frame 4–4 × 9– 6 & store for reuse = 4 fr.

Cut pocket for column seat 18 in. × 12 in. × 12 in. = 2 ea.

Cut pocket for column seat 18 in. × 18in. × 12 in. = 1 ea.

Cut pocket for column seat 48 in. × 12 in. × 48 in. = 1 ea.

Conc. col. seats   *FORMS*

2/	1–6 × 1–0 × 1–0	=	3 CF		10 SF
	1–6 × 1–6 × 1–0	=	3		6
	4–0 × 1–0 × 4–0	=	16		40
			$\overline{22 \ CF}$		$\overline{56 \ SF}$
		=	$\overline{1 \ CY}$		

Set col. base plate & U-bolts = 4 ea.

Shore 12-in. wall for cutting new doorway 4–0 × 8–0 = L. S.

Remove foundation wall for new doorway = 32 CF

Set 10-in. channel lintel 5–4 long = 2 pcs.

Patch foundation wall around 4–0 × 7–6 opg. = 1 opg.

Cut beam pocket in brick wall & set 8 × 12 base plate & make good = 2 ea.

Cut chase 4 in. deep for 12-in. channel lintel

$$2 \quad \times \quad 26 \text{ ft} \quad = \quad \underline{52 \text{ LF}}$$

Cut chase for 10-in. channel lintel

$$2 \quad \times \quad 25 \text{ ft} \quad = \quad \underline{50 \text{ LF}}$$

Cut holes through 4-in. brick for $1\frac{1}{4}$-in. pipe spreaders $\quad = \quad \underline{20 \text{ ea.}}$

Set inner 12-in. channel lintel $\quad = \quad \underline{26 \text{ LF}}$

Set outer 12-in. channel lintel $\quad = \quad \underline{26 \text{ LF}}$

Set inner 10-in. channel lintels (3 pcs.) $\quad = \quad \underline{26 \text{ LF}}$

Set outer 10-in. channel lintels (3 pcs.) $\quad = \quad \underline{26 \text{ LF}}$

Nonshrink cement dry pack over lintels $\quad = \quad \underline{104 \text{ LF}}$

Remove 12-in. ext. brick wall

$$
\begin{array}{rcccl}
25\text{–}8 & \times & 15\text{–}9 & = & 404 \text{ SF} \\
9\text{–}9 & \times & 1\text{–}8 & = & 16 \\
9\text{–}6 & \times & 7\text{–}8 & = & 73 \\
15\text{–}0 & \times & 7\text{–}4 & = & 110 \\
& & & = & \overline{603 \text{ SF}} \\
& & & = & \underline{603 \text{ CF}}
\end{array}
$$

Cut chase 4 in. $\times$ *6 in. in top of brick wall for slab seat (D-D)* $\quad = \quad \underline{21 \text{ LF}}$

Face-brick patching

$$
\begin{array}{rcccl}
3\text{–}0 & \times & 7\text{–}0 & = & 21 \text{ SF} \\
& & & = & \underline{150 \text{ pcs.}}
\end{array}
$$

Common-brick patching

$$
\begin{array}{rcccccl}
21 \text{ SF} & \times & 0\text{–}8 & & = & 14 \text{ CF} \\
3/4\text{–}4 & \times & 2\text{–}9 & \times \; 1\text{–}0 & = & 35 \\
& & & & & \overline{49 \text{ CF}} & \times \quad 20 \quad = \quad 980 \text{ pcs.} \\
& & & & & & = \quad \underline{1 \text{ M}}
\end{array}
$$

Tarpaulins & protection for bldg. while open (approx.) $\quad = \quad \underline{700 \text{ SF}}$

Truck away rubbish (approx.) $\quad = \quad \underline{10 \text{ loads}}$

Attend on struct. steel sub. erecting 4 cols. $\quad = \quad \underline{\text{L. S.}}$

Generally make good where disturbed $\quad = \quad \underline{\text{L. S.}}$

NOTES ON THE TAKE-OFF (W. D. 8.3, 8.4)

The most important consideration in this take-off is that the work be planned so that no costly shoring of the wall or its load will be necessary. The lintels are set by cutting the chase for one side first and setting that lintel before the chase at the other side is cut and that lintel set; thus the lintels are in place before the wall below is removed. The alternative would be to shore and needle from roof level down to basement level, a very costly operation.

Following the take-off through, the temporary partition is taken off as 2 × 4 studding on 16-in. centers, using a 12-ft stud with a plate over it and a 10-ft stud above that to reach the total height of 22 ft. The three pieces of 2 × 4 taken off at 26 ft are for the plates—top, bottom, and between the 12-ft and 10-ft studs. The first two pieces at 24 ft are for intermediate bridging; the second two pieces at 24 ft are for head and bottom plates for the two low partitions: the total length of the two partitions (9 ft 6 in. plus 16 ft) less 2 ft 6 in. for the distance the partition will be set back from the wall. It would not be practical to erect the partition too close to the wall; some working space will be needed behind the wall for getting out the windows and erecting the inner lintels.

The plywood item is notated "taped joints" because a dustproof partition was specified. In pricing that partition, some consideration should be given to the fact that the material will be recovered and will have some reclaim value.

The scaffolding is taken off for one side, measured from the basement floor up to about 2 ft above the lintels. For the work that is to be done, it is apparent that a complete scaffold will be required.

The windows and sashes that will be reused are separated from the windows that will not be reused. Considerable care will be needed in taking out windows that are to be reused.

The items for cutting out for beam plates, column bases, and the concrete pads for the columns, follow the respective details shown on the drawing. The new basement doorway is taken off item by item, although an experienced estimator might handle it in one descriptive item for a lump-sum price, as: "Shore, set lintel, cut door opg. 4–0 × 7–6 and make good."

The cost of setting lintels B, C, D, and E is made up of several items: cut chases, set inner lintels, set outer lintels, and dry pack. The chase is measured for both sides. Note that for the two lintels that meet at the corner (E–9), the chase is taken off at 25 ft, which allows the deduction for the 12-in. corner that need only be taken off once. The 25 ft allows 9 ft 6 in. for Elevation 1–1 and 15 ft for Elevation 2–2.

The face brick item is for patching the window opening at the F line. The common brick is for patching both that opening and where the basement windows were removed.

Tarpaulins will be needed to protect the open area until the new wing is up and covered. Rubbish to be removed will consist of the masonry and concrete that has been broken out. Finally, items should be allowed for attendance on the structural-steel sub and for general making good. It might be found necessary to cut out the brickwork for the columns and then set the columns before cutting out for the lintels, so that the columns could take the load from the lintels; the item for attendance on the structural-steel erector provides a place for pricing that extra cost. The general making-good item is one that is always needed in taking off alteration work. There are always factors that do not show on the drawings, and some allowance must be made for unanticipated costs.

REMODELING

Working Drawing 8.5 shows alteration work in a building that is to be remodeled to provide a canteen and two new offices. The following information was taken from the specifications and supplements the drawing: from floor to underside of slab above to be 9–9; allow $280 for supplying finish hardware; plastering not included in the contract, nor is linoleum; all hollow metal door frames to have transoms and are 3–0 × 8–9 for single doors and 5–4 × 8–9 for a pair of doors; new entrance doors to have 2-in. × 2-in. staff beading on outside of frame, 1-in. × 6-in. casing inside; ceiling height to be 8–9 in all rooms.

The removal work is taken off room by room, so that each item can be readily identified when the site is visited before pricing the estimate.

THE TAKE-OFF (W. D. 8.5)

ALTERATIONS (Fig. 9.5)

Ext.   *Shore 12-in. wall for cutting new opg. 4–0   ×   8–9   =*   <u>1 opg.</u>

                 Remove 12-in. masonry to form door opg. 4–0   ×   8–9 & set
                 3 angle-iron lintels   =   <u>1 opg.</u>

                 Waterstruck-face-brick patching
                         23–0   ×   0–8   =   16 SF
                                          =   <u>120 pcs.</u>

                 Common-brick patching   =   <u>240 pcs.</u>

                 Set. ext. door frame 4–0   ×   8–9   =   <u>1 fr.</u>

                 Set ext. wood door & hardware   =   <u>1 pr.</u>

2 × 2 staff bead   =   <u>26 LF</u>

1 × 6 door casing   =   <u>26 LF</u>

Rms. 2 & 3   *Remove 1 pr. wood doors   +   H. M. fr.*   =   <u>L. S.</u>

Cut new doorways 3–0   ×   8–9 in 8-in. brick ptn. & set lintel

                                                      =   <u>2 opgs.</u>

2 × 4 stud ptn.

$$3 \times 16\text{–}0 = 48 \text{ ft}$$
$$13 \times 10\text{–}0 = \underline{130}$$
$$\underline{\underline{178 \text{ LF}}} = \underline{180 \text{ LF}}$$

Rm. 6   *Remove 1 pr. doors & frame*   =   <u>L. S.</u>

Remove single door & frame   =   <u>1 dr.</u>

Cut doorway 5–4   ×   8–9 in 8-in. wall & set lintel   =   <u>1 opg.</u>

Cut doorway 4–0   ×   8–9 in 8-in. wall & set lintel   =   <u>1 opg.</u>

Remove 6-in. terra cotta tile ptn.

$$22\text{–}4 \times 9\text{–}8 = \underline{216 \text{ SF}}$$

Remove wood base   =   <u>144 LF</u>

Remove wall plaster for new dado tile

$$88\text{–}0 \times 4\text{–}0 = \underline{352 \text{ SF}}$$

5-in.   ×   8-in. glazed facing tile dado, 2 in.

$$88\text{–}0 \times 3\text{–}7 = 316 \text{ SF}$$
$$\text{Less} \quad 14\text{–}0 \times 0\text{–}10 = \underline{12}$$
$$304 \text{ SF}$$
$$\times \quad \underline{3.35}$$
$$1{,}018 \text{ pcs.}$$
$$+\ 5\% \quad \underline{52}$$
$$= \underline{1{,}070 \text{ pcs.}}$$

Extra for Group 1

Drs.	4	×	6	= 24 pcs.
Window	2	×	1	= <u>2</u>
				<u>26 pcs.</u>

Extra for Group 2

Sill	14 pcs.
Cap	70
Base	84
	168 pcs.

Extra for Group 4

Base miters	4 pcs.
Sill miters	2
Jambs — dr. 4 × 2	8
Jambs — window	2
	16 pcs.

Clean & point fcg. tile   =   **304 SF**

Remove window stool & apron   =   **14 LF**

Cut & fit window jamb casing to new tile dado   =   **L. S.**

Patch floor as necessary

$$26\text{–}6 \ \times\ 22\text{–}4 \ =\ \textbf{592 SF}$$

Reset H. M. door frame 4–0 × 8–9   =   **1 fr.**

Reset H. M. door frame 5–7 × 8–9   =   **1 fr.**

Set new H. M. door frame 4–0 × 8–9   =   **2 fr.**

Patch & reset wood int. door & hdwr.   =   **5 drs.**

Common-brick patching

(8 in.)	2/ 6–0 × 9–8				
(8 in.)	4–8 × 9–8	22–0 × 9–8	=	213 SF
(8 in.)	8/ 0–8 × 9–8			×	14
					2,992 pcs.
				=	3 M

Sand wood floors

2 & 3	2/ 14–6 × 11–9	=	341 SF
5	35–6 × 13–2	=	469
5	26–6 × 22–4	=	592
			1,402 SF

Finish hardware allowance   = $\underline{\$280}$

General cut & patch & make good   =   <u>L. S.</u>

Remove rubbish   =   <u>L. S.</u>

Trucking   =   <u>L. S.</u>

NOTES ON THE TAKE-OFF (W. D. 8.5)

The new entrance is taken off item by item. Patching around the opening allows 8 in. width all around. The common brick is 8 in. thick; therefore its quantity should be twice that of the face brick. For the interior, the removal work and cutting of new doorways are taken off, but items for patching the masonry and setting the doors and frames are not taken off yet, as it will be simpler to take off all the brick patching in one item and all the setting of doors and frames in another.

For the new canteen, the plaster removal item is taken off at 4 ft in height, which allows working space for the new facing-tile dado. The 88-ft perimeter is twice the sum of 26–6 and 22–4, less the two doorways. Two courses of facing tile are deducted at the window (14 ft × 10 in.). The 5 × 8 tile courses 5⅜ in. × 8 in., or 3.35 tiles per SF. The locations of the specials in each group are noted on the take-off sheet. The Group 1 items are for the vertical jambs excluding the base and cap pieces, which are Group 4.

The common-brick patching item allows 4 in. at each jamb of the old doorways—5–4 plus 2 times 0–4 gives 6–0, and 4–0 plus 2 times 0–4 gives 4–8; where cutting out has to be done, 8 in. is allowed at each jamb. Cutting out for openings disturbs the surrounding wall, so more patching will be needed for such jambs than for filling in present openings.

The last three items—general cut and patch, remove rubbish, and trucking—can be expensive; some allowance should be made for them.

MISCELLANEOUS ITEMS

Demolition

Major demolition work, such as tearing down entire buildings or removing a large part of a building, is usually handled by a wrecking company. If it is, the item should be listed on the subcontractor's sheet of the estimate and prices requested from wrecking contractors. Wrecking contractors will usually include all the demolition work down to ground level but exclude the removal of foundation walls and floors below ground level. Before completing the take-off the estimator must ascertain the extent of demolition included by the wrecking sub; if work below ground is not included by the wrecking sub, it must be taken off to be done by the general contractor.

Foundation walls should be measured either in square feet or cubic feet, and ground slabs in square feet, with the items described as completely as possible. If an existing basement is of appreciable size in proportion to that of the new building, the building excavation item should be adjusted to allow for the present hole. If an existing basement or cellar hole is to be filled in, an item for fill is *always* taken off.

Shoring

If walls or columns that support floors or other loads are to be removed, it is usually necessary to take off an item (or items) for shoring. For example, if the 43-ft-long end wall of a 3-story building was to be removed and the floors and roof were supported by that wall, then the take-off should include the following item: "Shore floors and roof through 3 floors for removal of end wall—43 LF."

Partitions and interior walls

If removal of partitions is to be part of the alteration work, an item for patching and making good the floor will probably be required. The item would be measured in lineal feet; for example: "Patch and make good floor after removal of ptns.—........LF."

Roofs adjoining new roofs

Both the drawings and the present building should be examined to ascertain what work will be involved at roof level. There will probably be removal of the eaves cornices and patching of the old roof at its junction with the new, and some roof covering may have to be stripped and relaid. Whatever will be necessary should be taken off item by item, with each fully described, in lineal feet or square feet.

Occupied buildings

In taking off alteration work for a building that is to be continuously occupied during remodeling, the working conditions must be carefully studied. The limited areas available to the contractor at any one time may necessitate costly handling of materials. If material will have to be wheeled to a particular spot and then hauled up and through a window, the additional cost of such an operation should be covered in the estimate. If men will be working in a building where smoking is not permitted, that too must be noted in the take-off; a no-smoking rule can cause a reduction in output. Any number of factors must be considered in taking off alteration work: confined working space, protection for the public, lack of room to store material, dust screens, temporary ramps, and many other items depending on the particular job. Every item or condition that is likely to cause expense should be included in the take-off and described as fully as possible.

CHAPTER 9 **Job Overhead**

The job-overhead (or general-conditions, as it is sometimes termed) sheet of the estimate is relatively simple to write up, but can be very difficult to price. It requires a clear understanding of the distinction between job overhead and main-office overhead. The cost of maintaining the contractor's main office is normally not included in the job estimate; the job overhead items that are carried in the bid are items of direct cost to that job. It could properly include such items as trucking to and from the yard and work at the yard loading or unloading for the job, but not such items as rent and taxes on the yard. Vehicles used on the job for that job alone could be charged as direct job overhead, but staff cars used for visiting the job from the main office would be more properly charged to main-office overhead. One cannot be dogmatic in affirming that certain items belong on the overhead sheet rather than elsewhere on the estimate. The question of which are main-office costs and which should be charged to the individual jobs, should be referred to company policy; as long as the estimate follows that policy, the various estimated and actual costs can be accurately compared.

Once it has been decided which items are direct job costs, the question still remains whether certain items should be carried on the overhead sheet or on the applicable trade sheets. The item for a trade foreman is a good example of this question. Having totaled a particular trade sheet, it would be quite proper to add the foreman for that trade as an item at the bottom of that sheet. If the general contractor intends to accept sub-bids for what could be called general contractor's work, such as formwork or masonry, it will be advantageous to have *all* the costs for that work contained on the trade sheet, so as to have a full total that can be properly compared with the sub price. For work that sub-bids will be accepted for, the estimate might even be set up so that the trade sheet would also include fringe benefits, scaffolding, hoisting, insurances, and payroll taxes. As long as all the cost items are included in the estimate, their allocation to either the trade sheets or the overhead sheet is a choice that should be considered as: which way would be best for *this* bid, or for *this* company?

After having priced many jobs, the estimator will have some idea of the proportion that the overhead should be of the total bid. For jobs of a similar type, the overhead should decrease in proportion to the total cost as the size of the job increases. For a small school of, say, $200,000, the overhead sheet might total $16,500; for a school of similar design but five times the cost, the overhead might be $60,000. In this example, the overhead is 8¼ per cent for the smaller school and only 6 per cent for the larger. Any such ratios that an estimator might have in the back of his mind, however, can be no more than a rough guide. An individual overhead sheet should be properly compiled for every job. It is when checking the priced overhead sheet in proportion to the total cost, with regard to the size and nature of the job, that the experienced estimator may legitimately feel that his overhead sheet is light or heavy. And even then, nine times out of ten, he will also realize that certain special job conditions support and justify his overhead sheet as compiled. Only in the odd instance will he discover an item on the overhead sheet that needs adjusting.

Performance and payment bonds

A performance bond guarantees the faithful performance of all work required to complete the contract. A payment bond guarantees the payment of all bills for labor and material used in the work (including lumber purchased for the job, even if not incorporated in the work) and all rental of equipment and trucks used for the work. The two bonds may be written either jointly or separately, but whether the contract requires one or the other or both of them, the premiums are as follows:

On the first	$100,000	$10.00 per $1,000
On the next	$2,400,000	6.50 per $1,000
On the next	$2,500,000	5.25 per $1,000
On the next	$2,500,000	5.00 per $1,000
On everything over	$7,500,000	4.70 per $1,000

Stipulated completion not over 24 months. Surcharge if over 24 months: one per cent of regular premium for each additional month.

Minimum bond premium: $10.

Many contractors add the bond premium as an item at the very end of the summary sheet—that is, after the summary sheet has been completed, including the fee. They do so because only then do they know just what the bond will cost. The disadvantage of that method, however, is that it does not show the bond premium included in the total cost of the general contractor's work. By the time the overhead sheet is to be compiled, it should be possible to gauge the total value of the bid fairly closely, and thus to carry an approximate bond item on the overhead sheet based on that anticipated value. The total cost without the fee would then include all expenses—the best figure possible to use in deciding on the fee. A minor adjustment could later be made on the summary sheet when the fee is being decided upon.

Bid bonds

Bid bonds cost only $5 for a year for what is termed "bid service undertaking." For $5, a surety company will provide the contractor with all the bid bonds he needs in the course of a year. This item is not considered a job expense.

Maintenance bonds

Maintenance bonds are sometimes required. If a payment or performance bond (or both) is included in the contract, there is no charge for the first year. After that, a maintenance bond costs either $1.50 per $1,000 of the total value of the job (per year) or $7.50 per $1,000 on that part of the work that is to be guaranteed under the bond (per year), whichever is less. Thus a maintenance bond for part of a contract cannot cost more than 0.15 per cent (per year) of the total value of the contract.

If no performance or payment bond had been given, a maintenance bond would cost either $7.50 per $1,000 per year or the combined cost of the performance and payment bonds, whichever was less.

Permit bonds

Some local authorities require a contractor to file a permit bond to indemnify the authority against any costs arising from the contractor using public streets, crossing curbs, connecting to public utility lines, and the like. A permit bond costs $5 per year for each $1,000 of bond. A single permit bond usually covers a contractor for all his work within a particular town or city during that year.

Supply bonds

A supply bond guarantees the quality and quantity of material supplied to the owner. These bonds, which cost from $2 to $5 per $1,000, are not usually applicable to construction contracts.

Insurances

There are several types of insurance that may be the responsibility of the contractor: workmen's compensation, public liability and property damage, contingent liability, and hold harmless. The last two types have standard rates dependent on the amount of coverage, and so can be priced on the overhead sheet without any difficulty. The rates for workmen's compensation and for public liability and property damage vary according to the trades involved and the state that the work is done in. There are hundreds of different classifications, each with its own particular rate, but we are concerned with only a few of them. Because of the wide variation in rates, many contractors either carry these insurance items on the applicable trade sheets or use the labor totals from those trade sheets to compute a total insurance item for inclusion on the overhead sheet. Other contractors would depend on their accounting departments to give the estimators insurance costs as percentage figures of payroll costs for particular types of jobs.

The insurance-company auditors who visit a contractor's office to audit the payrolls for insurance breakdown, not being technically trained construction men, will simply allocate wages into whatever classification might seem reasonable. This practice can be expensive for the contractor; it is strictly a guessing game for the auditor, who tends to put all doubtful items into the most costly of the various probable classifications. For example, carpenters shown on the payroll at the time cement finishing was being done might be placed in the concrete-formwork classification—which might cost 8.5 per cent for workmen's compensation—although they were actually setting door frames—a finish-carpentry classification that would run more like 1.8 per cent. To avoid such an incorrect allocation of payroll items, give the insurance auditor the job-cost book when he comes to the office. Once he has ascertained that the total labor in the cost records agrees with that on the payroll, he will have every item on the payroll properly allocated for him to use in preparing his breakdown. The insurance auditor will appreciate this help, and the contractor will be assessed at the correct insurance rates.

Fire insurance

Fire-insurance premiums are based on either the amount of the contract or the value of the structures excluding excavation work. The fire-insurance requirements should be read carefully. In many contracts, the owner is required to arrange and pay for the fire insurance; he is so required in all contracts that include the "General Conditions" of the American Institute of Architects. In other contracts, fire insurance might be required on the structures only, so that the insurance coverage would exclude the value of excavation and site work. It might not be necessary to take out such a policy until the foundation work was started.

Even if fire insurance was not required on the contract work or was not to be paid for by the contractor, it would still be necessary to carry a fire insurance item to cover the contractor's own equipment—tool sheds, job shacks, and similar items not incorporated into the building.

Health-and-welfare funds

Payment into the various trade health-and-welfare funds is an item that can run 5 per cent or more of the payroll. It can be handled in any one of three ways: (1) The health-and-welfare contribution rate can be added to the hourly wage rate as part of the gross figure used to set the unit prices. This method is generally unsatisfactory, because health-and-welfare rates vary from district to district and in many areas there are no health-and-welfare funds. (2) The health and welfare item can be entered at the end of each trade sheet in the estimate, with the total labor cost expressed in hours and the health-and-welfare cost computed and added into the sheet. This is a satisfactory way to handle the item, except that it involves several separate calculations at a time when the estimator is working under pressure. Only the very best estimators, who are systematic and who have their estimates well in hand on the day *prior* to bid day, can cope with this method. (3) Health-and-welfare contributions can be expressed as a percentage of the payroll total, and computed either as a single item or as a series of items trade by trade, carried either on the overhead sheet or at the bottom of the priced trade sheets. This method is quite satisfactory if the payroll percentage is calculated accurately, according to the labor rates and the health-and-welfare rates for the area where the job is located.

Pension funds

Contributions to the pension funds of labor unions are handled in the same way as those to the health-and-welfare funds. Should you be bidding a job in an area where such fringe benefits do not apply at present, you should check into the expected trend; such benefits might well become a cost factor before the completion of your job.

Government payroll taxes

This item covers the employer's contributions for social security (F.I.C.A.), federal unemployment tax, and state unemployment tax. The three items can be combined and expressed as a percentage of the payroll, and the estimated amount computed. State unemployment tax rates vary from state to state. The employer's share for social security is presently 3 per cent of the gross wages, up to a maximum of $4,800 per person per calendar year. Federal unemployment and state unemployment tax together total 3 per cent of all wages up to a maximum of $3,000 per person per calendar year. The federal unemployment tax is actually 3 per cent of all wages up to the maximum, but with credit of up to 90 per cent allowed in a state that levies unemployment tax also; thus in some states the employer would pay 2.7 per cent to the state unemployment fund and 0.3 per cent to the federal fund.

Superintendent

An item for the superintendent should always be carried on the overhead sheet. Whether the item should be carried at full salary for every week throughout the anticipated length of the job, at full salary part of the time, or at partial salary all of the time, depends on your analysis of the needs of the particular job.

Foremen

The labor cost for foremen can be priced on the overhead sheet if it is decided to include the item. Some contractors may choose to work on the theory that the foreman should cover his own cost by increasing the production of his crew, a theory that might prove valid provided that unit prices had not already been figured at rockbottom throughout the estimate. The great variation in foreman requirements, however, from district to district and job to job, causes this to be a variable item that can be more properly priced as an overhead item. One district will have working rules that require a masonry foreman for every ten men, another nearby district will require a foreman for every four men. If you anticipate using a super who is himself a tradesman, you may elect to reduce your foreman item for that trade.

Engineering

For a large job, it may be necessary to carry an engineer for laying out the site and giving grades and lines throughout the entire job period; in fact, it might even be necessary to carry a rodman as well. Other jobs might justify only a few weeks for an engineer to lay out the building and the foundation work. If the contract calls for a registered engineer to lay out the building, the cost of the layout should be carried on the overhead sheet.

Timekeepers and material clerks

For large jobs, it is customary to carry overhead items for the job's clerical help, stock or toolroom men, waterboys, and all such general, nonproductive employees. If a job accountant is to be employed at the site doing work that would normally be done in the contractor's head office, he is not usually considered a job expense.

Watchmen

Watching is an item that often costs more than it is worth. Some jobs must be watched both day and night to prevent theft and vandalism, but others would not require even a night watchman. In many urban districts, site-watching would be necessary only during daylight hours after work, and from early morning until dusk on weekends.

Pilfering is a common problem on construction jobs. No amount of watching will prevent losses if the material and tools are leaving the site before the watchman takes over. Restricted parking areas for all cars can cut down on pilfering, provided the parking areas are not too close to the building and shanties.

Job offices and shanties

Temporary portable wooden shacks were the recognized type of building for job offices and toolrooms until recent years. They are still probably the most convenient buildings for these purposes, but are more expensive to dismantle, truck, and reassemble than the office trailers and converted truck trailers that are now commonly seen on construction jobs, and which also make very good job offices, toolrooms, lockers, and storage units. Trailers can be transported very cheaply and also filled before being moved; they not only arrive at the new site ready for use, but also save trucking. Two secondhand truck trailers would cost much less than one large wooden shack, would provide as much working area or storage space, and would last many more years.

The overhead item for temporary buildings will vary according to the type of shack or trailer that you intend to use, but it should include all installation and maintenance costs: transportation and erection, attendance for cleaning and taking care of heating, and fuel. The general contractor usually provides attendance for cleaning the clerk-of-works shack.

Trucking

General trucking is an item that often costs much more than the contractor anticipates. Trucking from the yard to the job, back to the yard, to the dump, and to pick up odd items that are needed in a hurry; it all adds up to a sizable item. It is not easy to determine how much trucking a particular job will require. You can only estimate so many loads at so much per load, considering the distance from the yard to the site. Some contractors keep a separate record of trucking costs and use those figures as a basis for pricing trucking in a subsequent estimate. Any trucks, pickup trucks, or cars that will be used either on the job or especially for the job, should be included on the overhead sheet.

Temporary light and power

If the general contractor is to pay for light and power, the item will probably have to include the cost of hooking up the temporary service, providing extension cords, temporary wiring, and bulbs, and paying the electric company's monthly bills. The light-and-power costs should be checked in the specifications, however, to see just what is to be covered by the general contractor; some contracts provide for splitting the responsibility for temporary services.

Temporary water

If the general contractor is to pay for the water used during construction, the local water department should be contacted to obtain the water rates. Very often a flat fee will cover all the water used; in other districts, the water might be metered and be quite an expensive item.

Temporary heat

Temporary heat may be required for drying out a building and keeping it warm enough for satisfactory completion of the finishing trades' work. The heating system of the building itself is generally used for heating during construction if it is possible to do so, but very often the heating system will not be ready to supply heat when the contractor needs it. In such an instance, it would be necessary to provide some alternative heating units—usually hot-air blowers. Before pricing the temporary heat item, you must decide when the building will probably need heat. It would be unusual for a building to require temporary heat before the plastering was begun, but after that the building might have to be heated almost continuously until its completion (except, of course, during weather warm enough to dry out the building).

Once you have decided how many weeks of temporary heating should be allowed for and the type of heating that should be used, the cost of labor, equipment, and fuel can be estimated. If local regulations should call for continual attendance while a heating system is in operation, it would be necessary to figure how many hours the system must be operated. Could the heating be shut down for a few hours each day—perhaps from 4 to 8 p.m., then operated from 8 p.m. to 4 a.m., and shut down again for 4 more hours before being started up for the day shift? Would the building retain sufficient heat during the shutdown period? The time of year and location of the job would enter into these considerations.

Permits

Building permits are necessary except for some public jobs; the cost of the permit is set by the local authority. The building department of the town or city where the job is located will give you the permit rates.

Equipment

Some contractors carry items on the overhead sheet for equipment such as hoists, cranes, pumps, and compressors. Any equipment that had *not* been covered on the detailed, priced estimate sheets, should be covered on the overhead sheet, priced for both labor and material. For example, the job being bid might require a crane for various tasks, such as moving formwork material, hoisting concrete, stocking masonry materials, and lifting reinforcing steel. If the crane was to be covered on the overhead sheet, the item should include the cost of the rental, gas and oil, operator, and oiler. Whether or not you would carry equipment items as overhead would depend entirely on how you priced the various trade items. If your unit prices provided for the equipment required, then you would not price the equipment again on the overhead sheet.

Small tools

Some allowance for small tools should be made on the overhead sheet. Such tools as wheelbarrows, concrete buggies, vibrators, and saws inevitably get damaged, wear out, are lost, or mysteriously disappear. The office records

of small tools purchased for previous jobs should provide a guide for estimating this item. (The number of tools that disappear in the first month
of the job will tell you whether or not you allowed enough for the item!)

Clean-up

Rough cleaning up for the various trades, such as cleaning and stacking
formwork lumber or clearing up and removing masonry debris, should be
charged against the applicable trade labor items, so that such cleaning up is
provided for in the unit prices carried for the items. A considerable amount
of cleaning up, however, cannot be allocated to any particular trade, including sweeping out the building to make it ready for the flooring trades,
picking up and burning cartons, removing accumulated rubbish, and cleaning and polishing hardware and fixtures. The labor required for this general
and final cleanup must be estimated and carried on the overhead sheet. The
item should also include the cost of material used—soap, sweeping brushes,
cleaners, rags, and the like.

Glass cleaning

If the contract requires the general contractor to clean glass at the completion of the job, the item should be carried on the overhead sheet. It is
often possible to obtain a price for glass cleaning from a company that
specializes in that kind of work.

Glass breakage

If the contract requires the general contractor to replace all broken glass,
that should be covered on the overhead sheet. Almost every building has
some glass breakage during construction, and, except if due to vandalism or
wind storms, the breakage is usually not covered by insurance.

Winter protection

Although some aspects of winter protection and winter working conditions may have already been considered in establishing the unit prices for
the various items of work, some general winter protection would still be
required. Covering concrete, heating sand, de-icing, snow removal, temporary enclosures—all kinds of extraneous costs are involved in winter working. The amount carried will depend on conditions peculiar to each job
that is bid.

Signs

The ordinary company-name sign that a general contractor puts up on
all his jobs is not considered a job expense. If the contract should call for a
special sign, however (perhaps one showing the title of the project, with the
names of the owner, architect, and engineer), then an item should be
carried in the estimate for it.

Progress photographs

Many contracts require the general contractor to submit photographs showing the condition of the job at certain stages to the owner or architect; these progress photographs can amount to a considerable expense. Four views of the building, with three prints of each view, to be submitted every month, would cost about $60 per month; for a job scheduled to take 16 months the item would cost $960.

Premium time (overtime)

Premium payments are the additional cost of overtime labor; that is, the difference between the basic rate and the overtime rate. Most construction jobs will involve some overtime work in addition to that already allowed for in the trade labor items. You might get caught pouring concrete at the end of the day, so six men work an extra hour; or they pour through the mid-day meal period; or two laborers must start half an hour early each day to get mortar ready for the masons; or the job simply falls behind schedule and you have to work a whole crew over several weekends. There will always be some unanticipated premium time, so an item should be carried for it. Payroll insurance rates are not paid on premium time, so either carry the item on the material side of the estimate or deduct it from the gross labor costs before computing the insurance items.

Labor wage increases

The probability of wage increases during construction must be considered in bidding a job. If existing labor agreements stipulate increases that will go into effect automatically at future dates, it should be possible to figure your unit prices on the basis of the exact rates that will be in effect at the time of the job. Probable future increases that can be anticipated and gauged within close limits should also be allowed for in figuring the unit prices. The real problem concerning wage increases occurs when it seems impossible to guess what the trades will ask for, what the contractors will offer, or what kind of a settlement will be made. You would be most likely to encounter such a problem in connection with a job scheduled to take over a year to complete.

If a trade has wage negotiations coming up in the immediate future, it should be possible to discover the local feeling and from that deduce how much of an increase may be expected. That is the kind of information that a good estimator will ferret out when visiting a job site. He will look around the area and see how much work is going on; he will talk to labor delegates, suppliers—anyone and everyone who might give him a lead or a little assistance. The information so collected enables an estimator to approach the bid adequately prepared. Whether or not an item is carried for wage increases would depend on how the labor unit prices were handled originally and how satisfied the estimator feels with those units in view of the expected wage increases.

The question of whether there will be enough tradesmen available locally to service the job should also be given some thought. Are you going to have to import labor at extra expense? Should you cover such extra expense in the labor increases item?

Travel time

All travel-time expenses for trades that have union agreements concerning the allowances required should be figured and the item placed on the overhead sheet. But again, there are the questions of future labor agreements and of bringing men in from other districts. It is not unusual to have to import workmen, particularly for a big job in a rural district, as was demonstrated by a large hospital bid in New England recently. The masonry work was extensive; it was estimated that the job would require about 60 masons for a year. At the time the job was bid, there was very little work being done in the area; out of 40 masons in the local district, it was assumed that 35 would be available. Thus it was necessary to allow a travel time item for 25 masons for one year—the men, to be drawn from surrounding areas, would each be entitled to $2 per day travel allowance. All the bids submitted, however, were rejected, some minor changes made in the drawings, and the job put out for rebidding about three months later. In that three months the local picture had changed drastically: several jobs had already been started in the area and a fair-sized job was just about to start. The estimator could no longer anticipate using 35 masons from the local area; in fact, it was difficult to see how more than 15 local masons could be mustered for the job. Moreover, the surrounding districts could not be depended upon to supply 45 masons; so it was necessary to figure travel-time allowances for 25 men from the surrounding districts, and also for 20 men from a metropolitan district some 25 miles away. An extra $0.15 per hour was also required for all 60 men, because local union rules said that the same hourly rate must apply to all the men on a job—that is, the highest rate due—and the rate for masons in the city area was $0.15 per hour higher than the rural rate. It can be seen from this example that travel-time expense can be an important item, and one that must be given serious thought.

Subsistence allowance

If workmen have to board and lodge away from home, their expenses usually fall upon the contractor. It should not be too difficult to compute this item: the number of men for so many weeks at so much for each per week. Usually only a few key men are sent to out-of-town jobs: perhaps the super, two or three foremen, and a few workmen—what are called in the industry "company men."

OVERHEAD IN GENERAL

The most common specific overhead items have been listed and explained, but they will not cover all requirements for every possible job. Special jobs will mean special considerations and unusual problems; an arbitrary limit cannot be set on the variety of items that might have to be allowed on the overhead sheet. You might be bidding a weather station on the top of a mountain: you would need more than just a general overhead sheet; you would have a major logistics problem. You would first have to decide how to get the material up and how to transport the workmen up and down. You would require a material compound somewhere near the foot of the mountain *and* trucking to that point *and* a materialman there *and* radio contact with the job site. How cold would it be 4,000 ft up? How many pairs of mittens should you allow? How much winter clothing? What of de-icing problems? Emergency rations? Temporary living quarters? Medical aid? Yes, a special job will have its own problems for the estimator.

You might hear that contractors get good prices "on the islands." Nothing to it, just a few miles off the coast. Simple—*if* you know what you are doing. Simple—*if* you include all the special items needed in the estimate, such as trucking to the pier and barge transportation to the island. Simple—*if* you can solve such problems as labor supply and transportation, and winter working.

There is no such thing as a standard overhead sheet. As we have seen, every job will have its own problems. There are, however, certain factors that should always be investigated, either when you visit the site or at some other time during the bid period. In your own home-office area, of course, many of those factors are known to you, but when you bid on a job in another area they will probably have to be investigated. For most out-of-town jobs, investigations and inquiries in the job area should cover:

  The site and everything applicable to the work thereon
  Wage rates and fringe benefits (both present and anticipated)
  Availability and quality of labor
  State and local taxes
  Material prices
  Gravel and fill prices
  Local subcontractors who may be bidding
  Distance from the site to the railway siding
  Distance from the site to the nearest dump.

Such inquiries cannot be made in two or three hours; thus it is not advisable to plan just a quick trip to see the site and back home to write up the bid. The best procedure is to have the take-off completed and the estimate sheets written up three or four days before bid day. Then, taking the estimate with you, make your site visit; stay in the district one whole day, two days, or even more, as long as you find necessary. After you have seen the site and checked on the local conditions, you should be able either to price the job or to brief whoever is going to do the pricing with you. If the take-off man is not sufficiently experienced to price the entire estimate alone, he still usually sits in on the pricing.

CHAPTER 10

Subcontractors' Bids

Checking and analyzing sub-bids is usually not the straightforward mechanical process that the uninitiated imagine. Time is the main difficulty. It is seldom possible to begin comparing sub-bids until the morning of bid day. There may be some sub prices in the day before bid day, perhaps even enough to enable some preliminary comparisons to be made. But you are going to have to wait for the morning mail on bid day to be able to compile the sub-bid sheet; the mail *and* the telephone calls—those last-minute bids or changes in bids, or your search for a bid for this or that item. The various sub prices must be analyzed to determine what items have been included or excluded, and some of the sub-bidders will have to be contacted by telephone to straighten out their bids. Add the routine but time-consuming work of totaling the sub sheet, completing the summary sheet, and compiling the various alternate prices (the "Add for this" or "So much if we deduct that" items)—plus writing up the bid form itself—and you have a hectic day.

Analyzing sub-bids is mainly a matter of reducing competitive bids to a common basis so that their prices can be accurately compared, and of making sure that you get all the required items covered without duplication. To do this, the sub-bids have to be read carefully. Other factors also must be checked: Does the sub-bid item comply with the specifications? Does the sub-bid provide an inferior product, which the architect will not accept? Does the apparently low sub-bid cover everything required? Does the sub-bid include items that you have already covered, either in your own work or that of another subcontractor? If the low sub-bid is very low and seems out of line with his competitors, should you call him and see what he has to say, or carry him and hope that he won't back away when you offer him a contract? These are questions that you will have to decide, and decide promptly. There can be no dilly-dallying around—not on bid day!

There are several items that frequently require particular care when analyzing sub-bids, and so should always be checked. They include the following items.

Plumbing

Check the excavation for utilities (interior and exterior), utilities piping, manhole, and catch basin items in the specifications. Some specifications call for the plumber to do all work for storm and sanitary sewers, including the excavation; others require the general contractor to do the excavation, back-fill, manholes, and structures, with the plumber responsible only for supplying and laying the pipe. No matter how the items may be spelled out in the specifications, however, it is what is included in the plumbing bid that counts. A sub-bid submitted "as per plans and specifications" can be taken as a definite offer to carry out *all* the work specified. If a sub-bid spells out certain exclusions, however, then those items must be covered somewhere else in the estimate.

The specified requirements for temporary water lines should also be checked to see whether or not the plumber is to include all or part of that work.

Heating

As for plumbing, the excavation items for heating lines must be checked; the general contractor is usually, but not always, responsible for this item. Other items worth checking in the specifications are: concrete for oil-tank trenches and oil-tank mats; insulating concrete for heating lines; pipe hangers; steel supports for heating units; intake and exhaust louvers.

Temporary-heat requirements must also be carefully followed through in the specifications. This item is one that is not always clearly spelled out in the specifications; just what should the general contractor pay for and what must the heating subcontractor provide? In deciding such a question, you must always remember that no matter how contradictory the specifications, no matter how vaguely worded the item; if temporary heat is necessary, the responsibility for providing it is the general contractor's. The division of the work between the general contractor and his heating subcontractor is something that they must settle between them, but the owner will look to the general contractor for the satisfactory completion of *all* the work. There is no contractual relationship whatsoever between the owner and the general contractor's subcontractors. Thus it is extremely important that you know what the heating sub-bid should include, determine what it does include, and satisfy yourself that your general contractor's bid has the temporary heat item covered.

Electrical

This sub item (like plumbing and heating) must be checked for excavation, and the following questions answered. Is the general contractor to excavate and backfill and do the concrete work for electrical lines and fire-alarm lines? Is the electrical subcontractor to wire up motors or oil-burner equipment for the heating sub? Did *both* subs cover this work? Or did neither?

How do the items for temporary wiring and the cost of maintaining temporary light and power read in the specifications? Does the electrical sub-bid comply with them?

Structural steel

Architects are liable to have included all sorts of sundry metal items in the structural-steel section of the specifications. The structural-steel bids must be checked to see what items are excluded and those items covered or accounted for, so that they are all included in your bid but included *once only*. Duplicating items in a bid is almost as bad as missing items; you could lose the job by duplicating some of the items and so increasing your bid above what it should be.

Items that often cause trouble in analyzing structural-steel bids are: loose lintels; setting wedge inserts for lintels; setting column base plates; painting steel in the field; unloading structural steel.

Miscellaneous steel and iron

This is a sub section that always has to be checked very carefully in analyzing the sub-bids. Too often, the miscellaneous-iron section of the specifications is used as a catchall for various metal items such as hollow metal bucks, fire-extinguisher cabinets, door louvers, flag poles, signs, and carpenter's iron. The specifications take-off should have broken down the section and separated the items that you would not expect the miscellaneous-iron subcontractor to bid, but you must still check the bids extremely carefully.

Labor allowed for setting the various items should also be checked. Which items will the sub erect, and which must you, the general contractor, include for setting costs? Have you covered all the items and their setting without duplication?

Roofing and flashings

The responsibility for setting flashings should be checked. There are also several items that may or may not be included in the roofing bid, such as skylights, skydomes and ceiling panels for skydomes, cants, asphalt shingles, roof insulation, and roof hatches. If the building requires any of these items, the roofing bids must be carefully scanned to see whether they are included. Here again, the specifications take-off will prove valuable: it should show where such doubtful items were specified.

Glazing

The items that sometimes cause trouble between the general contractor and the glass-and-glazing subcontractor are the cleaning of glass and the replacing of broken glass. Even if the glazing section of the specifications requires the glazing subcontractor to clean all glass and replace broken glass, glazing bidders will tend to exclude those items. The sub-bids must be checked for them; if they are not included, you must make sure that they are allowed for elsewhere (but not duplicated). If you have already priced those items on the overhead sheet and then the glazing sub includes them, you will have to adjust his price accordingly.

Metal windows and curtain walls

These two items may be in separate chapters of the specifications, but generally the curtain walls—of either metal or one of the combinations of porcelain panels, stainless steel, aluminum, and the like that are becoming so popular—are fabricated and erected by metal-window companies. The specified requirements should be carefully checked against the sub-bids. Items often included in curtain-wall or window chapters but excluded by sub-bidders include: unloading and protecting their material; asbestos-cement (or similar) panels; perimeter caulking; structural framing. The structural framing item can be especially troublesome if such items as angle irons or plates are shown on the architectural drawings but not on the structural drawings. The structural-steel subcontractor will disclaim responsibility for light framing not shown on the structural drawings (whether or not the item is mentioned in the structural-steel specifications) and the metal-window sub will contend that he is not a structural-steel contractor. Thus the item may be clearly shown as part of the job, but the general contractor has no one on whom he can palm off the responsibility.

Doors and door frames

Sub-bids on doors and door frames will normally be for supply only; setting costs should have been included in your carpentry take-off. Special door items, however—such as overhead doors, sliding wardrobe doors, and manual or automatic folding doors—are usually bid with the erection included. You cannot, of course, *presume* such an inclusion—the specifications must be checked and the sub-bids examined to ensure that erection is included.

Millwork

Millwork sub-bids must be carefully checked and compared. There are always troublesome items—items that you included in the carpentry take-off for both labor and material because you expected the millwork sub-bids to exclude them, only to find some of them covered in one millwork bid, but not in another, and so on.

It is difficult to generalize concerning millwork items. If you are in doubt about a particular item, you should take it off with the carpentry work, keeping it separate on the estimate sheet so that you will have the value of the item available if it should be necessary to adjust the millwork price on the sub sheet. The following items may or may not be included by the mill-work bidders: moldings, fascias, and the like that are to be metal covered; hardboards; hardware for casework; metal edging for counters; gutters;

pegboards; shelf-bearers; handrail brackets; linoleum or plastic counter tops; cutouts in casework (such as sink cutouts).

MISCELLANEOUS ITEMS

The following items should be checked in every sub-bid, and clearly spelled out in writing up the subcontracts:

Scaffolding: Make sure that the sub-bid does not specifically exclude this, for if it does, you as general contractor may have to provide the scaffold for the sub.

Hoisting: Same as scaffolding.

Clean-up: Be sure that this is not specifically excluded in either the sub-bid or your contract with the sub. Be sure, in fact, that you clearly state in the contract that the sub is to clean up all his own debris.

Cutting and patching: Unless the specifications or drawings—or both—require the general contractor to do this work for all trades, you should make sure that sub-bids (and contracts) include their own cutting and patching.

SUB-BIDS IN GENERAL

The examples of specific items to check given in this chapter do not exhaust the items that can be troublesome to you in analyzing sub-bids. Every job will present its own problems, and every bid day will bring with it particular problems involving sub-bids. One such problem might be an item included by two different sub trades, which would have to be taken out of one of their bids; it might be an item that was shown on the drawings but not specified, with the result that no one included it; or it might even be a sub trade for which you received no bid at all. Not receiving any bid for a trade is the worst of all bid-day problems, and often necessitates the estimator's making a hurried take-off to use in obtaining an approximate price by telephone. Much of such hectic scrambling on bid day can be avoided, however, as we shall see.

There is no certainty that on the day your bid is to go in everything will fall into place smoothly and easily. No matter how well you line up prospective sub-bidders, things can go wrong. Bidders will hold off until the last minute; the bigger the job, the longer they stall. It is not unusual to be without a single mechanical bid only an hour or two before your general-contract bid is due. You may have talked to twenty mechanical subcontractors, you may have fifteen bids promised; but they still have not come in. In addition, perhaps two or three other sub items have been troublesome because of their complexity or jurisdictional questions involved.

To minimize your problems on bid day, get everything set up beforehand as far as possible. When you put the estimate file away at the end of the day prior to bid day, the only things left to do should be to analyze the sub-bids and compile the sub sheet and the final figures to complete the bid summary. The general contractor's own work should be completely totaled, checked, and entered on the summary sheet. The bid form and bid envelopes should be written up as far as possible. The sub-bids that have been received should be sorted and checked, and (if possible) the sub-bid sheet partially completed. All these things should be done before you leave the office on the day prior to bid day. It may mean a long day, but long working days are part of estimating. There is no excuse for leaving things until the very last day; in fact, it is extremely important not to do so. Completing the sub-bid sheet and the bid summary, writing up the bid form, and getting the bid in, will give you enough to think about on bid day.

If a bid is to be delivered to an owner or authority at a considerable distance from the office where you are putting it together, it is customary and prudent to have your representative (with the bid documents completed as far as possible) stationed at the bid depository location. On receiving your last-minute telephone message, he can complete the bid form, and you save precious time.

Many bid-day problems could be minimized if architects and owners would make sure that bids close on convenient days and at a reasonable time of day. Monday is a bad day for a bid to close, for sub-bidders are reluctant to mail out their prices on a Friday, three days before closing day; consequently, the Monday mail is light, and the telephone becomes a frantic enemy of time. The day following a holiday is bad for the same reason. Bids that close at noon or earlier are very difficult to handle. Not everyone is first drop for the mailman; in fact, many business people do not receive their first mail until 10 a.m. or later. And even if the mail is picked up at the post office, the morning is generally just too short for all that has to be done. A long list of alternative prices can be a major problem in putting a bid together.

In the interests of sound bidding, to reduce the probability of errors and ensure that the owner will receive the lowest bid that the contractor can come up with, the following suggestions are made:

1. Bids close on Wednesday, Thursday, or Friday.

2. Bids close not earlier than 2 p.m.

3. Alternate prices be held to a minimum and confined to items of significant monetary value.

4. The architect spell out the requirements clearly even if it means listing two or three acceptable items. If it should be that a particular product is desired and is the only one that will be accepted, that restriction should be stated.

Consistently good bidding is not accidental, nor is it the result of a particular mechanical process. It stems from a careful and complete study of every job, a consideration of the special problems that each bid presents, and a use of all experience and resources to reduce the gamble that any bid entails. Good estimating starts with an accurate and complete take-off, and ends with a bid that goes together smoothly on the last day, reflecting the care and efficiency of the estimator.

CHAPTER 11

The Completed Take-off

A complete take-off of the general contractor's work on a school is given on the following pages. It includes: excavation, site work, utilities, paving, formwork, substructure and superstructure concrete, concrete finishes, exterior masonry, partitions, glazed facing tile, rough carpentry, millwork, finish carpentry, and alteration work. It is not a working example, with drawings and step-by-step explanation, but a copy of the actual take-off compiled for a recent school bid, the cost of which was approximately $900,000. It has been included to show how the various trades considered in previous chapters are set out in the completed take-off.

There are several items worth particular notice. In the excavation section, the building excavation item shows the perimeter separately, so that it will be accessible for use in computing the backfill item. The concrete quantities are used in computing the hand excavation item. The ground area of the building (22,020 SF) is computed once, then used for several items. At the end of the excavation-and-site section, the excavation and fill items are balanced to obtain the quantity of surplus earth to be removed.

The concrete items are taken off methodically: pier footings, piers, wall footings, foundation walls, and so on, through the finishes and sundries. Computations not shown were made on collection sheets.

It can be seen that the masonry is taken off exactly as was shown in the working examples in Chap. 6. Note that everything applicable to exterior masonry is taken off before beginning the interior partitions. The calculations for the truck weight of the facing tile and for the mortar should also be noted.

The carpentry for window grounds and blocking is taken off area by area for all items at once, and the totals then transferred to the applicable blocking or grounds items. Cutting and waste allowances are added to such items as boarding and gypsum board.

The alterations take-off describes the various items, so that they can be recognized when the site is visited.

The take-off is followed by the estimate (in Chap. 12) for the same bid—
the entire estimate as it was actually prepared, including all pricing.

TAKE-OFF FOR WARREN SCHOOL

EXCAVATION & SITE

Remove conc. retg. wall

$$16\text{-}0 \quad \times \quad 1\text{-}0 \quad \times \quad 1\text{-}10 \quad = \quad \underline{30 \text{ CF}}$$

Patch top of retg. wall   = $\underline{30 \text{ LF}}$

Remove benches   = $\underline{\text{L. S.}}$

General site clearing   = $\underline{\text{L. S.}}$

Strip & stack loam

260 ft	×	40 ft	=	10,400 SF
435	×	150	=	65,250
210	×	55	=	11,550
115	×	35	=	4,025
Site			=	91,225 SF × 6 in. = 1,690 CY

Machine exc. bldg.

160 ft	× 62 ft	× 4–0	= 39,680 CF				*Perim.*		
30	× 26	× 3–0	= 2,340	492–0	× 3–9	× 4–0	=	7,380	CF
60	× 88	× 3–3	= 17,160	62–0	× 3–0	× 3–0	=	558	
88	× 88	× 1–8	= 12,906	222–0	× 3–6	× 3–3	=	2,525	
			72,086	280–0	× 3–0	× 1–8	=	1,900	
	+ Perim.		12,363				=	12,363	CF ✓
			84,449 CF						
		=	3,128 CY						

Machine exc. wall trenches

225–0	×	1–6	=	338 SF
105–0	×	3–0	=	315
630–0	×	3–9	=	2,362
120–0	×	4–0	=	480
				3,495 SF × 4–0
			=	13,980 CF
			=	520 CY

Hand exc. ftgs.

Piers	172 CY	$\times$	$1\frac{1}{4}$				=	215 CY
Wall ftg.	58 CY	$\times$	$\frac{1}{2}$				=	29
Entr.	2	$\times$	11–0	$\times$	4–6	$\times$ 3–0	=	11
Areas			14–0	$\times$	4–0	$\times$ 4–6	=	10
								265 CY

Backfill — walls & ftgs.

Perim.	12,363 CF			=	458 CY
Trench	520 CY	$\times$	$\frac{3}{4}$	=	390
Ftgs.	265 CY	–	201 CY	=	64
					912
		+	10%		92
					1,004 CY

Trim for ground slabs

Lockers		135–4	$\times$	87– 2	=	11,796 SF
Vestibule	2/	9–0	$\times$	6– 0	=	108
Pump rm.		15–4	$\times$	8–10	=	136
Classrooms		159–6	$\times$	60– 6	=	9,650
		22–6	$\times$	14– 8	=	330
						22,020 SF

6 in. gravel for ground slab (compact 95%)

22,020 SF	$\times$	6 in.	=	11,010 CF
			=	408 CY
		+ 20%		82
				490 CY

Pumping = L. S.

Grading — cut

120 ft	$\times$	35 ft	$\times$	2–6	=	10,550 CF
72	$\times$	62	$\times$	3–6	}	28,644
60	$\times$	62	$\times$	3–6		
90	$\times$	65	$\times$	1–0	=	5,850
30	$\times$	26	$\times$	2–0	=	1,560
160	$\times$	38	$\times$	1–9	=	10,640
130	$\times$	30	$\times$	3–0	=	11,700
135	$\times$	15	$\times$	2–3	=	4,556
						73,450 CF
					=	2,720 CY

Grading — fill

$$60 \text{ ft} \quad \times \quad 18 \text{ ft} \quad \times \quad 1\text{--}6 \quad = \quad 1,620 \text{ CF}$$
$$84 \quad \times \quad 27 \quad \times \quad 2\text{--}4 \quad = \quad 5,292$$
$$\underline{6,912 \text{ CF}}$$
$$= \quad \underline{\underline{256 \text{ CY}}}$$

Area to subgrade

$$\text{Site} \qquad = \quad 91,225 \text{ SF}$$
$$\text{Less Bldg.} \quad = \quad \underline{22,825}$$
$$\underline{68,400 \text{ SF}}$$

Graded gravel bed for pavings (rolled)

$$520 \text{ SF} \quad \times \quad 8 \text{ in.} \quad = \qquad 350 \text{ CF}$$
$$2,960 \qquad \times \quad 4 \qquad = \qquad 990$$
$$6,700 \qquad \times \quad 6 \qquad = \quad \underline{3,350}$$
$$\underline{4,690 \text{ CF}} \quad = \quad 173 \text{ CY}$$
$$+ \quad 20\% \quad \underline{35}$$
$$\underline{208 \text{ CY}}$$

Edge forms for walks

$$1,060 \text{ ft}$$
$$\underline{1,140}$$
$$\underline{2,200 \text{ LF}}$$

$2\frac{1}{2}$-*in. bitumen paving* $=$ $\underline{58 \text{ SY}}$

2-in. bitumen paving $=$ $\underline{328 \text{ SY}}$

Conc. walks (5 in.)

$$5,982 \text{ SF} \quad \times \quad 5 \text{ in.} \quad = \quad \underline{\underline{2,492 \text{ CF}}}$$
$$= \quad \underline{93 \text{ CY}}$$

Broom finish & score (5 ft c-c) $=$ $\underline{5,982 \text{ SF}}$

$\frac{1}{2}$-*in.* $\times$ *4-in. exp. jointing* $=$ $\underline{220 \text{ LF}}$

Conc. platforms

$$690 \text{ SF} \quad \times \quad 0\text{--}5 \quad = \quad 288 \text{ CF}$$
$$172\text{--}0 \quad \times \quad 0\text{--}8 \quad \times \quad 1\text{--}0 \qquad \underline{115}$$
$$\underline{\underline{403 \text{ CF}}}$$
$$= \quad \underline{15 \text{ CY}}$$

Edge forms

$$172\text{--}0 \quad \times \quad 1\text{--}7 \quad = \quad \underline{272 \text{ SF}}$$

Float platforms   =   <u>690 SF</u>

½-in. graded gravel paving

$$2,000 \text{ SF} \times 8 \text{ in.} = \underline{\underline{1,334}} \text{ CF}$$
$$= \underline{50} \text{ CY}$$

Face-brick edging

$$316\text{--}0 \times 4\text{--}8 = 1,516 \text{ pcs.}$$
$$+ \text{ Waste } \underline{34}$$
$$\underline{1,550} \text{ pcs.}$$

Brick paving

$$66 \text{ SF} \times 7 = 462 \text{ pcs.}$$
$$+ \text{ Waste } \underline{38}$$
$$\underline{500} \text{ pcs.}$$

Exc. for curbs & walls

$$25\text{--}0 \times 4\text{--}0 \times 3\text{--}6 = 350 \text{ CF}$$
$$160\text{--}0 \times 1\text{--}6 \times 2\text{--}0 = \underline{480}$$
$$\underline{\underline{830}} \text{ CF}$$
$$= \underline{31 \text{ CY}}$$

Conc. foundation wall					*FORMS*
$22\text{--}0 \times 1\text{--}0 \times 0\text{--}6$	=	11 CF			22 SF
$22\text{--}0 \times 0\text{--}8 \times 3\text{--}0$	=	$\underline{44}$			$\underline{132}$
		$\underline{\underline{55}}$ CF			$\underline{154}$ SF
	=	$\underline{2}$ CY			

Face brick to wall

$$8 \text{ in.} \quad 22\text{--}0 \times 2\text{--}8 = 59 \text{ SF} \times 13.5 = \underline{800 \text{ pcs.}}$$

10½-in.   ×   *1½-in slate cap*   =   <u>23 LF</u>

Bench 12 ft long (See Drg. 2)   =   <u>L. S.</u>

Move boulder & set near front entr.   =   <u>$75</u>

Granite curb VB1   +   *exc.*   +   *gravel bed*   =   <u>154 LF</u>

Surplus earth to remove from site

$$\text{Exc.} = 6,633 \text{ CY}$$
$$\text{Fill} = \underline{1,260}$$
$$5,373$$
$$+ \text{ Bulkup } 15\% \quad \underline{807}$$
$$\underline{6,180} \text{ CY}$$

UTILITIES
Exc. and backfill trenches

Storm & san.	860–0	×	4–6	×	5–6	=	21,285 CF
Water	130–0	×	4–0	×	4–0	}	
Gas	55–0	×	4–0	×	4–0	}	2,960
Plmg., htg., & elec.	55–0	×	8–0	×	5–0	=	2,200
Elec.	170–0	×	4–0	×	3–0	=	2,040
M. H. & C. B.	13	×	150 CF			=	1,950
						=	30,435 CF
						=	1,130 CY

Exc. & backfill plmg. under slab

$$1,340 \quad × \quad 4–0 \quad × \quad 3–3 \quad = \quad 17,420 \text{ CF}$$
$$= \quad 645 \text{ CY}$$

8-in. transite pipe storm drain   =   80 LF

10-in. transite pipe storm drain   =   56 LF

12-in. transite pipe storm drain   =   630 LF

18-in. transite pipe storm drain   =   70 LF

Drain inlets 8–0   ×   *3–0*   ×   *3–8 deep*   =   3 ea.

Catch Basins 4–0 dia.   ×   *8–6 deep*   =   7 ea.

Manholes 4–0 dia.   ×   *6–9 deep*   =   3 ea.

24-in. C. I. cover & frames — Sub

Conc. base for utilities trench

55–0   ×   2–6   ×   0–4   =   2 CY | *4-in. edge forms*   =   110 LF

Gravel bed for drains   =   4 CY

CONCRETE (3,000 psi)   *FORMS*
Pier ftgs.

12/	6–6	×	6–6	×	1–8	=	845 CF		520 SF
22/	5–0	×	5–0	×	1–6	=	825		660
6/	3–0	×	3–0	×	1–0	=	54		72
4/	5–6	×	5–6	×	1–8	=	201		148
16/	6–8	×	6–8	×	1–6	=	1,067		640
2/	7–6	×	8–0	×	1–6	=	180		94
2/	6–6	×	7–6	×	1–6	=	146		84
8/	6–6	×	6–6	×	1–6	=	507		312
21/	5–9	×	5–9	×	1–2	=	810		564
							4,635 CF		3,094 SF
						=	172 CY		

Foundation piers

3/	1–2	×	1–2	×	0–8	=	3 CF		10 SF
11/	1–0	×	1–4	×	0–8	=	10		34
23/	1–0	×	1–0	×	1–6	=	35		138
							48 CF		182 SF
						=	2 CY		

Wall ftgs.

316–0	×	1–5	×	1–0	=	448 CF	
612–0	×	1–8	×	1–0	=	1,020	1,888 SF
16–0	×	1–4	×	1–0	=	21	
87–0	×	1–2	×	0–8	=	68	116
						1,557 CF	2,004 SF
					=	58 CY	

Foundation walls

12-in.

31 ft	×	11– 6	=	357			
181	×	10– 7	=	1,916			
11	×	5– 0	=	55			
61	×	4– 4	=	264	3,900	= 3,900 CF	7,800 SF
333	×	3– 5	=	1,138			
15	×	2– 1	=	31			
79	×	1– 9	=	139			

9-in.

40	×	5–10	=	234			
279	×	4– 4	=	1,209	1,806	= 1,355	3,612
99	×	3– 8	=	363			

Pilasters

20/	1–0	×	0–6	×	4–4	=	44	88
29/	1–0	×	0–6	×	3–6	=	51	102
						5,350 CF	11,602 SF
					=	198 CY	

Pilasters 1–0
× 0–6 × 4–0
(av.) = 49 ea.

Int. foundation walls

8-in.
   12–0 × 4–4 = 52   = 35 CF

6-in.
    8–0 × 4–4 = 208 ⎫
   14–8 × 2–6 = 37   ⎬ 398 = 199
   28–8 × 5–4 = 153 ⎭

                       234 CF
                     =   9 CY

	900 SF
2 × 4 *ftg. key* =	1,030 LF

Pipe trenches

      12–8 × 5–0 × 0–4 = 21 CF
      25–4 × 0–6 × 2–9 = 35
4/   6–6 × 1–4 × 0–4 = 12
      34–0 × 0–4 × 1–1 = 12
                     80 CF
                 = 3 CY

   ⎫ 2/ 26–0 × 3–0 = 156 SF
   ⎬
   ⎭ 2/ 34–0 × 1–6 = 102
                     258 SF

Encasing for oil tank

    4–4 × 5–8 × 0–6 = 12 CF
  18–0 × 2–7 × 0–6 = 23
                 35 CF
            = 1½ CY

           55 SF
           95
         150 SF

Visqueen vapor barrier for ground slab

              22,020 SF
   + 10% 2,200
              24,220 SF

½-in. × 4-in. exp. jointing

  2 × 224 ft = 448 ft
  2 × 15   = 30
  2 × 220 = 440
  2 × 11   = 22
            940 LF

6-in. × 6-in. × 10/10 mesh = 24,200 SF

4-in. conc. ground slabs

        22,020 SF × 0–4 = 7,340 CF
+ Ptns.
    300–0 × 1–0 × 0–8 =   200
                 7,540 CF
             = 280 CY

Slab edges and stops = 450 LF

Slab screeds = 2,300 LF

Conc. gym. entrance & balcony   *Forms*   *Float*   *Rubbing*

Walls	$6\text{--}0 \times 0\text{--}8 \times 3\text{--}4 = 14$ CF	44 SF	—	—
	$9\text{--}0 \times 1\text{--}0 \times 7\text{--}6 = 68$	160	—	—
Stair	$12\text{--}0 \times 1\text{--}0 \times 11\text{--}0 = 132$	230	120 SF	230 SF
Landing	$12\text{--}6 \times 6\text{--}0 \times 0\text{--}6\frac{1}{2} = 41$	80	80	10
Balcony	$31\text{--}0 \times 6\text{--}1 \times 0\text{--}6\frac{1}{2} = 102$	210	190	210
Balcony				
wall	$18\text{--}6 \times 0\text{--}4 \times 2\text{--}8 = 17$	126	—	120
	$= \overline{374}$ CF	$\overline{850}$ SF	$\overline{390}$ SF	$\overline{570}$ SF
	$= \underline{14}$ CY			

Conc.—cols.

Int.

$29/ \; 1\text{--}0 \times 1\text{--}0 \times 8\text{--}10 =$	256 CF	1,024 SF
$104/ \; 1\text{--}0 \times 1\text{--}0 \times 9\text{--}9 =$	1,014	4,056
$11/ \; 1\text{--}0 \times 1\text{--}4 \times 9\text{--}9 =$	143	500
$3/ \; 1\text{--}2 \times 1\text{--}2 \times 9\text{--}9 =$	40	136
$12/ \; 0\text{--}8 \times 1\text{--}0 \times 9\text{--}0 =$	72	360
	$\overline{1,525}$ CF	$\overline{6,076}$ SF
	$= \underline{57}$ CY	

Conc. beams   *Bottoms*   *Sides*

$205\text{--}4 \times 3\text{--}0 \times 1\text{--}0 = 616$ CF	616 SF	411 SF
$176\text{--}0 \times 0\text{--}8 \times 1\text{--}4 = 156$	117	469
$57\text{--}0 \times 1\text{--}0 \times 0\text{--}4 = 19$	57	38
$\overline{791}$ CF	$\overline{790}$ SF	$\overline{918}$ SF
$= \underline{29}$ CY		

Conc. suspended slabs

$3,230$ SF $\times 0\text{--}5\frac{1}{4} = 1,414$ CF	Slab forms	47,796 SF
$180 \times 0\text{--}6 \quad\quad 90$	Less Bms.	790
$44,386 \times 1\text{--}3\frac{3}{8} = 56,870$		$\overline{47,006}$ SF
$\overline{47,796}$ SF $\quad\quad \overline{58,374}$		

Less Pans

$12,040\text{--}0 \times 2\text{--}0 \times 1\text{--}0\frac{3}{8} = 24,832$

$\overline{33,542}$

$+$ Conc. only

$166\text{--}4 \times 1\text{--}0 \times 0\text{--}6 = 83$

$\overline{33,625}$ CF

$= \underline{1,245}$ CY

24-in. $\times$ *12-in. long pans*

$= \underline{12,040}$ LF

Slab stops 16 in. $= \underline{1,200}$ LF

Slab screeds $= \underline{5,100}$ LF

Conc. canopies

2/	18–0	×	3–0	=	108 SF		2,502 SF
42/	19–0	×	3–0	=	2,394		548
					2,502 SF × 5 in.		3,050 SF
			=		39 CY		

Conc. stairs

							Forms	Float	Rub
212 A & B									
4/	8–6 × 1–0 × 3–6			=	119 SF		240 SF	120 SF	240 SF
2/	7–4 × 4–0 × 0–5			=	25		70	60	70
214 A									
	11–0 × 9–6 × 1–0			=	105		170	70	170
215 A									
2/	6–0 × 5–0 × 1–0			=	60		120	36	120
217 A	5–0 × 7–0 × 1–0			=	35		80	30	80
218 A	9–6 × 4–0 × 1–0			=	38		70	40	70
203 etc.									
2/	4–6 × 3–6 × 1–0			=	32		70	30	70
6/	6–6 × 4–6 × 1–0			=	176		420	150	420
4/	10–0 × 3–9 × 0–7½			=	94		160	160	160
					684 SF		1,400 SF	696 SF	1,400 SF
			=		25½ CY				

Conc. — locker bases

315–0	×	1–0	×	0–4	=	105 CF	}	4-in. edge forms	= 760 LF
222–0	×	2–0	×	0–4	=	148			
						253 CF			
			=			9½ CY			

Cure slabs = 69,816 SF

Float roof slabs = 11,910 SF

Dust on finish and trowel floors = 57,906 SF

$\frac{3}{8}$-in. *Mastic underlayment for floors* = 26,300 SF

3 coats floor hardener (magn.- fluosilicate) = 16,300 SF

Grano. fill to pan stairs

12/	4–0	×	1–1	=	52 SF

Nonslip abrasive to stairs   =   <u>300 lb</u>

Grout slurry & rub ext. walls

$$
\begin{array}{rclr}
240\text{--}0 & \times & 1\text{--}6 & = & 360 \text{ SF} \\
880\text{--}0 & \times & 1\text{--}3 & = & \underline{1,100} \\
& & & & \underline{1,460 \text{ SF}}
\end{array}
$$

Grout slurry & rub clgs. & beams   =   <u>45,500 SF</u>

Extra cost for air-entraining admix for conc.   =   <u>1,430 CY</u>

Dovetail anchor slots

$$50 \quad \times \quad 10\text{--}0 \quad = \quad \underline{500 \text{ LF}}$$

$\frac{3}{4}$*-in. wedge inserts*   =   <u>100 pcs.</u>

Set sundry items for misc. iron sub   =   <u>L. S.</u>

MASONRY

Ext. face brick at $70 per M

	OUTS

Classrm. wing
76–0 × 28–10¼ = 2,194 SF

Classrm. wing
59–0 × 28– 1 = 1,657

Classrm. wing
399–0 × 2– 2¼ = 873

Gym
460–0 × 25– 2 = 11,576
                   16,300
                 − 3,227
                   13,073 SF
              × 6.7
                   87,590 pcs.

Headers — gym. end walls
$\frac{1}{6}$ × 12,380 = 2,064
                   89,654
  + Waste 4% 3,586
                   93,240 pcs.
         = 93.25 M

Sash
2/ 19–0 × 1–11 = 75 SF

Sash
10–0 × 9– 2 = 92

Lobby
22–6 × 18–10 = 424

Gym lobby
22–6 × 11– 9 = 264

Gym entr.
16–5 × 10– 6 = 172

Gym entr.
30–0 × 25– 2 = 755

Gym sash
241–4 × 4– 1 = 986

Gym sash
40–0 × 5– 5 = 217

Gym sash
10–0 × 24– 2 = 242

} 2,636 SF

                   3,227 SF

Face brick — lobby

11–6	×	17–6	=	201 SF
22–6	×	3–6	=	79
				280
Less Drs. 5–4	×	7–0	=	37
				243 SF
			×	6.7
				1,628 pcs
		+ Waste		72
				1,700 pcs
				1.7 M

12-in. cinder-block ext. walls

354–5	×	8– 8	=	3,072 SF
10–0	×	7– 0	=	70
10–0	×	7–11	=	79
				3,221
Less Sash 90–8	×	2– 1	=	189
				3,032 SF
		+ $\frac{1}{8}$		380
				3,412 pcs.
		+ 4%		138
				3,550 pcs. (8 × 16)

12-in. cinder block to patterns

2	×	13–0	×	21–0	=	546 SF
					=	640 pcs. (8 × 16)

8-in. cinder-block back-up

Gym.			=	11,576 SF
Less Outs			=	2,636
				8,940
+ 34–2	×	8–8	=	296
24–0	×	1–4	=	32
				9,268
Less 4 in. at beams			=	668
				8,600 SF
		+ $\frac{1}{8}$		1,075
				9,675 pcs.
		+ 3%		295
				9,970 pcs. (8 × 16)

6-in. cinder-block back-up

$$
\begin{array}{lrrl}
\text{Classrooms} & = & 4,724 & \text{SF} \\
\text{Less Outs} & = & 591 & \\
\hline
 & & 4,133 & \\
\text{Less } 74\text{--}8 \ \times \ 1\text{--}3 & = & 93 & \\
\hline
 & & 4,040 & \text{SF} \\
+ \ \tfrac{1}{8} & & 505 & \\
\hline
 & & 4,545 & \text{pcs.} \\
+ \ 3\% & & 135 & \\
\hline
 & & 4,680 & \text{pcs. } (8 \ \times \ 16) \\
\end{array}
$$

4-in. cinder-block back-up

$$
\begin{array}{lrcll}
\text{Gym} \quad 2 \ \times \ 668 \text{ SF} & = & 1,336 & \text{SF} \\
15\text{--}8 \ \times \ 8\text{--}8 & = & 136 & \\
10\text{--}6 \ \times \ 8\text{--}3 & = & 87 & \\
18\text{--}2 \ \times \ 9\text{--}0 & = & 163 & \\
\hline
 & & 1,722 & \text{SF} \\
+ \ \tfrac{1}{8} & & 215 & \\
\hline
 & & 1,937 & \text{pcs.} \\
+ \ 3\% & & 63 & \\
\hline
 & & 2,000 & \text{pcs. } (8 \ \times \ 16) \\
\end{array}
$$

Wash down face brick = 13,316 SF

Back parge face brick = 13,316 SF

Cavity wall ties = 4 M

Washed gravel for bottom of cavities = 3 CY

Exterior scaffolding = 17,800 SF

5-in. × 12-in. ceramic facing tile

$$
\begin{array}{llrll}
\text{2-in. soaps} & 344\text{--}0 \ \times \ 20\text{c.} & = & 6,880 & \text{pcs.} \\
 & 106\text{--}0 \ \times \ 1\text{c.} & = & 106 & \\
 & 409\text{--}0 \ \times \ 12\text{c.} & = & 4,908 & \\
 & 8\text{--}0 \ \times \ 19\text{c.} & = & 152 & \\
 & 180\text{--}0 \ \times \ 11\text{c.} & = & 1,980 & \\
\hline
 & & & 14,026 & \\
 & \text{Less Drs.} \quad 8 \ \times \ 40 \text{ pcs.} & = & 320 & \\
\hline
 & & & 13,706 & \\
 & + \ 3\% & & 414 & \\
\hline
 & & & 14,120 & \text{pcs.} \\
\end{array}
$$

4-in. G1F

$$140–0 \quad \times \quad 20c. \quad = \quad 2{,}800 \text{ pcs.}$$
$$106–0 \quad \times \quad 1c. \quad = \quad \underline{106}$$
$$2{,}906$$
$$+ \quad 3\% \quad \underline{94}$$
$$\underline{3{,}000 \text{ pcs.}}$$

Extra for Group 1   = $\underline{630 \text{ pcs.}}$

Extra for Group 2   = $\underline{460 \text{ pcs.}}$

Extra for Group 4   = $\underline{35 \text{ pcs.}}$

Extra for Group 6   = $\underline{55 \text{ pcs.}}$

Truck facing tile

$$14{,}120 \quad \times \quad 6.5 \text{ lb} \quad = \quad 91{,}780 \text{ lb}$$
$$3{,}000 \quad \times \quad 12.0 \text{ lb} \quad = \quad \underline{36{,}000}$$
$$\underline{\underline{127{,}780 \text{ lb}}}$$
$$= \quad \underline{63.9 \text{ tons}}$$

Wash down facing tile   = $\underline{7{,}360 \text{ SF}}$

6-in. waylite-block ptns.

$$616–0 \quad \times \quad 9–2 \qquad \qquad = \quad 5{,}646 \text{ SF}$$
$$\text{Less Drs.} \quad 14 \quad \times \quad 20 \text{ SF} \quad = \quad \underline{280}$$
$$5{,}366 \text{ SF}$$
$$+ \quad \tfrac{1}{8} \quad \underline{670}$$
$$6{,}036 \text{ pcs.}$$
$$+ \quad 3\% \quad \underline{184}$$
$$\underline{6{,}220 \text{ pcs.} \ (8 \ \times \ 16)}$$

12-in. cinder-block ptns.

$$170–0 \quad \times \quad 11–6 \qquad \qquad = \quad 1{,}955 \text{ SF}$$
$$30–0 \quad \times \quad 10–6 \qquad \qquad = \quad \underline{315}$$
$$2{,}270$$
$$- \text{ Drs.} \quad 9 \quad \times \quad 20 \text{ SF}$$
$$- \text{ Opg.} \quad 4 \quad \times \quad 18–0 \quad \times \quad 10–0 \ \Big\} \qquad \underline{900}$$
$$1{,}370 \text{ SF}$$
$$+ \quad \tfrac{1}{8} \quad \underline{172}$$
$$1{,}542 \text{ pcs.}$$
$$+ \quad 4\% \quad \underline{58}$$
$$\underline{1{,}600 \text{ pcs.} \ (8 \ \times \ 16)}$$

8-in. cinder-block ptns.

36–0	×	13–0	=	468 SF
70–0	×	11–6	=	805
40–0	×	10–6	=	420
129–0	×	9–2	=	1,182
28–0	×	8–8	=	243
154–0	×	4–4	=	668

3,786

Less Drs. 13 × 20 SF = 260

3,526 SF

+ ⅛ 440

3,966 pcs.

+ 4% 154

4,120 pcs. (8 × 16)

4-in. cinder-block ptns.

190–0	×	8–8	=	1,646 SF
35–0	×	10–6	=	368
143–0	×	9–2	=	1,311
48–0	×	5–0	=	240

3,565

Less Drs. 7 × 20 SF = 140

3,425 SF

+ ⅛ 428

3,853 pcs.

+ 4% 147

4,000 pcs. (8 × 16)

6-in. cinder-block ptns.   *OUTS*

306–0	×	8–8	=	2,652 SF		Drs. 18	×	20 SF	=	360 SF
270–0	×	10–6	=	2,835		Drs. 4	×	35	=	140
264–0	×	9–2	=	2,420		12–0	×	5– 3	=	63
212–0	×	5–4	=	1,131		48–0	×	4–10	=	232

9,038   795 SF

– 795

8,243 SF

+ ⅛ 1,031

9,274 pcs.

+ 4% 376

9,650 pcs. (8 × 16)

Clean & point cinder block

405–0	×	10–6	=	4,452 SF
286–0	×	9–2	=	2,622
292–0	×	8–6	=	2,482

9,556 SF

Glazed tile soap & grab dishes   =   <u>20 pcs.</u>

2-in. hardware cloth reinforcing to ptns.

$$\frac{7,360 \text{ SF at 1 ft per SF}}{}$$

=   <u>7,400 LF</u>

Rubber gasket and caulk ptns. at clgs.   =   <u>2,530 LF</u>

Set lintels   =   <u>47 pcs.</u>

Mortar (1:1:4)

Brick		95 M	×	18 CF	=	1,710 CF
Block	12-in.	58 C	×	10	=	580
Block	8-in.	141	×	8	=	1,128
Block	6-in.	206	×	6	=	1,236
Block	4-in.	60	×	5	=	300
F.T.	2-in.	141	×	4	=	564
	4-in.	30	×	6	=	180

5,698 CF

=   <u>211 CY</u>

Strap anchors $1\frac{1}{2}$ *in.*   × $\frac{1}{4}$ *in.*   ×   *12 in. long*   =   <u>90 pcs.</u>

CARPENTRY

Roof nailers & curbs

2 × 4   100 ft + 520 ft + 60 ft + 460 ft + 360 ft = 1,500 ft = 1,000 BF
2 × 6   50   + 180   =   230   =   230
4 × 4   300   =   400
1 × 4   360   =   120

<u>1,750 BF</u>

Window blocking							*2 × 4*	*2 × 6*	*1 × 2*	*1 × 6*
Link	2/	50–0	×	19– 8	=	1,966 SF	200 ft	80 ft	—	—
Lobby	2/	28–6	×	17– 6	=	998	120	72	—	—
Classrm.	2/	19–0	×	10– 6	=	399	60	68	40 ft	—
	33/	19–0	×	7– 0	=	4,389	660	660	660	462 ft
	6/	19–0	×	9– 2	} 1,220		120	120	120	120
	2/	9–6	×	9– 2			40	—	20	40
	2/	19–0	×	1–11	=	73	40	40	40	24
		10–0	×	9– 2	=	92	—	—	—	—
Gym.	2/	100–8	×	3– 0	=	604	—	400	120	—
	16/	9–0	×	2– 6	=	360	—	320	320	240
	4/	1–0	×	25– 0	=	100	—	10	200	100
	2/	13–0	×	3– 0	=	78	72	—	—	12
	2/	90–8	×	2– 1	=	378	—	200	—	—
						10,657 SF	1,312 ft	1,970 ft	1,520 ft	998 ft
						✓	✓	✓	✓	✓

Blocking

2	×	4	1,312 ft	=	875 BF
2	×	6	1,970	=	1,970
					2,845 BF
				=	2,850 BF

1 × *6 grounds* = 1,000 LF

1 × *2 grounds or furring*

Windows			1,520 ft	=	1,520 ft
Wall furring	147	×	10	=	1,470
Wall furring	92	×	12	=	1,104
Chalk & tack	12	×	64	=	768
Chalk & tack	13	×	84	=	1,092
Tack	19	×	24	=	456
					6,410 LF

1 × *3 grounds*

Chalk	25	×	12 ft	=	300 ft
Chalk	6	×	6	=	36
Chalk	2	×	8	=	16
					352 LF
				=	360 LF

2 × *8 rough bucks for door frames*

12	×	28 ft	=	336 ft	
20	×	24	=	480	
				816 ft	=	1,090 BF

2 × *4 frmg. pipe spaces*

17	×	4	×	10 ft	=	680 ft	
17	×	4	×	3	=	204	
		60	×	10	=	600	
12	×	4	×	10	=	480	
12	×	4	×	8	=	384	
		2	×	16	=	32	
				2,380 ft	=	1,600 BF	

Frmg. gym. ptn.

2 × 4	120–0 + 40–0 + 85–0 + 75–0 + 180–0	=	500 ft	=	334 BF
2 × 3	30/15–0 + 5/10–0 + 20/10–0	=	700	=	350
2 × 2	150–0 + 50–0	=	200	=	66
					750 BF

1 × 3 ceiling furring

Rms. 31 32	2	×	17	×	12 ft	=	408 ft
Rms. 41 42	2	×	4	×	4	=	32
Rms. 62 63	2	×	6	×	10	=	120
							560 LF

Plaster grounds

Ext. walls at clg.   =   500 LF

⅝-in. gyp. bd. to clgs.

60 ft	×	31 ft	=	1,860 SF
60	×	29	=	1,740
147	×	11	⎫	
15	×	11	⎭	1,782
				5,382
		+ 10%		538
				5,920 SF

⅝-in. gyp. bd. to wood ptns.

20–0 + 40–0 + 24–0 + 20–0 + 6–0 = 110–0 × 3–0 = 330 SF
+ 10%   40
                                                                370 SF

1-in. insulation bd. behind convectors

96–0	×	1–8	=	160 SF
10–0	×	2–0	⎫	
17–0	×	2–0	⎭	54
				214
		+ 10%		21
				235 SF

1-in. fiberglass insulation

Music rm.	56–0	×	10–0	=	560 SF
	Less 5	×	20 SF	=	100
					460
	+ 20–0	×	9–2	=	184
					644
			+ 10%		66
					710 SF

Vinyl-faced hardboard to walls

	56–0	×	9–2	=	512 SF
3/	11–0	×	7–0	=	231
					743
			+ 10%		77
					820 SF

Blocking for casework

	2 × 4				2 × 6			4 × 4
Art. rm.	4 × 22 ft	=	88 ft					
Rm. 59				2 ×	20 ft	=	40 ft	
Library	6 × 30	=	180					60 ft
Library	12 × 10	=	120					
Rm. 10			80				60	20
Shops	2 × 60	=	120	2 ×	25	=	50	
Darkrm.			80					
Rm. 53	4 × 30	=	120	2 ×	30	=	60	60
Displays	4 × 70	=	280					100
Rms. 2 & 14	2 × 90	=	180	2 ×	20	=	40	
Music rms.	3 × 130	=	390				20	
			1,638 ft				270 ft	240 ft
		=	1,092 BF				✓	✓
			270					
			320					
			1,682 BF					
		=	1,700 BF					

$\frac{1}{4}$-*in. plywood to walls*

100–0	×	3–6	=	350 SF
100–0	×	2–6	=	250
56–0	×	9–2	=	512
				1,112
Less 5	×	20 SF	=	100
				1,012
		+ 10%		102
				1,114 SF

1 × 3 floor sleepers (creosoted)

Link	52	×	22–0	=	1,144 LF

1-in. styrofoam to floor (mopped on)

50–0 × 22–0			=	1,100 SF
Less 52 × 22–0 × 0–2$\frac{1}{2}$			=	238
				862
		+ 5%		48
				910 SF

$\frac{3}{4}$-*in. plyscore to floor*

		1,100 SF
+ 10%		110
		1,210 SF

Temporary doors   =   6 ea.

Rough hardware   =   L. S.

Set only

  H. M. door frame   =   6 ea.

  Wood door fr. & transom   =   32 ea.

  Wood door fr. (single)   =   56 ea.

  Wood door & hardware   =   141 ea.

  Wood window units (& trim)   =   10,657 SF

SET MILLWORK

Wood glazed ptns.

5	×	5–3	×	10–6	=	276 SF
		93–0	×	10–6	=	976
		39–0	×	9–0	=	351
		9–0	×	8–0	=	72
						1,675 SF

$\frac{3}{4}$*-in. plywood panels*

	90–0	×	1–9	=	158 SF
2/	25–0	×	11–0	=	550
	25–0	×	3–9	=	94
	45–0	×	3–6	=	158
					960 SF

1 × *8 window stool* + *apron*   =   1,710 LF

1 × *6 window trim*   =   180 LF

Art-room casework   =   L. S.

Library casework   =   L. S.

Rm. 10 cabinets   =   L. S.

Shop 13 casework   =   L. S.

Shop 18 casework   =   L. S.

Storage shelving

	6	×	14–0	×	2–0	=	168 SF
	4	×	21–0	×	1–6	=	126
	18	×	22–0	×	1–0	=	396
4/	6	×	30–0	×	1–0	=	720
							1,410 SF

Classroom trim & cabinets   =   <u>22 rms.</u> (@ $125)

Storage cabinet Rm. 2 =   <u>L. S.</u>

ALTERATIONS

Link

   Remove brick entrance and platform   =   <u>L. S.</u>

   Remove window   =   <u>L. S.</u>

   Remove 1 pr. doors & frame   =   <u>L. S.</u>

   Cut opg. 6–0 × 9–0 at stair window, set lintel & patch   =   <u>2 opgs.</u>

   Face-brick patching

$$82 \text{ SF}   =   \underline{600 \text{ pcs.}}$$

   8-in. cinder-block patching   =   <u>100 pcs.</u> (8 × 16)

Boiler rm.

   Fill in old ash pits   =   <u>2 ea.</u>

   Remove conc. floor

$$25\text{–}0 \times 24\text{–}0   =   \underline{600 \text{ SF}}$$

   New conc. floor for boilers

$$600 \text{ SF} \times 1\text{–}0   =   \underline{22 \text{ CY}}$$

   12-in. edge forms   =   <u>100 LF</u>

   Excavate for tank

$$34\text{–}0 \times 10\text{–}0 \times 2\text{–}2   =   \underline{28 \text{ CY}}$$

   Conc. mat for oil tank

$$30\text{–}0 \times 9\text{–}0 \times 0\text{–}6   =   \underline{5 \text{ CY}}$$

   6-in. edge forms   =   <u>80 LF</u>

   Break out roof of bunker to admit new tank   =   <u>L. S.</u>

   Patch conc. roof:

   Forms 30 ft × 10 ft   =   <u>300 SF</u>

   12-in. conc. slab   =   <u>12 CY</u>

Cut window for and fit new louver (5–0 × 3–0) = 1 ea.

Cut window for and fit new louver (3–0 × 2–0) = 2 ea.

Common-brick patching

> 7–0 × 9–0 × 1–0 = 63 SF × 20 = 1,260 pcs.

Cut & patch in boiler rm. for mech. subs = L. S.

Stores:

Remove ceiling plaster & lath

> 40–0 × 17–0 = 680 SF

Refrig.:

Remove 3–6 window = 2 ea.

Remove temporary ptns. = L. S.

Boys rm.:

Remove all lockers (& store) = L. S.

Girls rm.:

Remove all lockers (& store) = L. S.

Remove all ductwork & fans = L. S.

Remove 6-in. ptns.

> 208–0 × 11–3 = 2,340 SF

Remove side entrance & steps = L.S.

Patch concrete floors (approx.) = 600 SF

Remove rubbish = L. S.

Make good work disturbed = L. S.

CHAPTER 12

The Estimate

The estimate shown on the following pages was prepared from the take-off in the previous chapter, with the addition of the overhead sheet, the sub-bid sheet, and the summary sheet. It constitutes the complete general contractor's estimate for our sample job, the Levi Warren School. The estimate has been completely priced, the sub-bid sheet completed, and the summary completed—right down to the total bid price. While the pricing is realistic and presents a good competitive bid for that particular job, it is not recommended as a basis for future bids by anyone. The sole purpose of including the pricing of the estimate is to round out the treatise by showing how a bid goes together. The unit prices shown were good for that job (and the conditions peculiar to that job) for the specific contractor concerned, at the time that it was bid. They would not apply to another bid; they would not even apply to the same bid at another time.

It may be found that in writing up the estimate from the take-off, some minor adjustments have been made. For example, reference to the sample take-off would show two items for face brick—one for 93.25 M and the other for 1.7 M. In writing up the estimate, those items were combined, and the total of 94.95 M rounded off to 95 M. Such minor rounding off of items is sensible and logical. You would not order 94,950 pieces of brick; the order would be for 95 M. At the same time, this very slight rounding off simplifies the calculations.

It should be noted that the cash extensions are rounded off to the nearest $5, fractional parts of $5 being either dropped or raised to the next $5. There are many estimators who figure their pricing to the nearest dollar, and one cannot really quarrel with them. For reasonably large bids, however, most of whose items are of a fair size, it should be quite satisfactory to round the items off to the nearest $5. By the time some items have been adjusted downward and others upward, the net difference between a bid figured to the nearest $5 and the same bid figured to the nearest $1 is very slight. This question, however, is one that the individual must decide for himself.

Certainly rounding off to the nearest $5 is the quicker method, but that may not be felt to be a sufficient argument in its favor.

The priced estimate is followed by some notes on it, which explain why certain items were handled in a particular manner and also give some general suggestions for putting a bid together. In addition to the information on pricing given in this chapter, Chap. 13 is devoted entirely to pricing the estimate, and provides a number of specific examples of how unit prices are built up.

THE ESTIMATE

ESTIMATE FOR WARREN SCHOOL

Bids due — June 9, 1959 (2:30 p.m.)
Architect — Architects Collaborative
Certified check — $45,000

	Summary	*Labor*	*Material*
Sheet			
1	Overhead	$ 20,835	$ 36,365
2	Excavation & Site	6,320	17,310
3	Excavation — Utilities	3,505	5,350
4	Concrete (Formwork)	37,340	10,425
5	Concrete	25,105	37,420
6	Masonry	36,260	29,495
7	Carpentry	16,560	3,570
8	Alterations	3,215	1,680
		$149,140	$141,625
			149,140
	Total general contractor's work		$290,765
9	Sub-bids		579,640
		Cost	$870,405
	+ Fee		43,520
		Bid	$913,925

Last-minute adjustment	*Deduct*	*Add*
Millwork	$1,800	–
Bond	–	–
Set structural	500	–
Ready-mix conc. 2,140 CY × $.50	1,070	–
Folding ptns.	750	–
Structural steel & bar joists	1,200	–
	$5,320	–
	Adjusted Bid	$908,600

Overhead   *(Sheet No. 1)*   *Labor*   *Material*

	Labor	Material
Bond (on $900,000)	—	$ 6,200
Fire insurance (on contractor's eqpt. only)	—	200
Insurances — W. Comp., P. L., P. D. ⎫ 13% × $149,140	—	19,390
Payroll taxes — F. I. C. A., fed. & state empl. ⎭		
Health & Welfare Fund 3% × $149,140	—	4,475
Pension fund (masons) 750 man-days = 6,000 hr × $.15	—	900
Superintendent 52 wk. × $180	$9,360	—
Engineering 6 wk. × $155	930	—
Labor foreman	—	—
Mason foreman 30 wk. × $180	5,400	—
Carpenter foreman (part) 35 wk. × $35	1,225	
Offices & shanties	350	200
Toilets	150	70
Telephones (2) 2 × 13 mo. × $40	—	1,040
Temporary water	—	—
Temporary light & power	100	750
Temporary heat	250	600
Trucking	—	200
Small tools	—	350
Crane (see sheet No. 5 for concrete crane item)	—	—
Hoist lab. 18 × $140 — mat. 4 mo. × $280	2,520	1,120
Clean glass	—	350
Glass breakages	—	100
Clean-up	450	50
Premium time	—	—
Progress photos	—	120
Winter protection	100	250
	$20,835	$36,365

Excavation & Site (*Sheet No. 2*)   *Labor*   *Material*

		L.	M.	Labor	Material
Remove conc. retg. wall	30 CF	$ 1.00	$ .80	$ 30	$ 25
Patch top of retg. wall	30 LF	1.20	L. S.	35	5
Remove benches	L. S.	15.	—	15	—
General site clearing	L. S.	350.	225.	350	225
Strip & stack loam	1,690 CY	—	.80	—	1,350
Machine excavate bldg.	3,128 CY	—	.95	—	2,970
Machine trench exc. bldg.	520 CY	—	1.30	—	675
Hand exc. bldg. ftgs.	265 CY	6.25	—	1,655	—
Backfill walls & ftgs.	1,004 CY	.20	.15	200	150
Trim for ground slab	22,020 SF	.015	—	330	—
6-in. gravel for ground slabs (compact 95%)	490 CY	1.20	1.70	590	835
Pumping	L. S.	400.	300.	400	300
Grading — cut	2,720 CY	—	.90	—	2,450
Grading — fill	256 CY	—	.30	—	75
Grading — area to subgrade	68,400 SF	—	.01	—	685
Graded gravel for pavings (rolled)	208 CY	.50	2.30	105	480
Edge forms for walks	2,200 LF	.15	.06	330	130
2½-in. bitumen paving	58 SY	—	1.80	—	105
2-in. bitumen paving	328 SY	—	1.65	—	540
Concrete walks (2,500 psi)	93 CY	4.00	14.00	370	1,300
Broom finish & score 5 ft c-c	5,982 SF	.10	—	600	—
½-in. × 4-in. expansion jntg.	220 LF	.10	.18	20	40
Platforms — edge forms	272 SF	.25	.09	70	25
Platforms — concrete (2,500 psi)	15 CY	3.00	14.00	45	210
Platforms — float	690 SF	.10	—	70	—
½-in. graded gravel paving (8 in.)	50 CY	1.50	3.00	75	150
Face brick edging	1,550 pcs.	.10	.07	155	110
Face brick paving	500 pcs.	.10	.07	50	35
Curb & wall — excavate	31 CY	2.00	1.50	60	45
Curb & wall — forms	154 SF	.30	.09	45	15
Curb & wall — concrete	2 CY	7.00	14.00	15	30
Curb & wall — face brick	800 pcs.	.11	.07	90	55
Curb & wall — 10½ × 1½ slate cap	23 LF	.65	2.10	15	50
Bench 12 ft long (Drg. No. 2)	L. S.	30.	15.	30	25
Move boulder and set near entrance	L. S.	75.00	—	75	—
Granite curb VB.1 + exc. + gravel	154 LF	1.20	3.30	185	510
Surplus earth to remove	6,180 CY	.05	.60	310	3,710
				$6,320	$17,310

Excavation & Site   (Sheet No. 3)   *Labor*   *Material*

		L.	*M.*	Labor	Material
Utilities					
Exc. & backfill trenches	1,130 CY	$ .20	$ 1.50	$ 225	$1,695
Exc. & backfill plmg. under slabs	645 CY	1.25	1.10	805	710
8-in. transite pipe storm drain	80 LF	.70	.90	55	70
10-in. transite pipe storm drain	56 LF	.85	1.05	50	60
12-in. transite pipe storm drain	630 LF	.95	1.15	600	725
18-in. transite pipe storm drain	70 LF	1.40	2.30	100	160
Drain inlets 3–0 × 3–0 × 3–8 deep	3 ea.	75.00	95.00	225	285
Catch basins 4–0 dia. × 8–6 deep	7 ea.	145.00	165.00	1,015	1,155
Manholes 4–0 dia. × 6–9 deep	3 ea.	130.00	145.00	390	435
24-in. C.-I. cover & frame	Sub	—	—	—	—
Edge forms 4 in.	110 LF	.20	.12	20	15
Conc. base for util. trench	2 CY	7.00	14.00	15	30
Gravel bed for drains	4 CY	1.30	2.50	5	10
				$3,505	$5,350

Concrete (Formwork) (Sheet No. 4)

Formwork		Quantity	*L.*	*M.*	*Labor*	*Material*
Pier ftgs.	↑	3,094 SF	$ .45	↑	$ 1,390	
Foundtn. piers		182 SF	.50		90	
Wall ftgs.		2,004 SF	.29		580	
Foundtn. walls (max. 11–6)		11,602 SF	.32		3,710	
Int. foundtn. walls		900 SF	.40		360	
Pipe trenches		258 SF	.40		105	
Encasing oil tank	Total 78,280 SF	150 SF	.40	L. S.	60	$7,875
Gym. entrance & balcony		850 SF	.48		410	
Columns		6,076 SF	.45		2,735	
Beams		1,708 SF	.42		715	
Susp. slabs		47,000 SF	.42		19,740	
Canopies		3,050 SF	.55		1,680	
Stairs	↓	1,400 SF	.60	↓	840	
2 × 4 ftg. keys		1,030 LF	.10	$ .10	105	105
Pilasters 12 in. × 6 in. × 4 ft av.		49 ea.	3.50	4.00	170	195
Slab edges & stops (4-in.)		450 LF	.15	.05	65	20
Slab screeds		7,400 LF	.06	.03	445	220
Slab stops 16 in.		1,200 LF	.30	.40	360	480
4-in. edges, locker bases		760 LF	.20	.06	150	45
24-in. × 12-in. metal pans to set		12,040 LF	.21	Sub	2,530	—
					—	—
Visqueen vapor barrier		24,220 SF	.01	.0225	240	545
6-in. × 6-in. × 10/10 mesh to slab		24,200 SF	.02	.025	485	605
$\frac{1}{2}$-in. × 4-in. expansion jntg.		940 LF	.12	.18	115	170
Dovetail anchor slots		500 LF	.12	.11	60	55
Dovetail anchors		1 M	—	15.00	—	15
$\frac{3}{4}$-in. wedge inserts		100 pcs.	.80	.95	80	95
Set sundry misc. iron		L. S.	120.00	—	120	—
					$37,340	$10,425

Concrete   (*Sheet No. 5*)   *Labor*   *Material*

		L.	M.	Labor	Material
3,000-psi Concrete					
Pier ftgs.	172 CY	$4.20		$ 720	
Foundtn. piers	2 CY	7.00		15	
Wall ftgs.	58 CY	2.30		135	
Foundtn. walls	198 CY	2.90		575	
Int. foundtn. walls	9 CY	3.10		30	
Pipe trenches	3 CY	5.00	$2,142\frac{1}{2}$	15	
Encasing oil tank	$1\frac{1}{2}$ CY	7.00	CY	10	$31,280
4-in. ground slabs	280 CY	3.10	$\times$	870	
Gym. entrance & balcony	14 CY	6.00	$14.60	85	
Columns	57 CY	2.00		115	
Beams & susp. slabs	1274 CY	1.60		2,040	
Canopies	39 CY	5.00		195	
Stairs	$25\frac{1}{2}$ CY	6.00		155	
Locker bases	$9\frac{1}{2}$ CY	9.00		85	
Crane for pouring slabs	13 days	— $170.00		—	2,210
Cure slabs (5 days wet)	69,816 SF	.01	.005	700	350
Float roof slabs	11,910 SF	.06	—	715	—
Dust-on finish & trowel floors	57,906 SF	.13	.0025	7,530	145
$\frac{3}{8}$-in. Mastic underlayment for flrs.	26,300 SF	.09	.11	2,365	2,895
3 cts. magn.-fluos. flr. hardener	16,300 SF	.02	.02	325	325
Grano. fill for pan stairs	52 SF	.30	.20	15	10
Non-slip abrasive to stairs	300 lb	—	.24	—	70
Grout slurry & rub ext. walls	1,460 SF	.15 } L. S.		220	120
Grout slurry clgs. & beams	45,500 SF	.17 } L. S.		7,735	—
Extra cost for air-entrained admix to concrete	1,430 CY	—	—	—	—
Float finish stairs & balcony	1,086 SF	.09 } L. S.		100	—
Rubbed finish stairs & balcony	1,970 SF	.18 } L. S.		355	15
				$25,105	$37,420

Total 2,142½ C.Y.

Masonry   (*Sheet No. 6*)

		L.	M.	Labor	Material
Face brick — ext. & lobby $70 per M	95 M	$95.00	$72.00	$ 9,025	$ 6,840
12-in. cinder-block ext. walls 8 × 16	3,550 pcs.	.50	.37	1,775	1,315
12-in. cinder block to patterns 8 × 16	640 pcs.	.60	.40	385	255
8-in. cinder-block back-up 8 × 16	9,970 pcs.	.40	.275	3,990	2,740
6-in. cinder-block back-up 8 × 16	4,680 pcs.	.36	.21	1,685	985
4-in. cinder-block back-up 8 × 16	2,000 pcs.	.30	.165	600	330
Wash down face brick	13,316 SF	.03	L. S.	400	50
Back parge face brick	13,316 SF	—	.02	—	265
Cavity wall ties	4 M	—	18.00	—	70
Wash gravel to bottom of cavities	3 CY	15.00	4.00	45	10
Exterior scaffolding	17,800 SF	.04	.06	710	1,070
5-in. × 12-in. ceramic facing tile:					
2-in. soaps	14,120 pcs.	.38	.26	5,365	3,670
4-in. G1F	3,000 pcs.	.38	.35	1,140	1,050
Extra for Group 1	630 pcs.	.10	.15	65	95
Extra for Group 2	460 pcs.	.10	.30	45	140
Extra for Group 4	35 pcs.	.10	.75	5	25
Extra for Group 6	55 pcs.	.10	.90	5	50
Truck facing tile	64 tons	—	—	—	—
Wash down facing tile	7,360 SF	.03	—	220	—
6-in. waylite-block ptns. 8 × 16	6,220 pcs.	.36	.29	2,240	1,805
12-in. cinder block ptns. 8 × 16	1,600 pcs.	.50	.37	800	590
8-in. cinder-block ptns. 8 × 16	4,120 pcs.	.40	.275	1,650	1,135
4-in. cinder-block ptns. 8 × 16	4,000 pcs.	.30	.165	1,200	660
6-in. cinder-block ptns. 8 × 16	9,650 pcs.	.36	.21	3,475	2,025
Clean and point cinder block	9,556 SF	.04	L. S.	380	40
Glazed tile soap and grab dishes	20 ea.	4.00	12.00	80	240
2-in. hardware cloth reinf. ptns.	7,400 SF	—	.02	—	150
Rubber gasket and caulk ptns. at clgs.	2,530 LF	.10	.15	255	380
Set angle-iron lintels	47 pcs.	4.00	—	190	—
Mortar 1:1:4	211 CY	2.50	16.50	530	3,480
Strap anchors $1\frac{1}{2}$ in. × $1\frac{1}{4}$ in. × 12 in.	90 pcs.	—	.30	—	30
				$36,260	$29,495

Carpentry   (Sheet No. 7)   *Labor   Material*

		L.	M.	Labor	Material
Roof nailers and curbs	1,750 BF	$ .17	$ .14	$300	$245
Window blocking	2,850 BF	.20	.13	570	370
Window grounds	1,000 LF	.10	.06	100	60
1 × 2 grounds or furring	6,410 LF	.12	.03	770	190
1 × 3 grounds	360 LF	.14	.04	50	15
2 × 8 rough bucks for door frames	1,090 BF	.20	.13	220	140
2 × 4 furring pipe spaces	1,600 BF	.16	.12	255	190
Framing at gym. ptn.	750 BF	.25	.12	190	90
1 × 3 ceiling furring	560 LF	.15	.04	85	20
Plaster grounds	500 LF	.12	.02	60	10
⅝-in. gyp. board to clgs.	5,920 SF	.11	.08	650	475
⅝-in. gyp. board to walls	370 SF	.10	.08	35	30
1-in. insulation board behind convectors	235 SF	.13	.09	30	20
1-in. fiberglass insulation	710 SF	.12	.14	85	100
Vinyl faced hardboard to walls	820 SF	.22	.26	180	215
Blocking for casework	1,700 BF	.18	.13	305	220
¼-in. plywood to walls	1,114 SF	.13	.14	145	155
1 × 3 floor sleepers (creosoted)	1,144 LF	.11	.05	125	60
1-in. styrofoam to floor (mop on)	910 SF	—	L. S.	—	300
¾-in. plyscore to floor	1,210 SF	.12	.21	145	255
Temporary doors	6 ea.	25.00	18.00	150	110
Rough hardware	L. S.	—	300.00	—	300

Set Only

		L.	M.		Material
H. M. door frame	6 ea.	8.50	▲		50
Wood door frame & transom	32 ea.	13.00			415
Wood door frame (single)	56 ea.	11.00			615
Wood door & hardware	141 ea.	25.00			3,525
Wood window units & trim	10,657 SF	.22			2,345
Wood glazed ptns.	1,675 SF	.25			420
¾-in. plywood panels	960 SF	.18			175
Window stool 1 × 8 + apron	1,710 LF	.30			515
1 × 6 window trim	180 LF	.22	Sub		40
Art rm. casework	L. S.	185.00			185
Library casework	L. S.	245.00			245
Rm. 10 casework	L. S.	80.00			80
Shop 13 casework	L. S.	145.00			145
Shop 18 casework	L. S.	185.00			185
Storage shelving	1,410 SF	.25			350
Classroom casework and trim	22 rms.	125.00			2,750
Storage cabinet Rm. 2	L. S.	70.00	▼		70
				$16,560	$3,570

Alteration Work (Sheet No. 8)		L.	M.	Labor	Material
Location					
Link:					
Remove brick entr. & platform	L. S.	$200.00	$75.00	$ 200	$ 75
Remove window	1 ea.	20.00	5.00	20	5
Remove 1 pr. doors & frame	L. S.	20.00	—	20	—
Cut opg. 6 ft × 9 ft at stair					
window, set lintel, & patch	2 opgs.	105.00	30.00	210	60
Face brick patching	600 pcs.	.12	.08	70	50
8-in. cinder block patching 8 × 16	100 pcs.	.50	.275	50	30
Boiler rm.:					
Fill in old ash pit	2 ea.	15.00	5.00	30	10
Remove concrete floor	600 SF	.12	.05	70	30
New conc. floor for boilers	22 CY	7.00	14.60	155	320
12-in. edge forms	100 LF	.30	.10	30	10
Excavate for tank	28 CY	6.50	—	180	—
Forms 6-in. for tank	80 LF	.25	.10	20	10
Concrete mat for tank	5 CY	10.00	14.60	50	70
Break out bunker roof to admit					
oil tank	L. S.	70.00	35.00	70	35
Forms — patch roof	300 SF	.45	.12	135	35
Concrete — patch roof	12 CY	4.50	14.60	55	175
Cut window for & set louver					
5 ft × 3 ft	1 ea.	25.00	30.00	25	30
Cut window for & set louver					
3 ft × 2 ft	2 ea.	20.00	20.00	40	40
Common brick patching	1,260 pcs.	.10	.05	125	65
Cut & patch in blr. rm. for subs	L. S.	140.00	50.00	140	50
Stores:					
Remove clg. plaster & lath	680 SF	.10	.05	70	35
Refrig.:					
Remove 3–6 window	2 ea.	15.00	5.00	30	10
Remove temporary ptns.	L. S.	25.00	—	25	—
Boys Rm.:					
Remove *all* lockers (& store)	L. S.	125.00	—	125	—
Girls Rm.:					
Remove *all* lockers (& store)	L. S.	175.00	—	175	—
Remove all ductwork & fans	L. S.	35.00	—	35	—
Remove 6-in. ptns.	2,340 SF	.20	.10	470	235
Remove side entrance & steps	L. S.	40.00	15.00	40	15
General:					
Patch conc. floors	600 SF	.22	.15	130	90
Remove rubbish (15 loads)	L. S.	120.00	95.00	120	95
Make good work disturbed	L. S.	300.00	100.00	300	100
				$3,215	$1,680

Sub-bids   (*Sheet No. 9*)

Section			Cost
G. C.	Allowance — finish hardware		$ 10,000
	Allowance — kitchen eqpt.		23,500
3	Reinforcing steel — buy		26,100
	Reinforcing steel — set	146 tons × $60	8,760
	Metal pan forms — rental		10,500
4	Structural steel — buy ⎫		24,000
	Bar joists — buy ⎭		
	Set structural steel & bar joists		4,400
6	Caulking & damp-proofing		2,000
7	Roofing & sheet metal		10,270
8	Chalk- & tack-boards + map-rails		1,800
	Wood doors & frames ⎫		20,000
	Wood windows ⎭		
	Millwork		31,600
	Finish wood floors		10,650
	Folding partitions		19,350
	Overhead doors	8 × $150	1,200
9	Metal windows		2,350
10	Metal toilet ptns.		5,320
	Metal book shelves		2,100
11	Misc. & ornamental metal		23,800
13	Resilient floors		7,800
14	Glass & glazing		12,850
16	Furring, lathing, & plastering		8,400
17	Acoustic ceilings		2,250
19	Painting		18,900
21	Plumbing		59,700
22	Heating & ventilating		149,300
23	Electrical		69,600
26	Gypsum roof		8,700
	Hollow metal door frames ⎫		240
	Pyro-bar fire door ⎭		
24	Lawns & planting		4,200
			$579,640

NOTES ON THE ESTIMATE

Although they are the first two sheets of the estimate, the summary and overhead sheets are handled last (that is, after the other general contractor's sheets have been priced). Before beginning to price the sheets it is often prudent and sensible to run through the drawings again. It might be two weeks or more since the take-off was started, time enough for your memory to need refreshing. If some of the pricing is to be done before the site is visited, the excavation, site work, and alterations items should be left until after the visit.

You will have enough trouble on bid day without deliberately creating your own difficulties; your general contractor's work should be fully priced, entered on the summary sheet, totaled, checked, and have had a last general looking-over before you leave it on the day prior to bid day. This rule has been emphasized before, but it is important enough to warrant repeating until it sinks in! If you leave dozens of loose ends for the morning of bid day, you will probably be in real trouble, trouble that might well result in a serious error. Bid day is usually hectic enough if confined to getting the sub prices together, completing the last two or three lines of the summary, and writing up the bid form.

In general, your procedure should be as follows: Complete the trade sheets, and then, with the trade labor figures available, compute all the overhead items except those dependent on the total amount of labor, such as insurances and payroll taxes. Next complete the labor side of the summary sheet, and then, using that total, go back to the overhead sheet and complete the insurance, payroll tax, health and welfare, and similar items. Finally, complete the material side of the summary sheet, and total the sheet for all the general contractor's work. By the time you are down to pricing the overhead sheet you should have a fair idea of what the job will cost, so you can then price the bond item. If you should later find that your guess was off, you can adjust the bond item at the last minute on the bottom of the summary sheet before closing out the total bid. Many estimators will leave the insurance, payroll tax, and bond items until the estimate is totaled on the summary sheet, and then add them in. With that method, the summary sheet is set up to show those items at the end of the sheet immediately above the total-cost line. There is absolutely no justification, however, for handling the insurance and payroll taxes in that manner, for the necessary figures are available as soon as your own labor total is ready. There is nothing actually *wrong* with handling the bond in that way, but it will prevent your obtaining your own general contractor's total beforehand. There is a certain satisfaction, and also much value, in having *all* your own work completely priced and totaled on the day prior to bid day. You can then mull over the figures, think about the total, and begin to shape your approach to the bid. Most important of all, however, a costly item will not be left "up in the air." In the mad rush to get a bid together, the bond item, if left to the end, could be missed.

The notes that follow are in the order of trades (excavation through alterations), followed by notes on the overhead sheet, the sub-bid sheet, and finally the summary sheet.

Excavation

The machine excavation item, which is priced on the material side only, is priced as if for rented equipment (rental of both machine and operator). The bitumen paving is priced as a sub item at unit prices obtained from a paving contractor.

Utilities

The manhole covers and frames had been listed in the miscellaneous-iron section of the specifications, and so were not priced on the utilities sheet.

Formwork

The lump-sum price for formwork material is broken down in Chap. 13. The formwork items for beams and slabs, shown separately on the take-off, are combined as a single entry on the estimate, because it would be almost impossible to keep the job costs for such intermingled items separate, and so for estimating and cost records they are best handled as one item. The metal pan forms are priced for handling and setting only; the forms themselves are a rental item, for which a sub-bid was received and entered on the sub-bid sheet.

The formwork total area is notated alongside the various items (78,280 SF) to give the estimator an idea of how much is involved, and also to enable the material cost to be checked. For the type of job being bid, in its particular locality, the formwork material should be approximately $0.10 per SF; thus it can be seen from the area total that the price is in line with past cost records.

Concrete

As for formwork, the concrete total volume is notated, and (being all 3,000-psi mix) used to simplify the pricing. The crane for pouring the superstructure concrete is included on this sheet; there being no other need for a crane, no crane item is carried on the overhead sheet. Air-entraining admix is not priced—there was no extra charge for it by the ready-mixed-concrete supplier.

Masonry

Notice that although allowance for buying face brick is $70 per M, the item is carried at $72. The $70 figure covered the cost of bricks "on the trucks at site," so $2 per M must be added for unloading and stacking. No labor is carried for the back parge item—that requirement was considered and allowed for in pricing the face-brick labor. Similarly, part of the labor for scaffolding and for mortar mixing comes out of the masonry unit prices.

The ratio of laborers to masons allowed in establishing the masonry labor unit prices provided for that factor. The item for trucking facing tile was deleted because the material was quoted as "stacked job site"; thus the material unit prices will cover the trucking.

Carpentry

Various millwork items are priced as lump sums; library casework, for example, is priced at $245 for setting labor. These items were priced by studying the plans and gauging the number of carpenter-days or -hours needed for them. Sometimes it may be better to detail and describe each item of cabinets, casework, counters, and the like, and then price each separately. It can be very difficult, however, to get accurate job costs for individual casework items if there are several different types of casework in one room. The carpenters would most likely move freely from one item to another; perhaps a man working on the blackboard trim would leave that for an hour to give another man help with a heavy cabinet. At the end of the day, the timekeeper or foreman would know how many men were working in each room, but he could not know exactly how their time was divided.

Many estimators do not price finish carpentry in any detail whatsoever, but simply at a percentage of the sub-bid price. They just take the combined sub-supply value of wood doors, door frames, windows, and millwork, and then price the setting labor at something between 30 and 50 per cent of that value. This is not a very satisfactory method, however, unless you are bidding a type of millwork job for which you have previous cost figures. And even if that is so, the method has one further serious drawback: since you would have to be extremely lucky to receive the sub-bids before bid day, you would be leaving the pricing of a substantial part of your own work until then—adding to the already considerable last-minute problems.

Alterations

All the demolition, removal, and related items must be priced *after* the site visit. The ideal way is to take the estimate sheets with you and price each item as you are looking at it. The final three items on this sheet are of a general nature and would be required for most alteration jobs. They are very difficult items to evaluate, and no estimator can hope to accurately assess all the factors involved. Cutting and patching in a present building, for example, would involve many unpredictable and expensive factors. Concrete slabs might be thicker and harder than could possibly have been anticipated, or they might be especially heavily reinforced. Plastered walls to be removed might sound solid, and even if we managed to detect that they were actually masonry, we still would not know whether they were solid brick, or structural clay tile, or even wood studding with brick nogging filling in between the studs. A bidder can only probe walls or floors to a limited extent in an occupied building.

Overhead

The bond item is figured on the basis of a preliminary guess on the value of the bid ($900,000); if the figure is off, that can be allowed for at the end of the summary sheet. The carpentry foreman item is priced only for the extra wages over the ordinary carpenter's rate, for that foreman will be a working foreman.

The crane item is priced on the concrete sheet for this bid, and so is not allowed for on the overhead sheet. The hoist item is figured for the anticipated duration of the exterior-masonry work: the labor side covers the operator's wages; the material side covers the rental of the hoist and also gas and oil.

The clean-up item allows for final cleaning only. Periodical cleaning up after each of the various trades should be charged against the trade concerned and go into the cost records for that trade.

The insurance, tax, and health-and-welfare fund items are priced on the total amount of labor at percentages provided by the office accounting records. These items are discussed in more detail in Chap. 9.

Sub-bids

It is a good rule to put all doubtful items on the sub-bid sheet, even if you have to notate them in some way. For example: You might not be sure of getting a sub price for the lawns item, so you would take it off on the site-work sheet and price it. You would also enter the lawns item on the sub sheet, with a note: "If not priced, on site-work sheet." You could then price it in either place; if you should price it on the site-work sheet and then get a bid or bids, you could use the sub sheet item to make any necessary adjustment. Or there might be doubt about whether or not a sub would include some item that was in his part of the specifications, so you would enter that item separately on the sub sheet with a query mark—"*Structural steel* (? field paint)"—and make a cross-reference notation on the base trade item(s) as follows:

Painting (field paint structural steel included?)
Field paint structural steel — if not included elsewhere

There were no real sub-bid problems in this particular bid. Notice that separate items must be carried for supplying and for setting if the fabricator or supplier does not do any field erection, as is common in both structural-steel (at least on small jobs) and reinforcing-steel bids. Steel may be handled in different ways, however, according to local custom: in some districts, reinforcing steel may be a general contractor's item; in other areas, it would usually be a sub-bid for both supply and setting; or in yet a third area, it might be included within a complete concrete sub-bid (covering forms, concrete, reinforcing, and finishing).

Summary sheet

Once the general contractor's work has been completed down to its total cost (on the day prior to bid day, please), there remains only the sub-bid sheet to be compiled and any last-minute adjustments to be made (for late subs or for items found after the summary sheet was totaled). Bond adjustment would be included in this last-minute addition or deduction. In our example, the bid was $8,600 above the approximate amount used to figure the bond item; that would be only about $60 in bond cost—not enough to worry about on a $900,000 bid—and so no bond adjustment was made. The adjustments made are all for late sub-bids that reduced the cost of the items concerned.

You have no doubt noticed that the bid carries a $43,520 fee, a fee of 5 per cent. This is an arbitrary figure, and is not presented as necessarily proper for the job. Many contractors believe that 10 per cent is too little fee for any job; others would consider that business was really good if they could win a job carrying 4 per cent!

CHAPTER 13   **Pricing The Estimate**

Pricing a general contractor's estimate is *not* a simple, straightforward job that can be given to a junior office engineer or estimator. Even a good take-off man, accurate, quick, and alive to the problems peculiar to the particular job being bid, may not be equipped to price the estimate. Pricing requires not only care, but also a developed judgment, an extensive knowledge of what can be accomplished by a workman or a crew under certain conditions, a sound knowledge of what each building operation involves, and the ability to evaluate these considerations in dollars and cents. The good estimator is, first of all, a good construction man. If he cannot visualize an operation, see how it can be done, and realize why it will be simpler or more difficult than previous jobs, then he cannot price the item.

Having prepared a complete and accurate take-off, you are well on the way to having a proper bid, but you are not home by any means. Too many estimators will spend a week taking off a job and writing up the estimate sheets, and then price the entire estimate in two hours, casually, robotlike, without studying the items, without visiting the site, without even checking on the wage scales for the area. It is such a casual, haphazard way of bidding that is usually accountable for the wide spread in bid prices for a given contract. There *are* times, of course, when bids vary because different estimators see the job differently, when a certain bidder may have his own good reason for being either high or low. It may be a bidder has "inside" information about the architect or owner, and has raised or tightened his bid acccordingly. Or perhaps one bidder is more familiar with the site, or has (or thinks he has) access to a gravel pit that will give him borrow fill for next to nothing. Such circumstances *do* result in bid variations; but more often than not, a wide variation in bids has no sound reason behind it, but is due simply to sloppy estimating.

Probably the most dangerous of all bidding methods to follow is the "price it to get the job" system. This kind of contractor for one reason or another wants the job badly (usually because he needs work), so he shaves his unit prices, slices 5 per cent or so off the sub totals, and adds little or no fee, then juggles his total around trying to guess what this or that competitor is likely to do, and finally throws in a bid price that he reckons will take the job. He is strictly a gambler, and if he gets the job will probably scheme and chisel to work his way out with a profit. But his kind do go broke, because consistently too-low bidding will catch up with a contractor unless he has unusually good luck on extras, site breaks, and purchasing. The contractor should not depend on this system—or any guesswork system. He should depend, ultimately, on good estimating.

THE GOOD ESTIMATOR

What, then, denotes a good estimator? A good estimator is one who can properly evaluate and price any job, giving due regard to the problems peculiar to that job. He recognizes and allows for all the factors that might affect the various operations and items of work. He realizes not only the *difficulties* of the particular job that is being bid, but also the *simplicity* of a particular part of the work that indicates a place to tighten up his unit pricing. And he is a good construction man, a man who knows what is involved in any operation, and who in fact goes through that entire operation mentally to determine each unit price. He is *not* a man who knows everything. He must have confidence in himself, but he must also be prepared to ask questions, to seek out the experts on a material or operation that is new to him and so obtain the information that will help him to evaluate and price the unusual, the tricky, or the new item.

The good estimator is not a man who has a head full of set prices, all ready to throw onto the sheets. If estimating was as easy as that, any half-baked construction man could buy an estimating handbook and, having memorized the prices in it (or sitting with the book open), price out a bid. But pricing cannot be learned from a book. There are many books devoted to pricing the construction estimate, and some of them contain a great deal of useful information. There are also many books on medical practice, but no surgeon is considered fit to operate on a patient on the strength of having read up on the diagnosed disease. Apart from the technical problems of the operation itself, there would be another vital consideration: did he correctly diagnose the disease? In order to make a certain diagnosis, the surgeon must also be familiar with the symptoms of all other possible ailments. Such familiarity comes only from experience. So it is in pricing the estimate— nothing can take the place of experience and first-hand knowledge. Books may supplement experience; they cannot supplant it.

The good estimator is adept at evaluating sub prices; he has his eye open for an incomplete sub-bid, and picks up the duplication if the same item is included by subs in different trades; if necessary, he can quickly take off an item for which he has received no sub price.

The good estimator never forgets that his is a difficult and exacting job. He always proceeds with caution if he is breaking new ground. He knows that no matter how experienced he is, he could not go to a new company (that is, new to him) and start pricing their estimates immediately. When joining a firm, the good estimator will want to get the feel of that company: their strengths and their weak points; their management control. He will want to study the cost records from recent jobs; he will want to know what kind of field force the firm has—what he can expect from the job supers and foremen. He will need the help and cooperation of all departments in the firm; he will ask endless questions and expect honest answers.

The good estimator has an alert, enquiring mind: he wants to know why a thing was done *that* way; how long those three men were on that piece of wall; how many men were used for yesterday's concrete pour. The general job picture is obtained from the job cost sheets, but the good estimator will want some direct and immediate information as well. When he visits the site, his eyes will be everywhere, noticing the type of operations being performed, the manpower, and the output. He is always watching, always asking questions, and always learning.

The good estimator prices the job in hand—prices it at what *this* job is worth, using the units that are right for *this* job—in order to arrive at the right bid. He tightens or raises tentative unit prices if his appraisal of the item tells him that it should cost less or more than was presumed. He never tightens his unit prices below what he believes the item to be worth. There is really only one place to either fatten or tighten the bid as a whole, and that is in the final item—the fee, or profit. The entire estimate, down to the total cost, should represent what the estimator firmly believes to be the actual value of the work.

BECOMING A GOOD ESTIMATOR

How then does one become a good estimator? Experience is the first requirement: experience in the field and in the office. He must also have the ability to observe, to absorb ideas, to learn what men can produce and why they will produce more or less under certain working conditions. Working on estimates priced by a superior helps, of course, but is not sufficient in itself. Given some time in an estimating office with access to the bidding papers, the budding estimator should soon learn that foundation wall formwork is being priced at (say) something between $0.28 and $0.36 per SF. But when $0.28—and why? When $0.36—and why? It is at this point that the budding estimator becomes a nuisance (if he is to become anything at all) and asks his questions, or else gets out old drawings and studies the foundation walls. In this way he finds out that the walls priced at $0.28 were simple, low, and in long, straight runs, while those priced at $0.36 were high (varying from 9 to 17 ft) and were broken up by pilasters and jogs. He may as yet have no conception of output as expressed in area of forms erected and stripped per man hour, but he has learned something.

The development of the ability to price a contractor's estimate is gradual and not very obvious as the weeks and months go by; it is a slow changeover from thinking in terms of money to thinking in terms of output. The ability to see an item as requiring so many man-hours of work per unit of measurement, is a sign that an estimator may be in the making. That is not to say that a good estimator can reel off output figures for any type of work. But he has a sound knowledge of what men can produce, and his experience and knowledge will take care of the normal and common items (items that he has cost records of and past experience with). That same experience and knowledge, together with his ability to gauge an item and his patient, enquiring mind, enable him to price new or "different" items soundly and confidently.

When an estimate is ready for pricing, it is time to visit the site, unless that has already been done. If the job being bid is in the contractor's home district, the site visit will probably involve only checking the site problems and perhaps determining the location of a borrow pit or clocking the mileage to the nearest dump. For bids outside one's own area, however, the site visit may have to supply information involving many items, and so require staying two or three days. The actual site problems—such as access, site clearing, loam stripping, water, and rock—are discussed on p. 18. In addition to those items, there are all manner of things to take care of and dozens of leads to trace down when visiting a site, including the following:

1. What are wage scales for the area, both present and future? When does the scale change? Any fringe benefits? Any special working rules such as "eight hours pay for seven hours work"? Any travel money? What are foremen's rates and conditions relating to foremen?

2. Are there any labor problems due to shortage of tradesmen? Is there much work in the area? What is the quality of the craftsmen in the various trades? Is there any apparent local animosity toward "outside" contractors?

3. Local material prices should be obtained. It is much easier to do this by contacting suppliers when in the district than trying to do it by long-distance telephone. The major suppliers, such as the ready-mix-concrete plants, may have to be visited, although as often as not an enquiry will bring the dealer to your hotel room.

4. Prospective subcontractors should be contacted to line up as many of the major items as possible. This preliminary work will save much wasted effort on bid day.

5. Major problem items of your own work should be given special attention. If there is a big item of "gravel fill to buy," then it should be attended to while you are visiting the site area. Most jobs will have some problem items of this nature.

6. Endless probing, questioning, and listening is also part of visiting an out-of-town site. All kinds of people you talk to will have information to give you—perhaps not exactly volunteered, but capable of being extracted one way or another. Listening is a useful part of your job!

Having seen the site and made all the enquiries that he considers necessary, the estimator should have the "feel" of the job and be ready to put the bid together.

EXAMPLES OF UNIT PRICES

The examples that follow show how some of the more important unit prices were compiled for the estimate given in the previous chapter. They show how prices are methodically developed by applying a knowledge of what may be expected of certain tradesmen under specific conditions. They do *not* provide standard unit prices—the prices given must not be considered as recommended basic units. They *do* show methods and they do point the way, but every estimator must build up his own unit prices, using his own experience and the cost records available within his own organization.

It should always be remembered that a unit price has to be an *average* for the item; therefore it must not be based simply on the output when everything is going well, but must allow for the time lost each day for coffee breaks, tradesmen whose day starts and ends in the shanty (rather than at the point of work), and dozens of similar time-consuming "hidden costs." It is because of such costs that the unit prices that follow are usually rounded off upward if any slight final adjustment is made.

EXCAVATION AND SITE WORK

> NOTE—These unit prices are for the applicable items in the estimate given in Chap. 12

Strip and stockpile loam

D7 bulldozer and operator	8 hr	$\times$ $14.25	=	$114.00
Material handled	20 CY per hr			
Lost time	0.75 hr			
Output	7.25 hr $\times$ 20 CY	= 145 CY	=	$0.80 per CY

Machine excavate building

Backhoe and operator per 8-hr day		=	$120.00
Material handled	140 CY		
Less 0.5 hr lost time	9		
Output	131 CY	=	$0.92 per CY
		Carry	$0.95 per CY

Granite curb VB1 (including exc. and gravel)

		L.	M.	Labor	Material
Based on 60 LF					
Granite curb	60 LF	—	$2.50	—	$150.00
Excavation (part hand work)	5 CY	$3.50	1.50	$17.50	7.50
Gravel bed	4 CY	1.20	2.30	4.80	9.20
Set curb — small backhoe	3 hr	—	10.00	—	30.00
Set curb — laborers	10 hr	2.60	—	26.00	—
Grout joints — masons	4 hr	3.80	—	15.20	—
Laying out — engineer	2 hr	4.25	—	8.50	—
Output		60 LF		$72.00	$196.70
Per LF:		Carry		$1.20	$3.30

Trench excavate and backfill, utilities

		L.	M.	Labor	Material
Lines and grades — eng.	2 hr	×	$ 4.25	$ 8.50	—
Backhoe and operator	8	×	15.00	—	$120.00
D6 bulldozer and operator	3	×	10.50	—	31.50
Hand trim — lab.	2.5	×	2.60	6.50	—
Tamp and hand backfill — lab.	2	×	2.60	5.20	—
Output		100 CY		$20.20	$151.50
Per CY:		Carry		$0.20	$1.50

8-in. common-brick manhole 4-ft dia. × 6–9

			L.	M.	Labor	Material
Excavate and backfill						
9–0 × 9–0 × 7–3	22	CY	$0.25	$ 1.35	$ 5.50	$ 29.70
Concrete base — forms	26	SF	0.27	0.10	7.02	2.60
Concrete base — concrete						
6–6 × 6–6 × 1–0	1.5	CY	4.00	15.00	6.00	22.50
Common brick	1,400	pcs.	0.08	0.045	112.00	63.00
Step irons	5	pcs.	—	1.10	—	5.50
Mortar	1.25	CY	—	16.50	—	20.62
					$130.52	$143.92
				Carry	$130.00	$145.00

The computation of common brick is as follows:

$$3\tfrac{1}{7} \ \times \ 4\text{--}8 \ \times \ 6\text{--}9 \ \times \ 0\text{--}8 \ = \ 21 \text{ CF}$$

At 20 pcs. per CF	=	1,320 pcs.
+ Waste		80
		1,400 pcs.

The diameter is to the center of the wall (4–0 plus 0–4 plus 0–4); the waste allows for cutting to the circular shape.

For variations in depth, per lineal foot:

			L.	M.	Labor	Material
Common brick	210	pcs.	$0.08	$ 0.045	$16.80	$ 9.45
Step irons	1	pc.	—	1.10	—	1.10
Mortar	0.25 CY		—	16.50	—	4.12
					$16.80	$14.67
Variation per LF of depth:	Allow				$17.00	$15.00

FORMWORK

NOTE—These unit prices are for the applicable items in the estimate given in Chap. 12

Formwork material

Pier footings	$\frac{5}{8}$-in. plywood	1,000 SF	×	$ 0.21	=	$ 210.00
Wall footings	2 × 12	800 BF	×	0.13	=	104.00
Foundation walls	$\frac{5}{8}$-in. plywood	3,000 SF	×	0.21	=	630.00
Foundation walls	Lumber	6M BF	×	130.00	=	780.00
Strapping	1 × 3	1,500 LF	×	0.04	=	60.00
Suspended slabs	$\frac{5}{8}$-in. plywood	6,000 SF	×	0.21	=	1,260.00
Suspended slabs	Lumber	12M BF	×	120.00	=	1,440.00
Suspended slabs	Strapping	1M BF	×	130.00	=	130.00
Adjustable shores	600 ×	3 months	×	1.50	=	2,700.00
Snap ties		4,000	×	0.11	=	440.00
Form oil & sundries					=	120.00
						$7,874.00
					Carry	$7,875.00

The pier footings item allows enough material for about one-third of the total work; the foundation wall quantity is for approximately a quarter of the job. The slab quantities, including the material available from the footings and walls, allow for about one-sixth of the total area. The total quantity of plywood allowed for formwork is 10,000 SF (1,000 SF plus 3,000 SF plus 6,000 SF), for approximately 60,000 SF of superstructure contact area.

The allowance for shores is approximately one for every 16 SF of the 10,000 SF to be decked in. It should be noted that the decking in of 10,000 SF here means having 5,000 SF ready to pour while another 5,000 SF are being made ready, so that by the time the second area is ready to pour, the formwork from the first area will have been stripped and moved over to a third 5,000-SF section.

The $1.50 per month rental rate on the shores is based on owning them—purchased at $18.00 each—and anticipating their being used, on the average, 50 per cent of the year; thus the $1.50 allowance covers $9.00 per year and figures to pay for the shores over a two-year period.

FORMWORK LABOR

NOTE—These unit prices are for the applicable items in the estimate given in Chap. 12

Formwork — foundation walls (11–6 max.) — labor

Erection crew	Carpenters	2 × 8 hr	× $3.50	=	$56.00	
	Laborer		× 2.60	=	5.20	
					$61.20	per day

Output (2 carp. fabricate and erect complete)   280 SF   Per SF $ 0.22

Stripping crew	1 carpenter	8 hr	× $3.50	=	$28.00	
	1 laborer	8	× 2.60	=	20.80	
					$48.80	

Output (Strip and remove, complete)   600 SF   Per SF $0.08

Clean and oil ready for next use   Lab.   8 hr × $2.60 = $20.80

Output   1,000 SF   Per SF $0.02

                              Labor cost total   Carry   Per SF $0.32

Formwork — cols.

Make-up crew	Carpenters	2 × 8 hr	= 16 hr	× $3.50	=	$56.00	
	Laborer	1	= 1	× 2.60	=	2.60	
						$58.60	per day

	Output (fabricate only) 310 SF	=	$0.19 per SF
Erection — 2 carp. $56.00 per day for 400 SF		=	0.14
Stripping (crew as previous item) $48.80 per day for 480 SF		=	0.10
Clean and oil forms ready for next use (crew as previous item)		=	0.02
	Labor cost total Carry		$0.45 per SF

Formwork — suspended slabs and beams

Make-up and erection crew	4 carp. 32 hr	× $3.50		=	$112.00	
	1 lab. 9	× 2.60		=	23.40	
					$135.40	per day

Output (make up beams, erect beam and slab forms) 450 SF	=	$0.30 per SF
Stripping (crew as in previous items) $48.80 per day for 480 SF	=	0.10
Clean and oil (crew as previously)	=	0.02
Labor cost total Carry		$0.42 per SF

It is virtually impossible to keep separate the labor on beams and that on slabs in allocating man-hours in the field. The ratio of beams to slabs must be considered in figuring the output rate. For this particular job, there are only 1,700 SF of beams to 47,000 SF of slabs; thus the beams are not a serious factor.

CONCRETE LABOR

> NOTE—These unit prices are for the applicable items in the estimate given in Chap. 12

Setting 24-in.   ✕   *10-in. long metal pan forms*

Crew	2 Carpenters	16 hr	✕	$3.50	=	$56.00
	1 Laborer	8	✕	2.60	=	20.80

$76.80 per day

Output (handle and set) 550 LF   = $0.14 per LF

Stripping crew — 1 carp. and 1 lab. (as before)

$48.80 per day for 800 LF   =   0.06

Clean and oil pans   Allow   0.01

Labor cost total   Carry $0.21 per LF

The laborer's time item includes unloading from truck and reloading on truck at the end of the job. The material cost is a rental item and appears on the sub-bid sheet.

Concrete foundation walls (40% barrowed, 60% shoot from truck)

Day's pour	=	32 CY	
Time taken	=	6 hr	
Crew	=	5 laborers	
Add setting up ramps	=	4 hr laborer	
Add cleaning barrows etc.	=	1 hr laborer	
Level top of wall & set dowels	=	1 hr laborer	
Laborers total time 36 hr	✕	$2.60	= $93.60 for 32 CY
Labor — placing concrete foundation walls		Carry	$2.90 per CY

Concrete — placing suspended slabs and beams (crane taken separately)

Day's pour		=	100 CY
Crew — Pouring 8 laborers ✕ 6 hr		=	48 hr
+ overtime 8 ✕ 0.5 hr		=	4
Setting runways ready for pour — laborer		=	4
Clean up after pour — laborer		=	2

58 hr ✕ $2.60 = $150.80

Labor $150.80 for 100 CY   Carry $1.50 per CY

The 100 CY of concrete figured to be poured per average day of pouring, explains the allowance of 13 days for a crane; the total quantity of super-structure concrete is approximately 1,300 CY. The half hour of overtime allowed is for pouring through the normal lunch hour in a locality that requires that the extra half hour be paid.

The two hours allowed for clean-up is for cleaning off runways and washing shovels and buggies.

Dust-on trowel finish floors

Average concrete slab pour   =   100 CY   =   3,700 SF per day

Crew	Cement finish foreman			12 hr	×	$4.25	=	$ 51.00
	Cement finishers 6	×	12 hr	= 72	×	3.80	=	273.60
	Overtime foreman			4	×	4.25	=	17.00
	Overtime cem. fin. 6	×	4 hr	= 24	×	3.80	=	91.20
	Laborer			14	×	2.60	=	36.40
				Output 3,700 SF			=	$469.20

Cost (screed, float, trowel, plus "dust-on" cement and
   2nd troweling)   = $0.127 per SF

                                                     Carry $0.13   per SF

The laborer item is for general assistance, particularly during the overtime period. Laborers get time-and-a-half for overtime, so for 12 hours' work he will get paid for 14 hours (8 plus 4 plus 2). Cement finishers, however, get double-time for all overtime, so for 12 hours' work they will get 4 hours' overtime pay.

Grout slurry and rub ceilings

Cement finisher	8 hr	×	$3.80	=	$30.40
Laborer	2	×	2.60	=	5.20
	Output		210 SF	=	$35.60 per day
	Labor cost		Carry		$0.17 per SF

MASONRY LABOR

   NOTE—These unit prices are for the applicable items in the estimate given in Chap. 12

Masonry labor costs

Crew make-up	8 masons	8 × 8 hr × $3.80	=	$243.20
	7 laborers	7 × 8 × $2.60	=	145.60
		For 8 Masons (per day)		$388.80
		Per mason man-day		$48.60
Add 1 lab. overtime	$\frac{1}{2}$hr + $\frac{1}{4}$hr = $\frac{3}{4}$hr × $2.60		=	1.95
		Labor cost per day Carry		$50.55

Output per mason day of $50.55

Face brick	=	530	=	$95.00 per M
12-in. cinder block	=	100	=	$0.50 ea.
8-in. cinder block	=	125	=	$0.40 ea.
6-in. cinder block	=	140	=	$0.36 ea.
4-in. cinder block	=	170	=	$0.30 ea.
5 × 12 glazed facing tile	=	135	=	$0.38 ea.

The 2-in. and 4-in. glazed facing tiles are considered together for one unit price, as it is almost impossible to keep separate job cost records for the two thicknesses. In addition to the basic unit price of $0.38 per piece for that tile, an allowance of $0.10 per piece is carried as an extra-cost-for-specials item. The special items are shown in the estimates as "Extra for Group........"; the quantities for the "specials" are included in the basic 2-in. and 4-in. items, and only the extra cost of $0.10 per piece is priced in the extra-cost items, which allow for handling the special shapes.

MASONRY MATERIAL

NOTE—These unit prices are for the applicable items in the estimate given in Chap. 12

Mortar   1 : 1 : 4

1 Cement	6.5 bags			×	$1.40	=	$9.10
1 Lime	6.5 bags			×	0.80	=	5.20
4 Sand	1 CY	=	1.25 tons	×	1.75	=	2.20
							$16.50 per CY

Mortar   1 : 1 : 5

Cement	5.3 bags	×	$1.40	=	$7.42
Lime	5.3 bags	×	0.80	=	4.24
Sand	1.25 tons	×	1.75	=	2.19
					$13.85 per CY

Mortar   1 : 1 : 6

Cement	4.5 bags	×	$1.40	=	$6.30
Lime	4.5 bags	×	0.80	=	3.60
Sand	1.25 tons	×	1.75	=	2.20
					$12.10 per CY

Prepared mortar cement $1 : 3$

1 Mortar cement	8.1 bags			$\times$ $1.10	=	$8.90
3 Sand	0.9 CY	=	1.15 tons	$\times$ 1.75	=	2.00
						$10.90 per CY

The mortar mixes given are based on sand weighing about 93 lb per CF. Sand varies considerably in weight; it may weigh anything between 80 and 100 lb per CF. The drier the sand, the greater the quantities of all materials required per cubic yard of mortar. Using dry sand at 80 lb per CF, for example, the 1:3 mortar cement would require 9 bags of mortar cement and 1 CY (1.25 tons) of sand, at a cost for material of $12.10 per CY of mortar.

ROUGH CARPENTRY LABOR

NOTE—These unit prices are for the applicable items in the estimate given in Chap. 12

Window blocking — based on windows for one typical classroom

Material per classroom		20 ft of 2	$\times$	4	=	14 BF
		20 ft of 2	$\times$	6	=	20
						34 BF

Labor	Carpenter	$1\frac{3}{4}$ hr	$\times$ $3.50	=	$6.10
	Laborer	$\frac{1}{4}$	$\times$ 2.60	=	0.65
			Output 34 BF		$6.75
				Labor	$0.20 per BF

Setting 1 $\times$ *2 grounds*

	Typical Classroom	=	250 LF		
	Carpenter	8 hr	$\times$ $3.50	=	$28.00
	Laborer	$\frac{1}{2}$	$\times$ 2.60	=	1.30
			Output 250 LF		$29.30
				Labor	$0.12 per LF

$\frac{5}{8}$-in. gypsum board to ceilings

Per day	Carpenters	2	$\times$ 8 hr	$\times$ 3.50	=	$56.00
	Laborer		$\frac{1}{2}$	$\times$ 2.60	=	1.30
						$57.30
Output per day (2 men)		16 sheets, 4–0	$\times$	8–0		512 SF
					Labor	$0.11 per SF

The laborer's time is for unloading lumber, carrying it into the building, and moving it as required to stock up for the carpenters. If local rules permitted laborers to lift and hold material for carpenters, the proportion of laborers to carpenters would be larger.

FINISH CARPENTRY LABOR

> NOTE—These unit prices are for the applicable items in the estimate given in Chap. 12

Setting wood door and hardware (average door 2–8 $\times$ 7–0 $\times$ 0–1$\frac{3}{4}$ solid core flush; hardware — 3 butts, mortice lock, & automatic closer)

Crew   2 carpenters   2 $\times$ 8 hr $\times$ $3.50   = $56.00 per day

Fitting doors   8 per day of $56.00   = $7.00 per door
Hang doors   10 per day of $56.00   =   5.60
Carpenter (1) set lock & striker 1$\frac{1}{4}$ hr
Carpenter (1) set door closer   1
Carpenter (1) final adjustment $\frac{1}{2}$
                                                        2$\frac{3}{4}$ hr $\times$ $3.50   =   9.60
Laborer (attend on carp. + unload & stack doors)
                                                        1 hr $\times$ 2.60   =   2.60
                                                                                        $24.80 per door
                                                                    Carry $25.00 per door

Set hollow metal door frame

Crew   2 carpenters   2 $\times$ 8 hr $\times$ $3.50   = $56.00 per day

Frames set and braced   7 per day   = $8.00 per frame
Add laborer unload, etc.   =   0.50
                                                        Carry $8.50 per frame

Set wood window units and trim (prefabricated units, plus 54 LF of 1 $\times$ 3 plain trim)

Typical classroom total windows 19–0 $\times$ 7–0 = 133 SF

Crew   2 carpenters 2 $\times$ 8 hr $\times$ $3.50   = $56.00 per day

Output 2 rooms per day   Per room $28.00
Add laborer $\frac{1}{2}$ hr $\times$ $2.60   =   1.30
                                                Output 133 SF $29.30
                                                        Carry $0.22 per SF

GENERAL REMARKS ON COMPILING UNIT PRICES

All the examples given of building up unit prices were based on previous experience from jobs similar to the Warren School; they represent the best knowledge that was available at the time of bidding. It could not be guaranteed, however, that the cost records of the completed job would corroborate all the unit prices used. Many factors can affect the actual job cost, and on every job there will be some costs that the estimator did not foresee: some items that he might have anticipated had he been more alert, and some that he could not possibly have expected. A winter that was abnormally severe would play havoc with job costs, yet the estimator could not know that such a spell of terrible weather was coming. A strike at a brick factory hundreds of miles from the site could bring the job to a stop for weeks. Abnormal rainfall might necessitate costly pumping.

Such happenings cannot be foreseen when estimating. Many less unusual cost factors, however, are often missed because the estimator was not awake when he priced the job. There can be no excuse for his not knowing, for example, that a concrete slab over an auditorium is to be 30 ft above the floor and so must be given special consideration in pricing the formwork. Having once had a job in a particular area and so knowing the shortage there of good tradesmen in a particular trade, only a poor estimator would ignore that fact when bidding again in that locality. Having worked for a particular architect before and so knowing that he is extremely fussy about masonry, a good estimator would remember that fact when another of that architect's jobs came up for bidding.

As the estimator receives and dockets such information, it should develop and revise his thinking. The wide-awake estimator is constantly enquiring; accumulating, sifting, and evaluating information; learning not to make the same mistake twice.

There will always be something for him to learn about estimating. When an estimator gets the idea that he knows it all, it is safe to say that he is not a good estimator and cannot be without first shaking off that dangerous and restricting conceit.

Mensuration and Tables

AREAS

Key to Symbols

L	=	Length	S	=	Number of Sides
W	=	Width	D	=	Diameter
H	=	Perpendicular Height	r	=	Radius
B	=	Length of Base	π	=	3.1416 or $3\frac{1}{7}$

Rectangle: Area   =   L $\times$ W

Parallelogram: Area   =   L $\times$ H

Triangle: Area   = $\frac{1}{2}$(B $\times$ H)

Regular polygon: Area   =   S $\times$ $\frac{1}{2}$(B $\times$ H*)

Circle: Circumference   = πD
                Area   = πr^2

Sphere: Surface Area   = $4\pi r^2$
               Cubic Volume   = $\frac{4}{3}\pi r^3$

Pyramid: Surface Area   = B^2 +   (2B $\times$ Sloping Height)
               Cubic Volume   = $\frac{1}{3}B^2$ $\times$ H

Cone: Sloping Area   = πD $\times$ Sloping Height
               Cubic Volume   = $\frac{1}{3}\pi r^2$ $\times$ H

Cylinder: Curved Surface Area   = πD $\times$ H
               End Surface Area   = $2\pi r^2$
               Cubic Volume   = πr^2 $\times$ H

*Perpendicular height from side to center point.

LINEAR MEASURE

12	inches	=	1 foot							
3	feet	=	1 yard	=	36 inches					
5.5	yards	=	1 rod	=	16.5 feet					
40	rods	=	1 furlong	=	220 yards	=	660 feet			
8	furlongs	=	1 mile	=	320 rods	=	1,760 yards	=	5,280 feet

SQUARE MEASURE

144	square inches	=	1 square foot		
9	square feet	=	1 square yard		
30.25	square yards	=	1 square rod		
4,840	square yards	=	1 acre	=	43,560 square feet
640	acres	=	1 square mile		

Inches converted to decimals of one foot

1 in.	=	0.083 ft
2		0.167
3		0.250
4		0.333
5		0.417
6		0.500
7		0.583
8		0.667
9		0.750
10		0.833
11		0.917

WEIGHTS OF MATERIALS

Material	Weight, in lb per CF
Ashes or cinders	40–45
Bricks (shale commons)	125
Cement	94
Clay (ordinary)	95
Earth (loamy soil)	75–90
Glass	156
Gravel (bank run)	90–105
Iron (cast)	442
Lead	712
Limestone	155–165
Lumber (pine or spruce)	30–32
Marble	160–165
Paper	33–44
Sand — dry	80–85
Sand — wet	90–95
Sandstone	150
Steel	489
Water	62.5
Water (solid ice)	56

CONVERSION TABLES

Lumber

board feet	divided by	12	=	cubic feet
cubic feet	multiplied by	12	=	board feet

Water

cubic feet	multiplied by	62.5	=	pounds
cubic feet	multiplied by	6.25	=	gallons (Imperial)
gallons (Imperial)	multiplied by	1.2	=	gallons (U.S.)
gallons (U. S.)	multiplied by	8.3	=	pounds
gallons (Imperial)	multiplied by	10.0	=	pounds

Temperature

To convert Degrees Fahrenheit to Degrees Centigrade:

Deduct 32 degrees and multiply by 0.555

To convert Degrees Centigrade to Degrees Fahrenheit:

Multiply by 1.8 and add 32 degrees

DUODECIMAL MULTIPLICATION

In computing quantities manually, whether because there is no calculating machine at hand or because you simply prefer not to use the machine or slide rule, you will find duodecimal multiplication very useful. Duodecimals are decimals in twelfths, based on the twelve inches per foot.

Example 1

9–8   ×   7–11

```
        9– 8
        7–11
        ─────
        8–10–4
       67– 8
       ───────
       76– 6–4   =   77 SF
       ═══════       ══
```

Explanation

11 in.	×	8 in.	=	88 sq in.			=		4(and 7 to carry)
11 in.	×	9 ft	=	99 (plus 7 carried)	=	106	=	8–10	
7 ft	×	8 in.	=	56 twelfths of a SF			=	4– 8	
7 ft	×	9 ft	=	63 SF			=	63	

```
                                      76– 6–4
                                      ═══════
                        =   76 SF 76 sq. in.
                            ══      ══
```

Further Examples

12–7 × 8–5	12– 7	
	8– 5	
	5– 2–11	
	100– 8	
	105–10–11 =	106 SF

9–4 × 11–3	9–4	
	11–3	
	2–4–0	
	102–8–0	
	105–0–0 =	105 SF

14–3 × 12–10	14– 3	
	12–10	
	11–10–6	
	171– 0	
	182–10–6 =	183 SF

RATIO MULTIPLICATION

It is often quicker to multiply by ratios (or fractions) than to use duo-decimals. Ratio multiplication simply applies the ratio between the number of inches and 1 ft by converting the inches to a fraction of a foot. Some of the examples given above would be handled as follows:

9–4 × 11–3		9–4	×	11 ft	=	102–8
	+	9–4	×	$\frac{1}{4}$	=	2–4
						105–0
					=	105 SF

14–3 × 12–10		12– 0	×	14 ft	=	168– 0
	+	0–10	×	14	=	11– 8
	+	12–10	×	$\frac{1}{4}$	=	3– 2
						182–10
					=	183 SF

9–8 × 7–11		7–11	×	9 ft	=	71–3
		7–11	×	$\frac{2}{3}$	=	5–3
						76–6
					=	77 SF

After some practice it will be found that, between them, duodecimal and ratio multiplication are fast and accurate methods for computing. The ratio method is actually a refinement of the duodecimal; it is simply a quicker way to figure the inches part of a calculation, particularly if one of the figures includes any of the following: 2 in., 3 in., 4 in., 6 in., 8 in., or 9 in. (the less cumbersome fractional parts of a foot).

$$2 \text{ in.} = \tfrac{1}{8} \text{ ft}$$
$$3 \text{ in.} = \tfrac{1}{4} \text{ ft}$$
$$4 \text{ in.} = \tfrac{1}{3} \text{ ft}$$
$$6 \text{ in.} = \tfrac{1}{2} \text{ ft}$$
$$8 \text{ in.} = \tfrac{2}{3} \text{ ft}$$
$$9 \text{ in.} = \tfrac{3}{4} \text{ ft}$$

These manual methods of multiplication should be given careful study. They are really quite simple, and can be mastered very quickly with little effort. Thereafter, they will often be of tremendous help. There are many times when an estimator or an outside engineer, foreman, or superintendent has to compute quantities without being able to turn to a calculating machine. Using these methods and knowing the "27 times" table, you should have no trouble in manually computing quantities. The "27 times" table is given again:

$$1 \times 27 = 27$$
$$2 \times 27 = 54$$
$$3 \times 27 = 81$$
$$4 \times 27 = 108$$
$$5 \times 27 = 135$$
$$6 \times 27 = 162$$
$$7 \times 27 = 189$$
$$8 \times 27 = 216$$
$$9 \times 27 = 243$$

Index